DISCOVERY OF THE UNIVERSE

*An Outline of the History of
Astronomy from the Origins to 1956*

by

GÉRARD DE VAUCOULEURS

520
V

THE MACMILLAN COMPANY

New York

© 1957 by Gérard de Vaucouleurs

Printed in the United States of America

First printing

Library of Congress Catalog Card Number: 57-10015

CONTENTS

CONTENTS

III. The Rise of Classical Astronomy: Positional Astronomy and Celestial Mechanics from the End of the Seventeenth to the Middle of the Nineteenth Century

IV. The Beginnings of Modern Astronomy from the End of the Eighteenth Century to the Middle of the Nineteenth Century

1. THE STELLAR SYSTEM

CONTENTS

CONTENTS

ILLUSTRATIONS

FOREWORD

When I was first asked to permit the translation into English of this short History of Astronomy, I hesitated for some time. It was first published in France in 1951,[1] and when I wrote it, some six or seven years ago, no book of similar scope had been published there for over thirty years. In particular, none had carried astronomical history forward into the twentieth century.

At the time, the situation in Great Britain differed hardly at all; the standard reference book was, I believe, even more out of date than its French equivalent. Since 1951, however, there have appeared in English—either original or translated—several excellent historical treatises on Astronomy; and I was inclined to wonder if it would serve any useful purpose to add my own version of the story. Nevertheless, after a careful reading of these various works I came to the conclusion that the outlook and contents of my book were sufficiently different to make its translation worth while.

One reason is that I have been concerned more with the evolution of ideas—the slow strengthening of Man's intellectual grasp on the Universe in which he lives, the philosophical implications of the main discoveries—than with biographical details. I feel that conventional histories often dwell too much on the more picturesque episodes in the lives of the great astonomers and thus run the risk of giving a distorted picture of the development of Astronomy. It is the result of a slow and continuous progress, not of a disconnected series of great 'revelations'. 'If I have seen

[1] *L'Esprit de l'Homme à la conquête de l'Univers—L'Astronomie, des Pyramides au Mont Palomar*, Spes, Paris, 1951, 256 pp. (Collection 'L'Homme dans l'Univers').

farther than others,' said Newton, 'it is because I was standing on the shoulders of giants.'

I have often felt, too, that many popular accounts are unbalanced and uncritical in their selection of material. A recital of the obsolete speculations of the Ancients, a minute review of the innumerable maps of the Moon or of amateur planetary observations—which figure so prominently in some recent accounts—may have some appeal for those interested in details, but they deserve only little space in a volume which aims at giving its readers a comprehensive survey of the whole history of astronomy in a few hundred pages.

Moreover, in an effort to reduce the unavoidable overlap with earlier works, I have expanded still further the chapters devoted to contemporary astronomy; in particular, the last one (Chapter IX)—on the very considerable post-war developments—is entirely new. The bibliography has been revised and enlarged. Many new illustrations have been added.

I am indebted to Dr. B. Pagel for his collaboration in the translation of Chapters I to VIII and to Mrs. G. V. Simonow for her valuable help in preparing the material for publication.

G. DE VAUCOULEURS

Mount Stromlo, Australia
November 1956

Ancient Astronomy, from its Origins to the End of the Middle Ages

1. The origins of astronomy

The origins of astronomy are lost in the mists of time. The oldest documents that have reached us—the Egyptian pyramids, the Assyrian tablets and the Chinese tradition—date back more than 5,000 years and give evidence of rudimentary but codified knowledge among the ancient peoples; going still further into the past, easily recognizable pictures of constellations, such as the Great Bear, have been found engraved on the walls of certain caves.

Thus Man, as soon as his mind had risen above the purely animal, could not fail to note the general permanence as well as the great motions and fundamental rhythms of the celestial vault.

It is certain that, like all sciences, astronomy arose from the needs of everyday life and from primitive man's fears of natural phenomena. Thus in its first expression and for a long time afterwards, astronomy was closely associated with arithmetic, geometry, astrology and the religious beliefs and philosophic systems of primitive tribes.

The regular daily motion of the Sun, Moon and stars; their rising and setting; the Moon's phases, their periodicity, and the Moon's motion among the stars; the permanence of the figures or constellations formed by the stars on the celestial vault; the annual disappearance and reappearance of some constellations according to the season while others were always visible towards the north (Septentrio = Septem Triones, the seven bright stars of the Great Bear); these first items of knowledge were obtained long before historical times.

Owing to the practical use of this knowledge for navigation (the cardinal points being marked by the rising and setting of the Sun—Orient and Occident—and by its position at midday—the Meridian), for the determination of times favourable for sowing or reaping (the heliacal rising of Sirius watched for by the Egyptians, cf. section 2) and the essential part obviously played by the Sun in all human activity, it was natural that Man should soon attribute personal, individual and characteristic powers to the heavenly bodies, and that he should see in them the manifestation of superior forces and divinities either favourable or adverse. The influences of these had to be predicted in order that divine wrath might be prevented and benevolence induced through offerings and sacrifices carried out by men specially trained to perform this essential function. This is the probable origin, in the very distant past, of the sun-rites of the Incas, of hierarchic religions and of astrology.

2. Primitive astronomy in China, Chaldea and Egypt

Among the sources of fear to which primitive man was subject, unexpected disturbances of the regular order of things took a very prominent position: tempests, thunderstorms and above all eclipses because of their greater rarity. These latter suddenly deprived mankind of the warmth of the Sun by day or of the reassuring light of the Moon by night, and thus came to be considered as omens of some particularly terrible calamity. Large comets, with their sword or javelin shapes, were rarer still and seemed to be unmistakable signs of celestial wrath.

It is thus obvious how much practical importance was immediately attached by the primitive mind to the observation of the heavenly bodies, and that it was not a disinterested love of exact knowledge or a regard for scientific culture that led the Emperors of China, the Pharaohs of Egypt and the Kings of Chaldea to engage the services of priests, astrologers and astronomers, but rather the desire to know their personal destiny and to assure success to the activities of their peoples. The heavens were thus subjected to painstaking and precise examination from the very earliest times.

The men to whom these important functions were assigned could not fail to be loaded with honours and favoured with handsome salaries; but the profession was not an undangerous one and woe betide the one who did not carry out his duties with sufficient diligence; legend reports that, in the twenty-fourth century before our era, the Chinese Emperor Yao had his ministers Hi and Ho beheaded because, through their addiction to drink, they had failed to warn him of the occurrence of an eclipse.

One may imagine that, after this, astronomers paid considerable attention to eclipses and made great efforts to predict their recurrence! In fact, these play an important part in the few written documents that are still extant from those distant times.

Thus certain Assyrian tablets found in the ruins of Nineveh, dating from 1,000, 2,000 and even nearly 3,000 years B.C., record eclipses of the Sun and Moon and also the consequences that these events were supposed to have for the future of the king. In addition, these tablets have records of the motions of the planets, the phases of the Moon and the lunar calendar.

In Egypt, on the other hand, no special significance seems to have been attached to eclipses, since only a few are mentioned in the earliest records, while the calendar, the seasons and astronomical orientation play an important part. Twenty or thirty centuries B.C. the annual overflow of the Nile followed shortly after the *heliacal* rising of Sirius (its first appearance at the moment of dawn before the rising of the Sun). The Egyptians therefore observed this event with special care.

The regular pursuit of these observations over a period of centuries enabled the Egyptians to determine the approximate length of the year—the period after which the sun returns to the same position among the stars; this period, fixed originally (fifty centuries B.C.) at 360 days, was probably fairly soon corrected to 365 days.

The Egyptian pyramids bear witness to observational abilities which were already adequate for the orientation of the earliest of them within a few degrees and for the orientation of the later ones within some tenths of a degree. This orientation doubtless had a religious significance and was perhaps considered favourable for the repose of the dead Pharaoh or for the future of his soul. It seems further that these structures served the Egyptian priests simultaneously as temples and observatories. Indeed it has been pointed out that the principal ascending corridor which emerges on the northern face of the Great Pyramid must at the time of its construction (c. 3400 B.C.) have pointed towards the star alpha Draconis, which was then the Pole Star. But it is not known what use may have been made of it.

On the other hand, the remarkable supposed relations that have been 'discovered' by certain naïve or unscrupulous authors, between the dimensions of the pyramids and the secret sensational scientific knowledge which they are supposed to demonstrate, are the grossest fantasies.

What little is known concerning the astrological practices of other nations indicates knowledge and beliefs that were either similar or inferior to those of the Egyptians (e.g. the astronomical alignment of menhirs among the Celts, sun temples among the Mayas and the Incas, etc.).

3. The cosmology of the primitive peoples

The world systems of these primitive peoples reflect the rudimentary condition of their outlook and their science, and are affected also by local conditions and the influence of religious beliefs. In its broad outlines their cosmology is practically the same everywhere—it is no more than a simple translation of the most obvious natural phenomena: the Earth is flat and circular like the horizon or, in the case of Egypt, rectangular like the country; it is surrounded by a large river or ocean, on which it floats; above is a hollow cap formed by the heavens, on which the chariots of the gods (i.e. the heavenly bodies) move round; above this vault there is more water (rain). The Earth is sometimes mounted on pillars (e.g. among the Chinese and the Hebrews), sometimes on elephants (among the Indians)[1]; below the Earth or in underground caves are the land of the dead, Hades, etc.

---

[1] How the pillars are supported is not stated, but the elephants have been described as resting on a giant tortoise!

Each country is of course considered to be the centre of civilization and is therefore placed at the centre of the Earth's surface, the 'barbarians' being relegated to the periphery. The king or emperor is usually the 'Son of Heaven' and its earthly representative; his power is thus justified and reinforced.

Irregular events, especially eclipses, are regarded as acts of aggression committed by monsters, dragons or serpents, against the god of the Sun or the goddess of the Moon. On such occasions a loud uproar must be raised in order to scare the monster away and liberate the tutelary star.[1]

It would be pointless to describe in detail these naïve legends, due to primitive imagination and mysticism as well as to the economic and social structure of the societies in which they arose; but, although they may bring a smile to the educated man of the twentieth century, they also seem to deserve his attention as a topic for reflection because, basically, they are still the essential core of the cosmological and religious beliefs of at least three-quarters of humanity in this 'enlightened' age.

4. The astronomy and cosmology of the Greeks

While earlier peoples had observed celestial phenomena only for practical, mystical or utilitarian purposes and always in a purely descriptive way without seeking to explain their observations except by the most primitive legends, the Greeks from the fourth century B.C. onwards were the first to study celestial phenomena and motions in a disinterested and purely scientific fashion, and to seek a rational explanation, without attempting to predict the future from them.

This sudden change from mystical to rational modes of thought, which in many ways could not have been expected or predicted, has been justly called the 'Greek miracle'; for, just as the appearance of a practical mind in the anthropoid ancestors of man marked

---

[1] This practice persisted until the nineteenth century and even later among certain peoples in Central Africa, Asia Minor, Upper Egypt, Indo-China, Malaya and Madagascar. . . . There, at each eclipse, visitors have seen and still see the entire population come out of its dwellings, shout, beat on domestic utensils, and fire shots throughout the event.

the birth of 'homo faber', so the rise of the theoretical mind in the latter may have indicated the emergence of a genuine 'homo sapiens'.

However this may be, unknown as are the causes of this fundamental change, its consequences have been of supreme importance not only to the development of astronomy but also to the whole of western civilization, which has in fact resulted from it.

Let us then summarize the astronomical science of the Greeks and see what has lasted, as distinct from the unbelievable confusion of contradictory philosophic doctrines of their various 'Schools'.

(A) THE IONIAN SCHOOL (sixth and fifth centuries B.C.) was founded by Thales (c. 640–560 B.C.) of Miletus in Asia Minor. The main achievement of this geometer (Thales' Theorem) and philosopher was the collection which he made in the course of his travels of the knowledge and observations accumulated by the Chaldeans and Egyptians and his importation of them into his own country. He is supposed to have predicted an eclipse of the Sun which occurred in 585 B.C. Unless the success of this prediction was due to a fortunate coincidence, it may well have resulted from a knowledge of the eclipse cycle of eighteen years' period called the 'Saros', imported from Chaldea, where astrologers ventured to predict eclipses as early as the seventh century; but there is no formal proof that he had this knowledge. These predictions were probably based on more or less clearly marked recurrences established by a long series of Chaldean observations lasting through two millennia (section 2); in the absence of precise knowledge of the cause and mode of action of eclipses, they cannot in any way have had the assured character of modern forecasts. Hence, when confirmed by the events, their success must have seemed still more remarkable.

In other respects the astronomical knowledge possessed by Thales does not seem to have surpassed that of the nations which he visited and his cosmology gives no evidence of higher scientific attainment.

His pupils and successors Anaximander (c. 610–545 B.C.), Anaximenes (c. 565–500 B.C.), Heraclitus (c. 540–480 B.C.) and

Anaxagoras (499–428 B.C.) were more fortunate and their ideas, though still very flimsy, indicate distinct progress: to them the Earth was a circular disc of small thickness, floating unsupported or floating on a vortex of air, isolated at the centre of a spherical universe while the Sun, Moon and planets moved round it in circles. But they believed the stars to be nearer than the Sun and Moon, and likened them to golden nails embedded in a crystal sphere. Furthermore they were the first to assign distances to these bodies (9, 18 and 27 terrestrial diameters), but we do not know how these figures were obtained.

These results, modest as they were, led Anaxagoras, who had come to teach at Athens about 450 B.C. to believe that the Moon was as large as the Peleponnesus and the Sun larger still. This statement was considered to be sacrilegious as well as completely contrary to the evidence and was exploited by his enemies in accusing him of atheism, for which he was condemned to death; his life was saved by the intervention of his powerful pupil and friend Pericles, but he was exiled to Asia Minor, where he died.

Further achievements of Anaxagoras were his conception that the Moon and planets were stony in nature like the Earth (he even believed the Moon to be habitable); his inference that the Moon shone by reflected light coming from the Sun; and, finally, his explanation of lunar eclipses as a result of the immersion of the Moon in the Earth's shadow. He even seems to have been the first spiritual and monotheist philosopher (this is probably why he was an 'atheist' in the eyes of his contemporaries, accustomed as they were to their multitude of Olympian deities of all ranks).

(B) THE PYTHAGOREAN SCHOOL (sixth, fifth and fourth centuries) was founded about 540 B.C. at Crotona (the modern Taranto) in Southern Italy by the famous geometer Pythagoras of Samos (c. 580–500 B.C.) and consisted of a secret religious and philosophic sect. After 2,500 years the name of this man still represents the ABC of arithmetic (the multiplication table) and of geometry (Pythagoras' Theorem), but we really have no precise knowledge either of his life or of his work, especially in astronomy. He is supposed to have studied in Egypt and to have discovered the spherical shape of the Earth, the obliquity of the ecliptic and the cause of eclipses.

It appears that these achievements must in fact be divided among his pupils and successors: Parmenides (c. 520–450 B.C.), Democritus (c. 470 B.C.) and Philolaus (c. 450–400 B.C.), who recognized and interpreted correctly a large number of facts that were already known and perhaps even some new ones. Their most important discovery was certainly that of the sphericity of the Earth, their proofs of which have now become classic: the disappearance of the masts of a ship on the horizon, the appearance or disappearance of stars when one travels southwards and, above all, the argument which became the most immediate one once the cause of lunar eclipses was known and agreed upon, namely the circular shape of the Earth's shadow projected on to the Moon during an eclipse. They may also have been the first to realize that the evening star and the morning star are merely alternate appearances of one and the same planet—Venus.

Believing on aesthetic grounds that uniform circular motion is the most perfect in existence and that the heavenly bodies must necessarily have this motion, they considered the planets, Sun, Moon and stars to travel about the Earth in concentric circular orbits. Further, as a result of their musically based cosmological fantasies concerning the 'Harmony of the Spheres', which played an essential part in their doctrines, they assigned to these spheres radii proportional to a series of musical intervals. They placed the heavenly bodies in the following order of distance: Moon, Mercury, Venus, Sun, Mars, Jupiter, Saturn, stars.

Finally it seems that Democritus put forward the idea that the appearance of the luminous belt of the Milky Way, spread out across the sky, results from the agglomeration of a very large number of stars at great distances—a truly remarkable presentiment.

But it must be understood that these important ideas were drowned in a medley of prejudices, mistakes and false hypotheses which at that time were an integral part of their philosophic system and were therefore accepted on the same basis as the more rational content of their theories.

For example, in order to explain the simple fact of the general diurnal motion which appears to carry the heavenly bodies and the celestial sphere round the Earth, they imagined that the Earth and a hypothetical planet—the 'Counter-Earth'—revolved along with the other planets about a central fire hidden from our view by that mysterious body. Outside these spheres they again imagined an external fire, the heat of which was concentrated for our benefit by the Sun in the manner of a magnifying glass (the Greeks knew the use of glass lenses for lighting fires in the sun).

It is quite clear that much care is needed before crediting the Ancients with the discovery of effects observed a great deal later. Only very gradually, and through a long series of mistakes and failures, has the truth finally been grasped.

(c) THE PLATONIC SCHOOL (fourth and third centuries), founded by the illustrious Athenian philosopher Plato (c. 427–347), continued and perfected the teaching of the Pythagoreans. The esotericism and aristocratic political outlook of the latter school had aroused violent opposition among the 'democratic' parties, which had massacred many and driven the rest out of Italy.

The chief exponents of the Platonic School in the astronomical field were Plato's pupils Eudoxus (409–356 B.C.), the famous Aristotle (384–322 B.C.) and Heraclides of Pontus (388–315 B.C.).

They re-established the spherical Earth in its fixed position at the centre of the universe; from that time on, for nearly 2,000 years, the immobility of the Earth continued to be a sacrosanct article of philosophy, supported by the authority of Aristotle.

The heavenly bodies were supposed to describe circular motions about the Earth, carried on spheres which Aristotle unfortunately believed to be material in nature; these motions were compounded geometrically by Eudoxus, who succeeded in representing the observed positions of the planets with more or less accuracy (rather less in the case of Mars). This result, however, was obtained at the price of a highly complicated mechanism comprising no less than 55 spheres.

This world system of Eudoxus and Aristotle should not be confused with that of Ptolemy, which will be discussed later; it was in fact virtually abandoned long before Ptolemy's time.

Mention should finally be made of the achievement of the last main representative of this school, Heraclides of Pontus, a pupil and contemporary of Plato and Aristotle, who as early as the second half of the fourth century B.C. appears to have stated clearly that the Earth rotates on its own axis in 24 hours, thus explaining the diurnal motion. He is even supposed to have discovered that Venus revolves about the Sun and not about the Earth. However, these deviations from tradition and from the authority of his masters were regarded as proofs of his mistaken outlook, not of the originality of his mind.

5. The School of Alexandria and the beginnings of positional astronomy

At the height of classical Greek civilization astronomy had consisted mainly of mathematical investigations and cosmological suppositions based essentially on previous observations taken from the Greeks and Chaldeans. The collapse of Alexander's empire and its subsequent dismemberment at the end of the fourth century B.C. led to the establishment on the shores of the Mediterranean of an important cultural centre, supported by the patronage of enlightened princes, at Alexandria, capital of the new kingdom of Egypt. Here the spirit of exact observation grew up, and the foundations of classical positional astronomy were laid in an admirable series of systematic investigations.

Indeed this appears to have been the first time in the history of science that a specifically scientific institution was established, provided with specially appointed buildings and an immense library; supported by the prince from state revenue, the scholars who frequented this centre of astronomical research were enabled to devote themselves to pure and disinterested scientific investigation.

This remarkable institution, which was to last for a period of nearly a thousand years in all, was apparently founded by Ptolemy, one of Alexander's generals, who had proclaimed himself King of Egypt some years after the death of the great conqueror. It must be said to the credit of the Romans—usually little interested in science—that they respected this remarkable cultural centre during their conquest of the Nile Valley (end of the first century B.C.) and

that they left at the disposal of the scholars most of the facilities
and subsidies that they had enjoyed up to that time. However, it
must also be pointed out that no valuable contribution to astronomy
came from Egypt after the Roman occupation.

Among the earliest scholars who worked at Alexandria reference
must be made to the celebrated Euclid (c. 300 B.C.), a mathematician
rather than an astronomer, whose 'Elements' still form the well-
known basis of instruction in geometry at our schools.

The first actual observers of whom we still have knowledge were
Aristillus and Timocharis in the following century, the third B.C.
Their observations, which were very imprecise and still made with
crude instruments, concern some stars, some solstices, some occultations of stars by the Moon and, finally, a lunar eclipse which—
thanks to Hipparchus—was to play an important part in the discovery of the precession of the equinoxes a century and a half later.

It appears that the greatest astronomers of that time were not
working at Alexandria itself; but their science resulted from the
same inspiration as that of the Alexandrian observers, whose results
they frequently used; furthermore, since their work is known to us
only through the writings of Ptolemy, the last great astronomer of
Alexandria, they are usually linked with this tradition.

(A) ARISTARCHUS (beginning of third century B.C.)

Born on the island of Samos, where he was working at the beginning of the third century B.C., he was not only a great observer, but
also a theorist of genius; unfortunately, his work is for the most
part unknown to us. We know only that he was the first to propose
a method as ingenious in principle as it is unfortunately inaccurate
in practice for the determination of the distance of the Sun; the
method he proposed consisted in observing the angular separation
of the Sun and Moon at the exact instant of first quarter (Fig. 1).

If the distance of the Sun is not incomparably greater than that
of the Moon, this angle should be slightly less than 90° and its value
immediately gives the ratio of the distances of the two bodies.
Aristarchus found by observation that this angle was 87° and
concluded that the Sun was 18 to 20 times further distant than
the Moon. This admittedly crude result (20 times too small)

nevertheless shows a highly remarkable outlook in the geometric clarity of the principle on which it is based, and it held the field for nearly 1,800 years, for, until the rise of classical science, no other method of determining the distance of the Sun was known.

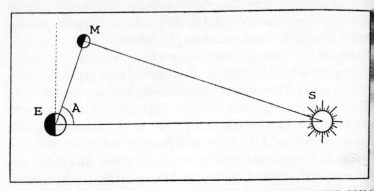

FIG. 1. MEASUREMENT OF THE DISTANCE OF THE SUN
ACCORDING TO ARISTARCHUS

A measurement of the angular separation A between the Sun and the Moon, at the instant of First Quarter, determines in principle the angles of the right-angled triangle EMS; hence the ratio $\frac{ES}{EM}$ between the solar and lunar distances may be found.

Aristarchus also indicated the principle of an equally ingenious direct determination of the distance between the Earth and the Moon, but it does not seem to have been applied until a century and a half later, by Hipparchus.

However, the most important sign of Aristarchus' genius is the fact that he—virtually alone in that remote period—clearly asserted the principle of the heliocentric system; seventeen centuries before Copernicus he maintained that the Earth moved, and that the distances of the stars were immensely greater than the dimensions of its orbit. As a result of this he was naturally accused of impiety and his system completely discredited.

(B) ERATOSTHENES (276–194 B.C.)

This scholar, philosopher, poet and grammarian was certainly a very great man, but unfortunately none of his works has reached us. It is known, however, that, on being called to direct the library at Alexandria towards the end of the third century, he had installed under the porch of the Academy instruments known as armillae or armillary spheres, with which he made various measurements; one of these was that of the obliquity of the ecliptic, i.e. the inclination of the plane of the annual motion of the Sun to that of the celestial equator, defined by the diurnal rotation of the heavens.

His most remarkable and famous achievement, however, was his measurement of the Earth's circumference, which he carried out by a method equally notable for its simplicity and for the precision of the result obtained. According to Aristotle the circumference of our globe had already been found by authors unknown to us to be approximately 400,000 stadia (about 37,500 miles). Eratosthenes immediately obtained a much more accurate value. His method was founded on the observation that, at the time of the summer solstice, the wells at Syene (the modern Aswan) in Central Egypt were illuminated to their remotest depths, from which it follows that on that day the sun passed exactly through the local zenith. At the same instant, in Alexandria, he determined with his instruments a zenith distance for the Sun equal to one-fiftieth of the circumference of a circle. Now, as Eratosthenes realized (Fig. 2), this angle is equal to the difference of latitude between the two cities on the Earth. He thus concluded that the circumference of the Earth is equal to 50 times the distance between Syene and Alexandria, which had been fixed at approximately 5,000 stadia, probably in the course of the contemporary Alexandrian surveys. The Earth's circumference was thus fixed at 250,000 stadia. The stadium is believed to have been 520 ft. in length, which would give a value of approximately 24,660 miles for the circumference of the Earth, compared with the modern value of 24,680 miles. This truly remarkable agreement is probably in part accidental owing to the drastic approximations and inevitable errors inherent in the old measurements.

More than a century later, Posidonius (133–49 B.C.), who lived on the island of Rhodes, is supposed to have made a further measurement of the Earth's circumference by deducing the difference in latitude between Rhodes and Alexandria from the difference of the meridian altitudes reached by the brilliant southern star Canopus at the two places. He found a value of 240,000 stadia or 23,500 miles, but this relative precision actually resulted from the fortunate mutual compensation of two serious errors in each of the two figures on which the calculation was based.

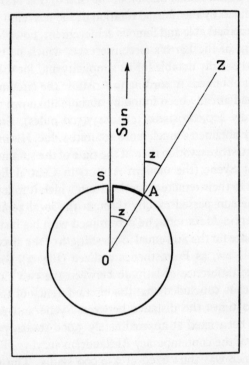

FIG. 2. MEASUREMENT OF THE EARTH'S CIRCUM-
FERENCE ACCORDING TO ERATOSTHENES

When the Sun passes through the zenith at the summer solstice and illuminates the bottoms of the wells at Syene (S), it transits in H, equal to the meridian at Alexandria (A) with a zenith distance Z, the difference in latitude between the two towns, which are separated a known distance AS. The Earth's circumference follows from this.

(C) HIPPARCHUS (end of second century B.C.)

Hipparchus was the greatest astronomer of antiquity and actually the originator of positional astronomy founded on a strict scientific basis. Very little is known about his life apart from the fact that he was born at Nicea in Bithynia and worked on the island of Rhodes.

Among his numerous investigations, which are known to us through the works of his distant successor Ptolemy, are to be found the precise measurement of the period of revolution of the Moon and of the inclination of the lunar orbit to the ecliptic, the discovery of the eccentricity of the lunar orbit,[1] and of the motions of its line of apsides and line of nodes.[2]

By a study of older observations he determined the inequality of the seasons, the existence of which had already been discovered, and he fixed the length of the year at 365 days plus $\frac{1}{4}$ minus 1/300th; the error in this value is only 6 minutes.

He was the first to measure the lunar parallax and hence its distance, which he deduced by comparing the apparent diameter of the Moon with that of the Earth's shadow during a lunar eclipse. He constructed precise tables of the motions of the Sun and Moon over a period of several centuries and, using them, finally succeeded in predicting eclipses correctly—a task which had defied the efforts of his predecessors for so many centuries.

The achievements of Hipparchus, however, were incomparably greater than those of his remote successors, because they were in possession of a theoretical science that was already highly developed, while he had to create one for the most part by himself; thus, in order to make use of his observations, he created trigonometry, which was entirely unknown until his time, and even spherical trigonometry.

Nor was this all. The unexpected appearance of a nova (or more probably a comet) about the year 130 B.C. led him to construct the first systematic star catalogue known to history; he made precise measurements of the celestial coordinates of these stars in order

---

[1] This term does not have its modern meaning, which refers to the properties of the ellipse, but its etymological meaning of a displacement with respect to the terrestrial sphere of the centres of the circular orbits assigned at that time to the heavenly bodies.

[2] The *apsides* are the closest and most distant points of the Moon's orbit, marked by the maximum and minimum apparent angular velocities of the Moon on the celestial sphere, which were already known. The *nodes* are the points of intersection of the lunar orbit with the ecliptic.

that any unusual appearance in the future might be definitely established, and that any possible relative motions of the stars among themselves might be discovered as he had been led to expect that such motions might occur. This catalogue of 1,025 stars, which has reached us in the form of a copy made by Ptolemy, is the first of the fundamental catalogues; it gives the distribution of the stars into constellations and even the first known estimates of their relative brightnesses or 'magnitudes'.

For more than sixteen centuries we shall find the chief astronomers occupied in repeating observations of the stars in Hipparchus' catalogue. After an interval of eighteen centuries it was indeed as a result of his observations that Halley was able to discover the proper motions of stars (III, 1).

In the meantime a series of successive comparisons with his catalogue made it possible to determine precisely another fundamental effect also discovered by him, namely the *precession of the equinoxes*—the slow retrograde displacement along the ecliptic of the point of intersection of the latter with the celestial equator (Fig. 3). This discovery resulted from a comparison between the longitude of the star known as Spica (Alpha Virginis)[1] as observed by him and the value observed 150 years earlier by Timocharis. The value deduced from this observation, 46″.8 per year, differs very little from the value of 48″ deduced for that epoch from present data. However, Hipparchus himself—allowing for accidental errors in the measurements—concluded only to a *minimum* value of 36″.

To complete this monumental work, Hipparchus also left to his successors an enormous number of planetary observations, the periods and inequalities of which he determined with precision. Considering in addition that he put forward the first scientific method of determining geographic longitude and invented the stereographic projection, it becomes clear that he was one of the

[1] This longitude was deduced from a measurement of the angular separation between the star and the Moon during a lunar eclipse, the longitude of the apex of the Earth's shadow being known exactly from that of the Sun (the difference is exactly 180°); this latter was deduced by Hipparchus from his tables.

intellectual giants of mankind. He has been called 'the true father of astronomy'; however this may be, he was certainly the real founder of classical positional astronomy.

It is of interest to note that the greatest permanent contribution of antiquity to science was made by a scholar who was essentially an observer, while on the other hand the theoretical dogmatism of Aristotle actually helped to prevent progress for nearly 2,000 years.

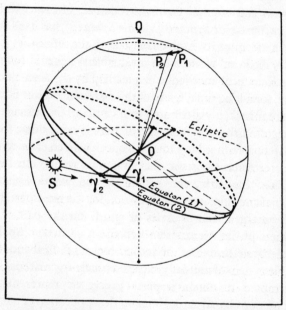

FIG. 3. THE PRECESSION OF THE EQUINOXES, DISCOVERED BY HIPPARCHUS, causes a retrograde motion along the ecliptic of its point of intersection with the equator (Vernal Equinox, designated by γ). It is due to the precessional motion of the Earth's axis marked by the celestial pole P) about the pole of the ecliptic Q, with a period of about 26,000 years.

D) PTOLEMY (second century A.D.)

After Hipparchus, Greek astronomy failed to produce any important results for nearly three centuries. We may just mention his immediate successor Posidionius, named above, and the astronomer Sosigenes of Alexandria (first century A.D.), who is known chiefly because he was consulted by Julius Caesar in connection with the reform of the Roman calendar (the introduction of the leap year every four years)[1] and because he discovered the variations in apparent diameters of the Sun and Moon.

To find the real spiritual heir and successor of Hipparchus we must proceed to Claudius Ptolemy, who was born in the Thebaid and lived and worked at Alexandria during the second century A.D. It is through his writings that we are acquainted with the works of Hipparchus and of other Greek astronomers of earlier times. His chief work, the *Great Syntaxis* (*Megale Syntaxis*), has itself survived only in the form of its Arabic translation, the *Almagest*; it served the entire medieval world as an invaluable systematic compilation of the astronomical knowledge bequeathed by the Ancients.

Hence, for a long time, many of the discoveries described in this work were mistakenly attributed to its author. In particular it has been suggested that his catalogue of stars is none other than that of Hipparchus, reduced to Ptolemy's epoch with an erroneous value of the precession constant that was mistakenly attributed to Hipparchus. Similarly, the system of the world which bears Ptolemy's name (Fig. 4) is certainly not, for the most part, his own work. It emerged from a series of efforts on the part of earlier astronomers of the Alexandrian School, in particular Apollonius who, as early as the end of the second century B.C., abandoned the impossible system of mutually enclosed concentric material spheres and attempted to obtain a plane geocentric representation of celestial motions based throughout on the application of circles and of uniform motions. Subsequent Greek astronomers, particularly Hipparchus and, later on, Ptolemy, succeeded in this task with considerable geometrical elegance, using a judicious superposition of eccentric circles and epicycles.[2] The system was finally

---

[1] The Julian Calendar, based on this $365\frac{1}{4}$-day year which is more than 11 minutes too long, has been kept until modern times in the countries of Eastern Europe; the discrepancy between this calendar and the seasons would now amount to thirteen days. For this reason the anniversary of the Russian Revolution of October 1917 (old style) is commemorated in November (new style).

[2] *i.e.* small secondary circles described about a centre which in turn moved with uniform speed along the principal circle (or deferent).

verthrown as a result of the complexity which arose when an ever-increasing number of superimposed circles had to be postulated in order to represent the ever-multiplying inequalities in the planetary motions revealed by observational progress; but more than 1,500 years were to pass before this came about.

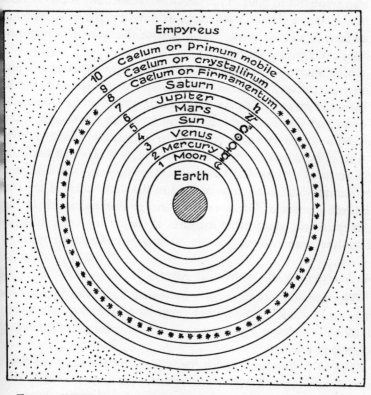

FIG. 4. PTOLEMY'S GEOCENTRIC SYSTEM OF THE WORLD

The Symbol of the ancient view of the Universe.

At all events, Ptolemy was certainly a good observer and the inventor of several new astronomical instruments, for he is credited with the discovery of the change in position among the stars of the pole of rotation of the celestial sphere, the result of the precession of the equinoxes (cf. Fig. 3), and of the less conspicuous inequality in the lunar motion known as *evection*. He was also the first astronomer to recognize clearly the apparent elevation of the heavenly bodies near the horizon known as *astronomical refraction* —a phenomenon which had only been suspected before his time— and he gives a clear description of it in his *Optics*. A description is also found in this book of the deviation (refraction) of rays of light passing into a glass of water; here we have a vague anticipation of modern experimental physics, a science the spirit of which had completely eluded the Ancients.

After Ptolemy, Greek culture falls into complete darkness. The material collapse of the Roman Empire under the pressure of Barbarian invasions (end of fourth century) and the abandonment of the Greek intellectual tradition in favour of submission to the authority of the Ancients through the influence of Christian doctrine, embodying a cosmology inherited from the Hebraic tradition (cf. section 3), arrested the development of astronomy and of science in general. The Arab invasions led to the destruction of the last Eastern centres of Greek culture; in 640 Alexandria fell to the Arabs and the inestimable treasures of the library, comprising at that time more than 700,000 manuscripts, were destroyed by fire.

6. Astronomy in the Middle Ages

Throughout this long period—more than 1,000 years in extent— astronomy made no significant progress of any kind. However, Ptolemy's heritage was preserved and, at infrequent intervals, slightly improved.

The only work worthy of mention is that of the Arab and then the Mongol astronomers, or rather astrologers; stimulated by the unchanging desire of all conquerors to read their future in the stars, they collected and studied the manuscripts left behind by the Greeks, continued their observations and perfected to a limited extent the mathematical techniques required in the prediction of celestial motions.

Among the Arabs we distinguish three principal schools distributed over the vast extent of their empire; their activities were centred respectively at Baghdad, Cairo and the Arabian West— Morocco and Spain.

(A) THE SCHOOL OF BAGHDAD (ninth to tenth centuries)

Baghdad was founded in the eighth century with the aid of astrological advice, and here the heritage of Ptolemy, translated by order of Caliph Al-Mamoun, was preserved best. The most famous astronomers of the Baghdad Caliphate were Al-Battani (Albategnius) (858–929), Al-Sufi (903–986) and Abul-Wefa (Abulfeda) (939–998).

Albategnius made new observations of the Sun's position, improved the value of the tropical year, rectified Ptolemy's precession constant and measured the obliquity of the ecliptic with special care; it was he who introduced the sine into trigonometry.

Al-Sufi is known chiefly for his *Uranographia*, in which he made new observations of the stars in the Ptolemy-Hipparchus catalogue in an endeavour to verify their relative magnitudes; his description of the distribution of stars over the celestial sphere is the first known to us since Antiquity.

Abulfeda published an original *Almagest* and developed the science of trigonometry; he may have been the discoverer of the inequality in the Moon's motion known as the variation.

After Abulfeda nothing remarkable appears in this part of the world for five centuries; in the thirteenth century the Arab Empire was superseded by that of the Mongols, who took over their knowledge and transmitted it as far as China. In this respect they were the direct heirs of the Baghdad School.

The only Mongol astronomer worthy of mention is Ulug-Beigh (1394–1449), grandson of the sanguinary conqueror Tamerlane, who had created an important cultural centre and even an Academy of Science at his capital of Samarkand.[1]

In an observatory specially constructed and equipped with a gigantic quadrant (200 ft. in radius), Ulug-Beigh observed the obliquity of the ecliptic, compiled tables of the Sun and planets and, most important of all, established a new catalogue of some

---

[1] Conquerors throughout the ages have been pleased to surround themselves between successive periods of carnage with men of genius and learning, in the hope that some of that higher glory of which they were themselves incapable might be reflected on them. Louis XIV, Frederick II of Prussia, Catherine of Russia, Napoleon I and Wilhelm II are more recent examples.

thousand stars—the first catalogue in which the coordinates were not simply taken out of Ptolemy. The circumstances of his death are a good illustration of the basically astrological character of Arab astronomy, and of the unhappy effects that this disastrous belief may have on those who trust in it. In 1449 he thought he had read in the stars that he would die by the hand of his son, and accordingly took the precaution of sending him into exile; the son, however, took the matter ill, rebelled, defeated his father and caused his assassination.

After Ulug-Beigh nothing further emerges from Asia.

(B) THE SCHOOL OF CAIRO (tenth, eleventh and twelfth centuries)

In the tenth century the Moors of North Africa drove the Eastern Arabs out of Egypt, founded Cairo and in turn set up an astronomical centre in their new capital. It was to Baghdad, however, that they turned in search of the first elements of their science. Their two most famous astronomers were Ibn-Younis (?–1088) and Alhazen (?–1038).

Ibn-Younis, who had been a pupil of Abul-Wefa at Baghdad, observed the Sun, Moon and planets at Cairo and established tables of their motion of which the Introduction alone is extant; this contains important mathematical advances.

Alhazen is supposed to have written over eighty treatises, almost all of them lost; his *Optics*, which has survived, shows great progress in comparison with that of Ptolemy.

After this time no more notable astronomers are found, but it is known that as late as the twelfth century there were still at Cairo astronomers paid to calculate ephemerides.

(C) THE WESTERN ARAB SCHOOLS (eleventh, twelfth and thirteenth centuries)

Very little is known about these Schools except that they flourished in Spain and Morocco; nor do we know how they obtained the *Almagest*.

The chief astronomers whose names have survived are Arzachel who observed at Toledo towards the end of the eleventh century and improved the precession constant, and Alpetragius, who worked in Morocco in the middle of the twelfth century. Alpetragius objected to the complexity of Ptolemy's system, but the one that he proposed in its place, in spite of the 'divine inspiration' which he claimed for it, was no better and did not survive him.

In connection with the Arab astronomers, whose protector and pupil he was, one should mention the first European to reappear in the history of astronomy—Alphonso X, King of Castile, who on the day of his accession in 1252 ordered the publication of the *Alphonsine Tables*; these tables were compiled by Jewish and Arab astronomers whom he had called to Toledo. Although these tables of celestial motions incorporate in their system a few of the errors added by the Arabs to Ptolemy's elements,[1] they show distinct progress in the improvement of certain fundamental constants—in particular the length of the year.

(D) THE AWAKENING OF ASTRONOMY IN CHRISTIAN EUROPE (fifteenth century)

Outside the sphere of influence of the Arabs nothing of note appeared in the Christian world until the fifteenth century. Between the collapse of the Roman Empire and the Renaissance the intellectual heritage of the Ancients was only kept, preserved and transmitted through the centuries in the monasteries, those oases of peace and learning, where generation after generation of monks dedicated their lives to reading, translating and endlessly commenting on the works of Aristotle in the light of the scriptures. Ptolemy's book itself did not arrive until rather late, in the form of its Arabic translation, and original Arab contributions filtered through only very gradually under the influence of the Crusades from the eleventh and twelfth centuries on.

Only in the course of the fifteenth century did science in general and astronomy in particular reappear in Europe. This revival resulted from many factors: the invention of printing in 1453 which facilitated the diffusion of knowledge, the fall of

[1] In particular a so-called movement of 'trepidation' of the equinoxes, superimposed on the precession, which they seemed very proud of having discovered, and which is entirely spurious.

Constantinople to the Turks (1453) and the consequent emigration
of Greek scholars to the West, and finally the great Portuguese and
Spanish naval expeditions (discovery of America in 1492) made
possible by the use of the compass inherited from the Arabs. This
raised the astronomical problem of the determination of longitudes and of positions at sea and finally demonstrated the spherical
shape of the Earth and its isolation in space.

The names worth mentioning in the fifteenth century are few in
number: George Purbach (1423–1461), who possessed a Greek
text of the *Almagest* and put forward a theory of the planets, and
especially his pupil John Müller (1436–1476) known as Regio-
montanus (because he was born near Königsberg), who translated
the *Almagest* into Latin and established an observatory equipped
with a workshop and a printing press at Nuremberg in 1471. He
left ephemerides covering the period 1475–1505, which are said to
have been used by Vasco da Gama and Christopher Columbus.

Finally, the Belgian Cardinal Nicolas de Cues (or of Cusa)
(1401–1464) was one of the first to revive and support Aristarchus'
hypothesis of the motion of the Earth; to his contemporaries,
however, this probably seemed no more than an intellectual sport,
and he was unable to support his conviction with decisive arguments. These did not become available until after the work of
Copernicus and his successors.

Plate I. THE LUNAR SURFACE AND ITS CRATERS

Photograph taken with the great 'equatorial coude' of 24 in. aperture and 60 ft. focal length at the Paris Observatory.

Over 30,000 craters of all sizes have been recorded on the surface of our satellite. The largest are over 100 miles in diameter, while the smallest craters visible in large telescopes are only a few hundred yards across. Their depth varies from about 4 miles in the case of the crater Theophilus visible near the middle of the plate to a few dozen yards for the smallest craters. Certain craters, probably among the older in origin, are more or less completely eroded or buried under material deposited or spread out in the course of ages; this is the case of the notched crater Fracastor, visible on the plate.

The lunar surface also shows large plains with relatively few features, such as the *Mare Nectaris* visible at the centre of the plate, and mountain ranges, probably eruptive in origin, of which the Altai Chain, visible on the plate, is a minor example. Near the South Pole of the Moon the Doerfel and Leibnitz Mountains reach altitudes of 27,000 ft., comparable with the heights in the Himalaya Chain on the Earth.

Photographs such as this, taken with the great coude refractor in Paris, were used at the turn of the century by the French astronomers Loewy and Puiseux to prepare a large 'Atlas photographique' of the Moon.

Scale in kilometres

0   100   200   300   400   500

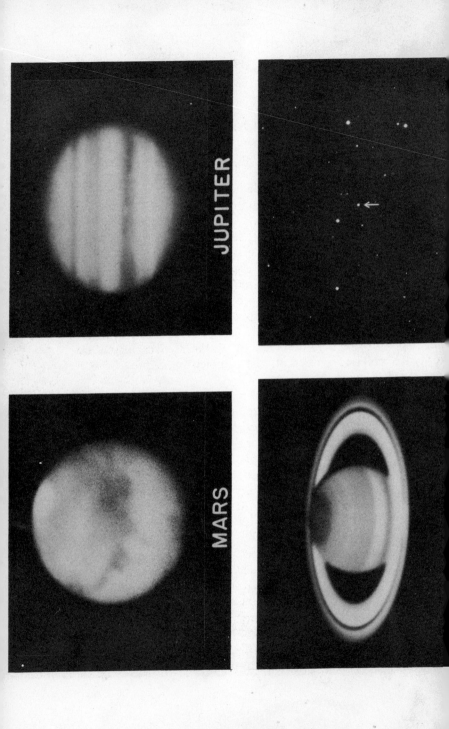

JUPITER

MARS

PLATE II. THE PLANETS MARS, JUPITER, SATURN AND PLUTO

(a) This photograph of Mars, taken with the 100-in. telescope at the Mount Wilson Observatory, shows the bright, snowy polar cap at the top and a number of dark regions in the upper half of the disc in which there occur seasonal variations suggesting the presence of some kind of vegetation. The so-called 'canals', which have caused so much speculation since their discovery by the Italian astronomer Schiaparelli in 1877, are seldom visible on photographs. They are observed mainly in the bright desert regions of the lower half of the disc.

(b) This photograph of Jupiter, taken with the 100-in. telescope, shows only an impenetrable atmosphere laden with thick clouds which are arranged in a series of bands parallel to the equator. Note the flattening of the globe due to its rapid rotation, first measured by Cassini about 1670, and the intense darkening at the limb of the disc due to absorption by the dense atmosphere. The Red Spot is not visible on this view. The discovery of radio emission from Jupiter, observed by Burke at Washington in 1955, has renewed interest in the complex phenomena of the Jovian atmosphere.

(c) This photograph of Saturn, again taken with the 100-in. telescope, shows plainly the globe, strongly flattened, with its bands of clouds parallel to the equator and strong atmospheric limb darkening, and the famous ring, discovered by Huygens in 1656. The ring has three main zones differing in brightness: two outer bright zones separated by the division discovered by Cassini in 1675 and an inner, darker zone, the 'crepe ring' (visible on the photograph only where it crosses the disc), discovered in 1850 by Bond in America and Dawes in England. No radio emission has been received from Saturn yet.

(d) This photograph of Pluto, taken with the 200-in. telescope on Palomar Mountain, shows it only as a mere point of light among the stars in the field. The most distant planet in the solar system was discovered in 1930 by Tombaugh at the Lowell Observatory after an exhaustive photographic search inspired by theoretical predictions of P. Lowell and W. H. Pickering. Its minute disc was first observed and measured visually by G. P. Kuiper with the 200-in. telescope in 1950.

41

* II *

The Copernican Revolution and the Beginnings of
Classical Astronomy in the Sixteenth
and Seventeenth Centuries

---

7. Copernicus (1473–1543)

It was the glorious achievement of the Polish cleric Nicholas Copernicus of Thorn that he opened the gateway to Classical Astronomy, and thus to all later progress, by establishing the true 'System of the World' which still bears his name; this he did in his immortal book *De Revolutionibus Orbium Coelestium*, published in 1543 (Fig. 5).

According to this the Earth, along with the other planets, revolves round the Sun, which remains fixed at the centre of the system; the dimensions of the orbits are negligible in comparison with the distance of the fixed stars.

This discovery, simple as it was fundamental, marks the beginning of the transition from the subjective, mystical, primitive conception of the Universe to the objective, rational view of modern times. It brought in its train an immense revolution of thought, in that it replaced reliance on the authority of the Ancients by submission to the facts as the source of all knowledge and set forth simplicity and adequacy as criteria of the truth of theories.

In actual fact the significance and full implications of this new view of the universe became apparent only by stages, and, in some respects, Copernicus' work represents no more than a resumption of the Greek intellectual tradition. Far from rejecting the authority of the Ancients, whose science and philosophy he had studied extensively in Italy, he invoked it in his own favour and relied upon it in the presentation of his system; Copernicus knew his predecessors—he quoted them and indeed stated explicitly that it was the perusal of their works which had caused him to consider motion of the Earth and to enquire whether such a hypothesis might not permit a *simpler* explanation of the motions of the heavenly bodies than that provided by the Ptolemaic system.

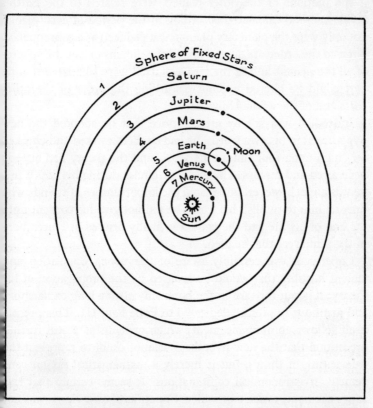

FIG. 5. THE HELIOCENTRIC SYSTEM OF COPERNICUS marks the arrival of the modern view of the Universe.

'Basing myself on this, I too began to consider the possibility that the Earth might be in motion. And, though the idea might appear absurd, I knew nevertheless that others before me had been at liberty to imagine such circles as they pleased in order to represent celestial phenomena. I therefore concluded that I too should be permitted to try to see whether, by supposing the Earth to be

43

endowed with a certain motion, it might not be possible to obtain representations more valid than those of other men for the revolutions of the celestial spheres.

'And thus, having supposed those motions which I attribute to the Earth in my book, I finally found by a lengthy application that, if the motions of the other planets were related to the Earth's revolution and calculated according to the period of each planet, not only were the planetary phenomena deduced as a consequence, but also the order of succession and the dimensions of the spheres of all the planets and of the Heavens itself were so related that no part could be altered without disturbing the order of the other parts and of the whole Universe.'

Indeed, it was not by mere caprice that he adopted the new hypothesis: in his own words, he had studied, worked and checked for 'nigh upon four times nine years' and the theory had already been aired and discussed in academic circles during his life. While he was alive, however, he resisted the importunities of friends who pressed him to publish his work; he did not give his consent until the end of his life and the book was finally printed at Nuremberg in the same year that he died.

Copernicus was certainly aware of the strong opposition and violent hostility that would be aroused by the propagation of his theory; it is put forward in the book only after a long explanatory and justificatory preface dedicated to Pope Paul III. This preface itself follows an announcement, which explains as a still further precaution that the new hypothesis cannot claim to represent the true nature of things, but is merely a mathematical fiction convenient in astronomical computations. It seems certain that this announcement, which contradicts Copernicus' own views, was not written by him; it is believed to stem from the prudence of the Protestant theologian Osiander, who was entrusted with the publication of the book.

Such precautions in the presentation of a new mathematical theory of celestial motions may seem strange to a twentieth-century reader living in a civilized country; but they were thoroughly justified in the sixteenth century when there was no trifling with any subject which could, however indirectly, touch on the authority of Aristotle and the accepted interpretation of the Scriptures. In spite of the high patronage under which it had been put forward, the work was in fact finally placed on the Index in 1616[1]; even in 1600 advocacy of the Copernican system appears among the 'crimes' cited by the Inquisition in order to send the unfortunate Giordano Bruno to the stake.

It would take too long to describe here, even in outline, the highly involved history of the battle aroused by the new system of the world; it lasted for more than three centuries, during which, as Bigourdan has pointed out, 'Science very frequently played only the smallest part.' We shall have more to say on this subject later in connection with the condemnation of Galileo.[2] In any case, the violence and long duration of the struggle bear witness to the fundamental character of the revolution which Copernicus effected in our conception of the world.

Credit is due to him essentially for having been the first to produce a clear and systematic exposition of the crucial arguments against the geocentric view of the Universe, and for having destroyed that tenacious optical illusion. This was the basic outrage that he committed, since in other respects he held to all the aesthetic and philosophic prejudices of his predecessors: like them he believed in a small spherical universe, in circular orbits, and in uniform motions; since these hypotheses are inadequate to describe the observations, he was obliged to reintroduce eccentrics and epicycles after he had rejected those of Ptolemy; he even took up Aristotle's idea of moving material orbs or spheres; for him the part played by the central Sun was purely optical, and gravity provided only the internal cohesion of the separate bodies.

In other words, Copernicus' great service to science lay rather in the later developments which he made possible when he liberated astronomy from the idea of the Earth's immobility than in any immediate progress arising from his representation of the celestial motions, which was really hardly better than that of Ptolemy; the more so because the case that he made for his system was often

[1] It was to remain there until the beginning of the nineteenth century.
[2] The interested reader may consult the works on this subject mentioned in our Bibliography.

specious, inaccurate and infested with non-scientific considerations borrowed from the Ancients.

If it had not been for the series of men of genius who perfected Copernicus' work in the 150 years following his death and provided the conclusive proofs which he still lacked, no great progress would have been achieved and his system could not have prevailed.

8. Galileo (1564–1642)

The most striking arguments and direct proofs that were calculated to lead to the triumph of the heliocentric view of the Universe were provided chiefly by Galileo Galilei, the great Italian physicist and mathematician of Pisa.

This genius, the founder of dynamics and creator of the experimental method in physical science, was already famous for his lectures on mathematics delivered from 1589 onwards, first at the University of Pisa and subsequently at that of Padua; his greatest achievement, however, was his study of the heavens from 1609 onwards, for the first time in history, through the telescope, which had been invented by accident in the previous year by some Dutch spectacle makers; after hearing a rumour of the invention, he independently rediscovered its principle by 'a more profound study of the theory of refraction'.

'Sparing neither trouble nor expense', he finally constructed a telescope giving a magnification of over thirty diameters, with which he discovered the mountains and valleys of the Moon and the 'infinite multitude' of telescopic stars, resolved the Milky Way into stars and finally made what he regarded as his most important discovery, that of the four major satellites of Jupiter, at the beginning of January 1610. All these discoveries he made public in his *Nuntius Sidereus*, the *Sidereal Messenger*, published in 1610, and immediately pointed out that the last in particular constituted 'an important and splendid argument' in favour of the Copernican System.

All these discoveries, however, were contrary to received teaching and to the authority of Aristotle, and were not received without a struggle. From every side the followers of the old philosophy, then called the Peripatetics, rose up against them with various specious objections which today seem ridiculous: it was claimed that the discoveries were mistaken—illusions produced by the lenses of the telescopes[1]—and some even refused to look through the new instruments.

Fortunately, Galileo had observational evidence in his favour; all Europe applied to him to obtain lenses and telescopes constructed under his direction, and his observations were soon verified on every side.

Feeling, however, that they were losing the battle on the factual front, the defenders of the traditional teaching and of the principle of authority turned to the temporal power of the Church to assure the victory of their opinions. By a series of manœuvres and intrigues in which bad faith vied with ignorance, and after long and tortuous debate, they managed to have Copernicus' book placed on the Index in 1616; it thus became forbidden to teach or defend the 'absurd and false' doctrine of the motion of the Earth. Galileo was summoned to Rome and appeared for the first time before the Tribunal of the Holy Office; under threat of prosecution he was compelled to promise to 'abstain from supporting, teaching or defending this opinion in any way soever, in speech or in writing.'

But the battle of ideas had been joined and could not be arrested so easily; in the whole of Europe the new system gradually gained the adherence of scholars: Kepler adopted it to discover the laws of planetary motion (cf. section 10); Galileo, continuing his observations, discovered the phases of Mars and Venus, predicted by Copernicus, and thus refuted one of the objections that until then had been raised against his system.[2]

He also conceived, less fortunately, a mistaken theory of the tides, from which he claimed to have deduced a new proof of the motion of the Earth. Chafing under the burden of silence that had

[1] This was the case in particular of the sunspots, observed by Galileo and by the Jesuit father Scheiner, who for a long period had a contest over priority with Galileo; the observations of Scheiner were more thoroughly pursued, but Galileo's interpretations were more accurate.

[2] The phases of these planets are invisible to the naked eye, but can be noticed clearly with a very small instrument.

been imposed on him concerning the theory that he knew to be correct, he undertook in various works at least to demonstrate the impossibilities of the Ptolemaic System; particularly in *Il Saggiatore* (*The Assayer*), which was dedicated to Pope Urban VIII and was well received (1624).

In 1632, however, there appeared his *Dialogue on the Two Principal Systems of The World, those of Ptolemy and Copernicus*, in which his preference for the latter was too clearly noticeable. In spite of the precaution that he had taken in initially submitting the manuscript to Urban VIII and in obtaining permission to print from the Examiners of the Inquisition, Galileo was again denounced before the Roman Inquisition by his more far-seeing adversaries, who even succeeded in deceiving Urban VIII as to the true content of the book and in changing his feelings toward Galileo.

The scientist was therefore summoned once more before the Tribunal, and condemned in the middle of 1633 to 'abjure, curse and detest' his 'errors and heresies' concerning the motion of the Earth, according to the emphatic formulae of the time; after this he was kept under surveillance at Rome and then near Florence, until his death in 1642.[1]

9. Tycho Brahe (1546–1601)

While Galileo played the most distinguished part in spreading Copernicus' theory and introducing it to cultivated circles, it is quite certain that the adoption of the heliocentric system by men of science owes at least as much, if not more, to two astronomers whose talents complemented each other: a remarkable observer, Tycho Brahe, and an extraordinary computer, Kepler, who were led by destiny into a fortunate association.

By his success in greatly increasing the accuracy of measures of astronomical positions, and by his assiduous observation of them, Tycho Brahe discovered a number of new phenomena; but

---

[1] For the controversial details of this sentence, from which, incidentally, the Roman Catholic Church rather than science suffered, reference may be made to the works mentioned in our Bibliography.

above all he provided his pupil and successor Kepler with a series of observations of the highest quality for his theoretical researches into the laws of planetary motion.

The scion of an aristocratic Danish family, Tycho Brahe was attracted to astronomical studies from his early youth. After cultivating for some time chemistry, astrology and astronomy together, he devoted himself exclusively to celestial observations after the appearance in 1572 of a 'New Star' of unexcelled brightness (it is now known that it was actually a galactic supernova; cf. VIII, 44). The appearance of this star, which contradicted the theory accepted since Aristotle's time that the heavens were immutable, filled Tycho Brahe with amazement:

'In the month of November, on the eleventh day of that month, in the evening, after sunset, when, according to my habit, I was contemplating the stars in a clear sky, I noticed that a new and unusual star, surpassing the other stars in brightness, was shining almost directly above my head; and since I had, almost from boyhood, known all the stars of the heavens perfectly (there is no great difficulty in attaining that knowledge), it was quite evident to me that there had never before been any star in that place in the sky, even the smallest, to say nothing of a star so conspicuously bright as this. I was so astonished at this sight that I was not ashamed to doubt the trustworthiness of my eyes. But when I observed that others, too, on having the place pointed out to them, could see that there was really a star there, I had no further doubts. A miracle indeed, (perhaps) the greatest of all that have occurred in the whole range of nature since the beginning of the world, . . . For all philosophers agree, . . . that in the ethereal region of the celestial world no change, in the way either of generation or of corruption, takes place; but that the heavens and the celestial bodies in the heavens are without increase or diminution, and that they undergo no alteration, either in number or in size or in light or in any other respect; that they always remain the same, like unto themselves in all respects, no years wearing them away . . .'

It may be imagined that the occurrence of a celestial phenomenon so contradictory to all accepted teaching led contemporaries to regard it as a miracle announcing some sensational event: the arrival of Antichrist or the return of Christ, according to many authors of the time. As for Tycho Brahe, he contented himself with proving by very precise measurements that the body was indeed a star at a very great distance and with no appreciable parallax, and not some unusual meteor within the solar system. Furthermore, the appearance of this star gave him the same idea that it had to Hipparchus eighteen centuries before of establishing a precise star catalogue in order that future changes might be confirmed with certainty.

This catalogue, along with most of Tycho Brahe's other work, was executed from 1576 onwards on the island of Hven, near Copenhagen, where the liberality of King Frederick II of Denmark enabled him to erect an important observatory, named by him Uraniburg, which is justly regarded as the ancestor of the great modern observatories. For twenty years—from 1576 to 1596—he made an immense number of observations there, for which he caused the construction of much larger and more accurate instruments than were in general use at the time.

Among his principal studies one must mention that of atmospheric refraction—the apparent elevation of stars over the horizon due to the bending of light rays by our atmosphere; but he did not realize the general character of the effect and believed that the influence of refraction on the stars was somewhat less than on the Sun. Apart from this he discovered the inequality in the lunar motion known as the *variation* and even suspected that which is called the *annual equation*. In compiling his great star catalogue he employed a constant of 51″ for the precession of the equinoxes— a value which is very close to that adopted at present—and he discovered the *variation in the obliquity of the ecliptic* from changes in the celestial latitudes (measured from the ecliptic) of certain stars, that had occurred since the epoch of Hipparchus. These changes, though small, could already be measured thanks to the precision of his instruments (of the order of a minute of arc).

Though an incomparable observer, Tycho Brahe was much less fortunate as a theorist; unwilling for theological reasons to adopt the Copernican System, he attempted to construct a hybrid system, half heliocentric, half geocentric, which would enable him to save the phenomena and account to some extent for his observations. According to this system the planets revolved round the Sun, but the Sun itself, accompanied by its entire retinue of planets, revolved round the Earth. This system hardly survived its author and had no appreciable effect on the progress of astronomy.

After the death of his protector, the King of Denmark, Tycho was compelled to leave Uraniburg and in 1599 he took refuge at Prague where he became astronomer to Rudolf II, Emperor of Austria, who was infatuated with astrology. Here he died shortly afterwards, in 1601. Before his death, however, he had called to his side the young Kepler, who succeeded him as Imperial Astronomer in 1601. Tycho bequeathed to him the treasure of his collected observations, which Kepler ably exploited in establishing the laws of the true system of the Universe.

10. Kepler (1571-1630)

It was in the course of a difficult and agitated life that the genius of John Kepler manifested itself with the aid of Tycho Brahe's precious observations. As early as 1596 Kepler had written a treatise filled with mystical ideas concerning the *Harmony of the Spheres*, inherited from the Pythagoreans, in which he declared himself a partisan of the Copernican System. From that time on, his strange ideas had led him to inquire into the geometric relations between the orbits of the various planets, and he thought that he had found such relations by inscribing between them various simple geometric solids such as the cube, tetrahedron, octahedron, etc. Mistaken as they were, these ideas were valuable in so far as they started him on the road that was to lead to his most important discoveries.

In addition, his book bore witness to an originality of mind which was recognized by Tycho Brahe, who was led to appoint Kepler first as his assistant, then as his successor.

In this way, after innumerable attempts and gropings which the accuracy of Tycho's observations enabled him to check step by step, Kepler was led by his particular study of the motion of the planet Mars to discover the first two fundamental laws of planetary motion which have made his name immortal.

These two laws, published in 1609 in his *Astronomia Nova*, state first that the motion of the planets takes place not along circular orbits as had always been believed before, but precisely along *ellipses* with the Sun at one focus, and second (the Law of Areas), that the *radius vector*—a straight line described between the planet and the Sun—sweeps out equal areas of the ellipse in equal times.

It is interesting to note that Kepler's discovery of the elliptic form of the orbit of Mars was made possible by the great accuracy of Tycho Brahe's observations and by Kepler's complete confidence in them; indeed the deviation between the elliptic form and the previously assumed circular form of the planet's orbit is no more than 8 minutes of arc in longitude. Here is a striking example of the importance to scientific progress of a simple increase in the accuracy of measurements, for, in Kepler's own words, 'these eight minutes in themselves alone have led to a complete renovation of astronomy'.

It should also be pointed out that throughout his work Kepler continually used considerations as to the action of the Sun on the motion of the planets, and thus unmistakably anticipated the Law of Universal Gravitation, the enunciation of which three-quarters of a century later was to make Newton famous (section 11).

Furthermore, Kepler was the first to give a clear explanation of the phenomenon of tides through the attraction exerted by the Moon on the mass of the oceans. However, all this is drowned in a confusion of rather surprising mystical and extrascientific considerations—such as this law of the five geometric solids interposed between the orbits of the planets, which Kepler took very seriously.

Nevertheless, these very mistakes actually helped him, since they led him to study closely the relation between the periods of revolution of the planets and their respective distances from the Sun. After extraordinary labours, which took him no less than sixteen years of intricate calculation, and after innumerable failures, Kepler finally achieved decisive success in discovering that the squares of the periods of revolution of the planets are related to one another as the cubes of the major axes of their orbits (Kepler's Third Law). This fundamental result was published by Kepler in 1619 in a book that was called, significantly enough, *Harmonices Mundi*, the Harmonies of the World.

Thus were established the three fundamental laws of planetary motion. The accuracy of representation of the observations by means of these laws was so much superior to that provided by the hypothesis of circular orbits that the chief astronomers were rapidly convinced. The discovery of these laws directly paved the way for the investigations of Newton, who was to establish finally the principle of universal attraction responsible for Kepler's laws.

Furthermore, Kepler made a large number of other important investigations, in physics as well as astronomy; further publications of his are the *Epitome of Copernican Astronomy* (1618–1621) and a *Treatise on Comets* (1619), in which he pointed out that cometary tails are always directed away from the Sun and suggested their possible formation from matter of the cometary head repelled by the solar rays, thus anticipating by two and a half centuries the discovery of radiation pressure (VII, 40). He discovered an approximate law of refraction which enabled him to calculate astronomical refraction in a very simple way and to show that it does not reach zero until the zenith, instead of altitude 45° as believed by Tycho Brahe. He was the first to maintain that the atmosphere has weight and to explain correctly the reddish colour of the Moon during lunar eclipses, ascribing it to sunlight that has passed through the Earth's atmosphere. It was he also who proposed the substitution in astronomical telescopes of a convergent eyepiece for Galileo's divergent eyepiece.

Finally, in the last years of his life, he produced the 'Rudolphine Tables' of planetary motion, based on his laws and on Tycho Brahe's observations, which were used for more than a century in the calculation of ephemerides.

He died in utter destitution in 1630, during a journey that he had undertaken to obtain from the Emperor the stipend that the monarch always delayed paying him. In order to live Kepler had for almost all his life to continue the practice of astrology, in which, despite his mystical temperament, he hardly believed.

11. Newton (1642–1727)

It was the magnificent achievement of the English scientific genius Isaac Newton, mathematician, astronomer and physicist, that he established firmly the general law governing the motion of the heavenly bodies, thus completing the edifice that had grown for more than a century and a half through the work of Copernicus, Galileo, Tycho Brahe and Kepler.

Legend has it that in 1666, at the age of twenty-four, Newton was led by his observation of the fall of an apple to reflect on the force of gravity which causes bodies to fall on the surface of the Earth, and to consider whether this same force of attraction might not extend as far as the Moon and retain it in its orbit. However, the numerical data available at the time concerning the dimensions of the terrestrial globe had not made it possible for him to verify his ideas. In fact the idea of mutual attraction of the heavenly bodies had already been formulated before Newton's time, especially by Kepler and more clearly by the English physicist Hooke. Kepler had even spoken of a decrease in the attractive force with the inverse square of the distance. The essential achievement of Newton was his precise and convincing proof that the attraction of the Earth diminishes effectively according to this particular law.

He did not succeed in his task until sixteen years later, after the French astronomer Picard had, in the course of very careful geodetic operations north of Paris in 1671, obtained a new value of the Earth's diameter much more accurate than previous figures. With this, Newton was able to compare correctly the fall of bodies at the surface of the Earth with the 'fall' of the Moon towards the Earth—the deviation of the lunar orbit from its tangent at a given point; he found that the observed values of these two effects were exactly, within the limits of the errors of measurement, in the ratio corresponding to a law of attraction varying as the inverse square of the distance from the centre of the Earth.

Newton was thus led to state formally the law of universal attraction, according to which *everything occurs as if matter attracted matter in direct ratio (proportionally) to the masses present and in inverse ratio to the square of the distance between them.* It should further be noted that Newton refrained in this connection from proposing any metaphysical hypothesis (*hypotheses non fingo*) 'for whatever is not deduced from the phenomena is to be called an hypothesis; and hypotheses, whether metaphysical or physical ... have no place in experimental philosophy' and that, having stated the properties of the attractive force he avoided any reference or assumption as to its 'fundamental nature'.

This Principle of Universal Gravitation was published in 1687 in Newton's immortal book on the *Mathematical Principles of Natural Philosophy*, in which he established once and for all the fundamental laws of celestial mechanics and deduced Kepler's three laws from his Principle and from the mechanics of Galileo, elaborated by Huygens (section 12, c).

With the aid of the Principle, Newton was also in a position to explain and make precise calculations of the tides, to calculate the motion of the Moon and of the planets with greater accuracy, taking into account the mutual perturbations of the planets, and even to compute cometary orbits. This last point was a striking achievement, since it brought into the natural order of things bodies that up to then had been regarded as free from subjection to the ordinary laws applicable to the other celestial bodies.

His contemporary Halley (III, 13) made a famous application of these calculations of cometary orbits to the great comet of 1682, which now bears his name, predicting its return in the year 1759 three-quarters of a century later. The exact realization of this prediction produced the final and conclusive proof of the truth of Newton's Law and of the validity of the methods of celestial mechanics. It may be added that the general acceptance of Newton's theories and of his mechanics on the Continent dates only from that time, near the middle of the eighteenth century: for reasons in which nationalist prejudice played a greater part than scientific doubt, Newton's ideas were in general badly received outside England in most European countries, where the odd and now forgotten ideas of the French philosopher Descartes concerning the nature and structure of the Universe had at that time a considerable following.

In astronomy a further achievement of Newton's was his

theoretical prediction of the polar flattening of the Earth. He was also the first to explain that the phenomenon of the precession of the equinoxes is connected with this flattening of our globe, and that the precession is due to the influence of the Sun's attraction on the Earth's equatorial bulge. At the beginning of the eighteenth century this question of the flattening of the terrestrial globe raised lengthy debates which were not finally resolved in Newton's favour until after the French geodetic expeditions to Lapland and the Equator, undertaken for the purpose of comparing the lengths of arcs of the meridian of equal angular size in these two regions (III, 16). This comparison showed that the distance corresponding to an arc of $1°$ was greater in Lapland than at the Equator and that the meridian was consequently flattened towards the poles, in accordance with Newton's theory.

Finally, Newton was also the first to construct a *reflecting telescope* with a metallic mirror, which was realized in 1672. This type of instrument was not much developed until a century later by W. Herschel (IV, 23), but since then it has assumed fundamental importance in modern research.

Newton's astronomical research virtually ceased with the publication of the *Principia* owing to administrative duties which unfortunately monopolized his later activities.

12. Other astronomers of the seventeenth century

In comparison with the brilliant founders of classical astronomy the remaining astronomers of the time pale into insignificance nevertheless, some of them did work worthy of mention.

(A) J. HORROX (1619–1641)

This English clergyman, clearly a precocious genius, had enough time in the course of his very short life to make observations and propound theoretical ideas that were equally remarkable. He was the first to observe a transit of Venus across the solar disc, in 1639.

[1] In 1631 the French philosopher Gassendi (1592–1655) had observed a transit of Mercury which already demonstrated the definite superiority of Kepler's '*Rudolphine Tables*'.

His main achievement was his early and wholehearted support for Kepler's theory of elliptic orbits, which he applied to the lunar theory in memoirs that were published in 1672, long after his death, and utilized by Newton. He discovered the explanation of the Evection and Variation—effects of the ellipticity of the lunar orbit —by introducing the idea that the Sun's influence leads to variations in the ellipticity and to oscillatory motion in the line of apsides. He also produced clearer evidence for the Annual Equation suspected by Tycho Brahe. His untimely death was certainly a great loss to astronomy, the more so because most of his works are lost.

B) J. HEVELIUS (1611–1687)

This wealthy merchant of Danzig had installed a well-equipped observatory on the roof of his house and was one of the most active observers of the seventeenth century. From a painstaking study of sunspots, between 1642 and 1645, he deduced a reasonably accurate value for the period of the solar rotation; he gave the first description of the bright areas in the neighbourhood of spots—the name of 'faculae', which he gave them, is still used. He also made observations of the planets, particularly Jupiter and Saturn.

In 1647 he published the first—comparatively detailed—map of the Moon,[1] based on ten years' observation, and diagrams of the different phases for each day of the lunation. He realized that the large, rather uniform, grey spots on the lunar disc consist of low plains, while the bright contrasted regions represent high mountainous relief. He also obtained much better values than Galileo for the heights of these lunar mountains (Plate I).

Hevelius was also interested in positional astronomy, and planned a new star catalogue which was to be much more complete than that of Tycho Brahe. This task, begun in 1657, could unfortunately not be completed because Hevelius' observatory was destroyed by arson in 1679. Nevertheless his observations enabled him to compile a catalogue of over 1,500 stellar positions, which was published

[1] In 1651 the Italian J. B. Riccioli (1598–1671) published in his *New Almagest* a somewhat better map, the nomenclature of which prevailed and is still in use.

posthumously in 1690; this *Uranographia* contains a fine celestial atlas in 54 plates.[1] Unfortunately, however, Hevelius continued the practice of observing positions with the naked eye, which considerably reduces the value of his work.

(c) c. huygens (1629–1695)

While the astronomers mentioned above were concerned mainly with the positions and motions of the heavenly bodies, the Dutchman Christian Huygens devoted most of his attention to their appearance and physical constitution.

His most famous discovery, if not his most important, was that of *Saturn's ring* (Plate II, *c*). With his primitive instruments Galileo had been unable to see more in Saturn than a strange form sometimes elongated, sometimes circular—which had perplexed him deeply, and for fifty years after Galileo's time observers had represented Saturn with the most extraordinary shapes; but no one had succeeded in finding an explanation of the curious and variable forms taken by the planet. With the aid of considerably more powerful instruments, Huygens succeeded in resolving the mystery of Saturn's shape in 1655–6; he found, as he tells us, 'that the globe of Saturn was surrounded on all sides by another body, a kind of ring, encircling it and concentric with it'. Huygens announced his discovery in a famous anagram, not translated by him until 1659, which simply says 'It is encircled by a thin, plane ring, nowhere attached, and inclined to the Ecliptic.' He also published a sketch explaining the variation in aspect presented by the planet and its ring as a function of its relative position with respect to the Earth.

Thanks to his powerful instruments, Huygens not only discovered Saturn's ring in its actual form, but also made another discovery of equal interest—that of Saturn's first known satellite,

[1] Early in the seventeenth century the German pastor J. Bayer (1572–1625) had compiled the first *atlas* of the constellations, published in his *Uranometria* (1603), in which he designated the stars by letters of the Greek alphabet rather than by the customary description of their positions in the associated mythological figures; as a result, the description of the starry heaven was greatly clarified, and Bayer's letters have remained in general use ever since.

Titan. Following this, other satellites of Saturn were discovered by Cassini in 1671-2 (section 12, D). About the same time, in 1656, Huygens discovered the nebula in Orion—that fine, large nebula which has occupied the attention of so many astronomers since then (Plate VIII); this was a remarkable discovery at the time, when only one other nebula was known.[1]

In 1665 Huygens went to work in France at the invitation of Louis XIV and stayed there for sixteen years; during this period he completed his wave theory of light, which opposed the emission theory of Newton. When in 1681 there was a revival in France of religious persecution directed against the Protestants he returned to Holland, where he died in 1695. Apart from his astronomical discoveries, we owe to him the extremely important invention of the cycloid pendulum clock described in his *Horologium Oscillatorium* published at Paris in 1673 and the invention of a composite eyepiece for astronomical telescopes—still in use today—which was greatly superior to Kepler's simple eyepiece. Finally, in 1698, three years after his death, there appeared at The Hague his *Cosmotheoros*, in which he summarized his ideas concerning the solar system and the universe outside it; some of these are truly remarkable for their time—in particular the idea of the plurality of inhabited worlds—the possibility that other planets might be inhabited, which gained so much success in the two centuries that followed.

The most important feature, however, is Huygens' clear exposition of an idea prematurely advanced by Giordano Bruno at the end of the sixteenth century, which neither Galileo nor Kepler had dared to uphold: that the stars of the sky are other suns at immense distances. On the basis of photometric comparisons, which, though rough, nevertheless provided an order of magnitude, Huygens estimated that the distance of Sirius, for example, was about 27,000 times that of the Sun. This value is some 20 times too small, but

---

[1] The first had been discovered in 1612 by the German astronomer Simon Mayer or Marius (1570-1624); this was the Andromeda nebula (Plate XI). It is, however, visible with the naked eye and had been noticed by the Arabs as early as the tenth century. The Orion nebula had been, unknown to Huygens, also observed by J. B. Cysatus in 1618.

it does give an inkling of the enormously large distances of th
stars. Furthermore, Huygens supposed that the number of th
stars surpassed the limits of human understanding and imagina
tion, and was not far from the idea that the stellar universe i
infinite in extent.

(D) J. D. CASSINI (1625–1712)

We have seen that, at a certain time, Tycho Brahe had had at hi
disposal an important observatory dedicated to astronomical re
search. Afterwards one of his pupils, Longomontanus, had founde
an observatory at Copenhagen in 1632; this observatory, however
was not finished until 1656 and was destroyed by fire in 1728. Som
private observatories were established in the same period b
amateurs, but until the middle of the seventeenth century ther
were not yet any important national institutions devoted to astro
nomical observation. Galileo, Kepler and Huygens had observe
from a window, a balcony or a garden.

In the reign of Louis XIV, however, the astronomer Auzou
pointed out to the king the interest that would attach to the creatio
in Paris of an institution in which the heavenly bodies might b
observed continuously; hence the foundation of the 'Académie de
Sciences' in 1666 was followed shortly afterwards by plans for th
construction of the Paris Observatory. This establishment wa
promptly built and was ready for occupation in 1671 when it wa
placed under the direction of the Italian astronomer J. D. Cassini
called to France by Louis XIV in 1669. Cassini ordered immens
telescopes for the observatory—'those large telescopes fit to frigh
ten people' as Molière called them—with which he carried ou
important observations of the Sun, Moon and planets. In particular, as has been mentioned, he discovered a second satellite o
Saturn—Iapetus—in 1671, and then a third—Rhea—in 1672
Eight years later, in 1684, Cassini discovered two further satellite
of Saturn—Dione and Tethys. In addition he noticed in 1675 a
circular median division in Saturn's ring, to which his name i
still attached (Plate II, c). In 1665, while still in Italy, he
had discovered the shadows projected by Jupiter's satellite
on to the planet which he distinguished correctly from intrinsic

narkings on the surface (Plate II, b). Observations of these markings, incidentally, enabled him to determine the period of rotation
of Jupiter on its own axis. Later on he continued these observations
at the Paris Observatory and obtained a very exact value for the
planet's rotational period—close to the one accepted at present. He
correctly remarked that the spots and bands on Jupiter are atmospheric and cloudy in nature. He also studied the rotation of the
planet Mars, on which he succeeded in identifying some surface
markings, and obtained a rotational period of 24 hours 40 minutes,
differing by less than 3 minutes from the modern value.

Finally, he devoted much time to eclipse observations of Jupiter's
satellites; following a suggestion already put forward by Galileo,
it was realized that the rapid motion of these satellites—especially
the one closest to Jupiter—formed a kind of celestial clock visible
from all parts of the Earth, which offered at least an approximate
solution to the difficult problem of determining longitudes at
sea. It thus became extremely important to establish the ephemerides of Jupiter's satellites as precisely as possible. Cassini published his first ephemerides in 1668, and returned to this problem
many times. This study of Jupiter's satellites, carried out at the
Paris Observatory in collaboration with the Danish astronomer
Römer, was to enable the latter to make a discovery of the greatest
importance.

c) O. RÖMER (1644–1710)

In 1672, after a trip to Denmark undertaken for the purpose of
determining the geographic coordinates of Tycho Brahe's
observatory at Uraniburg, the French astronomer Picard returned
with Römer, a young Danish astronomer, who became attached to
Cassini at the Paris Observatory and took part in the eclipse observations of Jupiter's satellites. These observations had shown that
Cassini's tables of the satellite motions, particularly those of the
first satellite—closest to the planet—contained an error; the
eclipses occurred sometimes earlier, sometimes later than predicted
in the ephemerides, according to the relative positions of Jupiter
and the Earth. It occurred to Cassini in 1675 that this difference
between the observed and calculated times of eclipse might

61

somehow be due to the time taken by the light in travelling from the satellites to the Earth, but he did not pursue this idea. Römer however, studied this question in considerably more detail and a early as 1676, using observations carried out from 1671 onward he announced that the periodic inequalities of the first satellite of Jupiter were certainly due to the time taken by the light to reac us. Thus, instead of being propagated with infinite velocity, as th Ancients had supposed, light took a finite time to travel from on point to another. Römer estimated that light takes about 1 minutes to traverse the radius of the Earth's orbit. It is no known that this value is too large and that the actual value of the period—known as the *light equation*—is approximately 8 minutes. The introduction of this inequality into the calculation provided greatly improved accuracy in the predictions furnishe by the ephemerides of Jupiter's satellites. Furthermore, this dis covery was to be confirmed and embodied in the framework of th heliocentric system half a century later with Bradley's discovery of aberration (III, 14).

(F) J. FLAMSTEED (1646-1719)

At about the time that Auzout obtained for France a nationa observatory, the same service was performed for England b Flamsteed on whose counsel the Royal Observatory was establishe in 1675 in Greenwich Park. This observatory was founded for th specific purpose of measuring stellar positions with improve accuracy so as to permit a better determination of positions at sea— a matter of vital importance to a maritime nation such as England Its first director was John Flamsteed, who immediately began th observations for which he had been commissioned. Until his tim all positional measurements that were recorded in catalogues ha been carried out with the naked eye, and the description of the sta places had remained rather rough and inaccurate.

At the Greenwich Observatory Flamsteed skilfully combine magnifying telescopes with measuring instruments so as to increas the precision of his observations and spent nearly thirty years, from 1676 to 1705, in accumulating the observations which finall enabled him to publish in 1712 a great star catalogue—known

s *Historia Coelestis Britannica*. This catalogue, revised and re-edited
1 1725, includes 2,866 stars; a star atlas based on this catalogue
vas also published, in 1729. Flamsteed carried out this gigantic
isk under extremely difficult conditions, working alone and un-
ssisted; but his catalogue is still a valuable document concern-
ig the appearance of the celestial sphere at the end of the
eventeenth century.

★

Thus, in the 150 years from Copernicus to Newton, the repre-
entation of the Universe had undergone a complete revolution and
1e ideas inherited from Antiquity had all been successively
ejected. The new observations and theories had decisively estab-
shed the fact that the Earth was not the centre of the Universe;
1at the Sun did not revolve round it, and that it was really the
arth—relegated to the status of a very insignificant planet—that
evolved round the Sun; that the orbits of the celestial bodies were
ot perfect circles described with a uniform motion, but in fact
1ore complex curves—only approximately representable by
llipses; that such fantastic and seemingly unpredictable bodies as
1e comets actually followed calculable and well-defined orbits
bout the Sun, and that their reappearance could be precisely
redicted using the universal laws of celestial mechanics; that the
eavens were not unchanging and immutable, that the brilliant
irface of the Sun showed variable spots, that stars could appear
1d then disappear from the heavens, and that the brightness of
ther stars was subject to periodic changes.[1]

There can be little doubt that this group of discoveries, and those
1ade during the same period in the realm of physics—which also
emolished the authority of Aristotle's theories—constituted a still
1ore important advance in the development of the human intellect
1an had the 'Greek miracle' 2,000 years before.

The discovery of the true system of the world removed all

---

[1] The first variable star was discovered in 1596 by the astronomer
. Fabricius; the periodic character of its changes in brightness was
tablished in the middle of the seventeenth century. Hevelius dubbed
is strange star 'Mira Ceti'—the Wonderful one of the Whale.

support from any creed or philosophy based on a geocentri[c] anthropocentric outlook: hence astrology in particular decline[d] rapidly after the end of the sixteenth century. Though still serious[ly] cultivated by Tycho Brahe, it was used by the unfortunate Keple[r] only to gain a livelihood, and since then no serious astronomer ha[s] practised it.[1]

[1] Doubtless the revival of astrology in the twentieth century, and th[e] tolerance now accorded to it, will later appear as a disgrace to our time[s].

PLATE III. THE SOLAR CORONA DURING A TOTA
ECLIPSE

A composite drawing from photographs taken by Britis
expeditions in 1870.

This careful sketch shows more clearly than do direct phot
graphs the ray-like structure of the inner corona and the coron
jets or streamers. The radial orientation of the jets and the
almost uniform distribution all round the Sun is characterist
of the phases of maximum sunspot activity. At spot minimun
the jets curve round towards the solar equator, leaving only fin
short tufts in the polar regions.

The corona emits a bright-line spectrum; the strongest line,
green one, was discovered by the American astronomers Harkne:
and Young at the eclipses of 1869 and 1870. For three-quarters (
a century the origin of this radiation remained one of the unsolve
problems of astronomical spectroscopy; not until 1941 was
shown, by the Swedish physicist Edlen, that the coronal lines a
emitted by very highly ionised atoms of iron, calcium and nicke
The presence of this high ionization is evidence of the existenc
in the corona of very high temperatures, of the order of a millio
degrees, the origin of which is still uncertain.

The study of the corona has advanced considerably since 193(
when the French astronomer B. Lyot introduced the 'coron:
graph', an instrument which permits the corona to be observe
in broad daylight outside eclipses. Nevertheless, this outc
envelope of the Sun still has many mysteries which are now bein
probed by the new techniques of radio-astronomy.

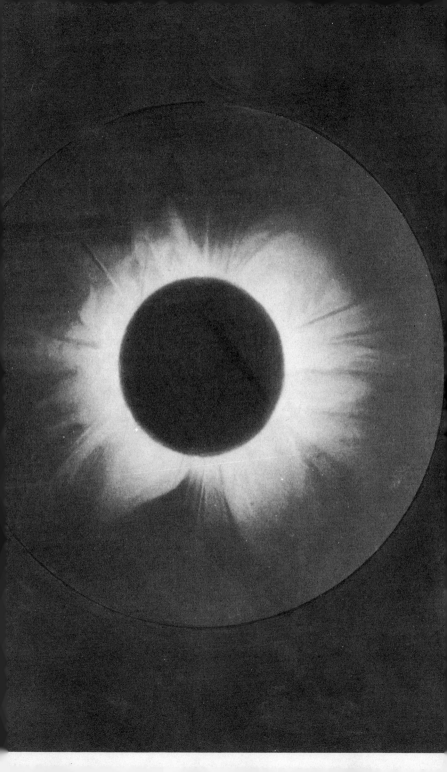

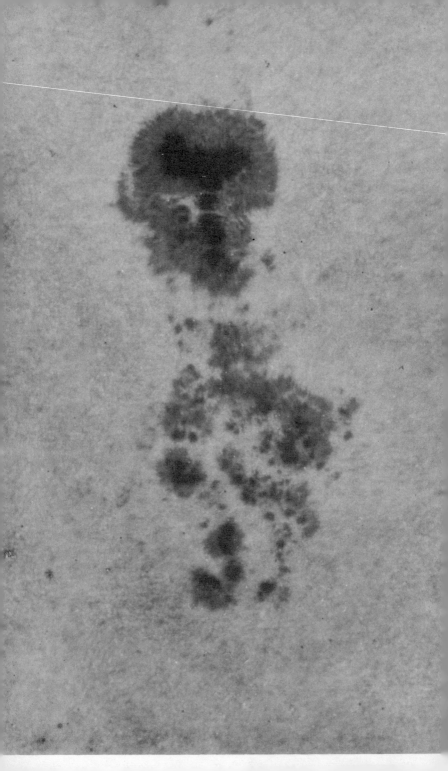

PLATE IV. A LARGE GROUP OF SUNSPOTS

A historical photograph taken by J. Janssen in 1885 by means of the photoheliograph of the Meudon Observatory.

Janssen's photographs, which are still among the best pictures of the Sun's surface that have ever been taken, show beautifully the photospheric granulation, the 'rice grains', and the radial filaments of which the spot penumbra consists. The black disc represents the Earth drawn on the same scale and gives an indication of the enormous sizes of these sunspots.

The central nucleus of a spot appears dark only by contrast with the dazzling background of the photosphere, the temperature of which is close to 6,000° C. (11,000° F.); the centre of the umbra is still quite bright, as its temperature of 4,500° C. (7,000° F.) is still higher than that of the electric arc. The periodic variation in solar activity, marked by a variation in the number of spots, was discovered by the German amateur Spörer in 1843; the last maximum of activity occurred in 1947 and the last minimum in 1954.

The variations in solar activity have a considerable effect on a large number of terrestrial phenomena: magnetic perturbations, solar aurorae, disturbances of telegraphic and radio communications, etc. In fact, our whole life is dependent on the Sun's rays.

* III *

The Rise of Classical Astronomy: Positional Astronomy and Celestial Mechanics from the End of the Seventeenth to the Middle of the Nineteenth Century

13. E. Halley (1656–1742)

Succeeding Flamsteed, Edmund Halley became the second Astronomer Royal at Greenwich. Halley had in fact been associated with the work of the Observatory for a long time and had drawn attention to his ability by some remarkable investigations. In 1676, when he was only twenty, he sailed for the island of St. Helena where he set up a temporary observatory and in the course of one year compiled the first catalogue of southern stars which was to supplement the respective catalogues of the northern hemisphere completed by Hevelius at Danzig and begun by Flamsteed at Greenwich. His catalogue, which contained 381 stellar positions, was published on his return in 1678 and brought him great fame at the early age of twenty-two. In 1679 he visited Danzig to work with Hevelius, and in 1680 proceeded to Paris to work with Cassini, whom he joined in observations of the great comet of that year, which attracted his attention to the study of comets. As has been mentioned, comets had hitherto been regarded as highly mysterious phenomena which hardly appeared to obey the laws valid for other celestial bodies. Tycho Brahe had observed several, but had been able to prove only one thing: that they were not terrestrial exhalations or close meteors, as was then believed, but more distant bodies somewhere in the solar system. He had even wondered whether comets might perhaps describe orbits bout the Sun, but he had not been able to test this idea, and Kepler till believed that they moved in straight lines within the solar ystem. In Galileo's time the Peripatetics had, in conformity with he theories of Antiquity, rejected all attempts to subject the notions of comets to the ordinary laws applicable to other bodies.

Following their observations of the comet of 1662, Cassini and Hevelius had suggested that these bodies might describe trajectories similar to those of the planets, though much more elongated; and Hevelius had even mentioned parabolas. It was Newton, however, who first showed conclusively that the paths of comets were very well represented by parabolic orbits with the Sun at the focus. Nevertheless, it was chiefly Halley who devoted himself to the calculation of cometary orbits. In his *Treatise of Cometary Astronomy*, published in 1705, he calculated parabolic orbits for twenty-four comets. Among these appeared a study of the comet of 1681–2, which was to lead him to a discovery of the greatest importance to the progress of astronomy.

Halley calculated the parabolic elements of this comet in 1682 and noticed their close similarity to the elements that he himself had found for the comet observed by Kepler and Longomontanus in 1607. Then he searched further back into the past and found a comet that had been observed by Apian in 1531, for which he again obtained very nearly the same elements. This coincidence of three comets that had appeared at almost regular intervals of seventy-five or seventy-six years with the same elements suggested to him that he was actually dealing not with three different comets, but with one and the same comet, returning periodically within sight of the Earth, and he ventured to predict that the same comet would return again towards the end of 1758. It followed that the orbit of the comet must be a highly elongated ellipse rather than a parabola. The small discrepancies in the period of return were explained by Halley, very simply and quite correctly, as a consequence of the perturbing action of the planets approached by the comet in the course of its journey. Halley did not, of course, himself live long enough to verify his prediction, the success of which aroused tremendous enthusiasm in Europe and, as has been mentioned, contributed largely to the final establishment of Newton's

theory on the Continent. Halley's comet did in fact return in 175
and continued to be visible in the early part of 1759, passing throug
perihelion no more than a month away from the date predicted
this was remarkable agreement, considering the length of th

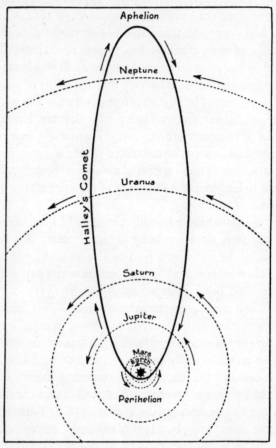

FIG. 6. ORBIT OF HALLEY'S COMET

The last passages at perihelion occurred in 1682, 1759, 1835 and 191

period of revolution. Halley's comet returned again in 1835 an
1910, and will be visible once more in 1986 (Fig. 6).

To Halley we owe many other discoveries important in th
development of astronomy.

In 1716 he suggested that the distance of the Sun might be determined by observing transits of Venus across the solar disc. Here again, Halley was unable to carry out the observations himself—the first transits of Venus to which his method was applied were not to take place until 1761 and 1769; however, for over a century this was the best method available for the determination of the solar distance (section 17).

In 1718 Halley made another fundamental discovery: that of the *proper motions* of stars. Since ancient times the stars had been considered completely fixed on the celestial sphere and it had been customary to refer to the 'sphere of fixed stars'. Comparing the positions determined by himself on Saint Helena with the observations of Hipparchus and Ptolemy, he noticed that four of them, Aldebaran, Sirius, Arcturus and Betelgeuse, showed small but appreciable, and certainly real, discrepancies in their positions; the only satisfactory hypothesis was that of an actual displacement with respect to the celestial coordinates. In the course of its development this brilliant discovery of proper motions was to open an immense field of new investigations of the stellar universe.

Finally, it was Halley again who discovered the *secular acceleration of the Moon*; this discovery (at first sight contrary to Newton's law) aroused much agitation until Laplace, a century later, showed that it was actually a periodic inequality with a very long period and that the acceleration would later be succeeded by a phase of retardation.[1]

4. J. Bradley (1693-1762)

James Bradley, the third director of the Greenwich Observatory was also a very great astronomer and we owe to him, apart from numerous observations of stellar positions, two highly important discoveries: *aberration* and *nutation*. In spite of the success with

---

[1] Later work has in fact shown that Laplace's periodic inequality, which is associated with long-period variations in the eccentricity of the Earth's orbit, is capable of explaining a part only of the secular acceleration of the Moon, and that there is a non-periodic residue; the residue has been attributed to a slowing down of the Earth's rotation through tidal action (cf. IV, 22).

which planetary motions had been explained by the application of the laws of Newton and Kepler to the heliocentric system, one of the fundamental objections to the Copernican view still remained unanswered. It had been argued against Copernicus and his successors that if the Earth moved through space in a heliocentric orbit, one would expect to observe a small apparent displacement of the stars on the celestial sphere, an effect of perspective resulting from the spatial displacement of the Earth. Investigation of this small displacement, or 'parallax' as it is called, was to occupy the attention of numerous astronomers in the eighteenth and early nineteenth centuries. Although more than 150 years of effort were required after Newton's time to obtain effective parallax determinations (IV, 25), these efforts led to several highly important discoveries on the way, two of which were made by Bradley.

The first of these was that of the *aberration of light*. While trying to measure the parallax of the star gamma Draconis, in 1725 and 1726, Bradley noticed a slight displacement of the star on the celestial sphere relative to the coordinates, and that this displacement was not in the direction of the parallactic displacement that might have been expected. Bradley then studied this new phenomenon by observing several stars in different parts of the sky and came to the conclusion that he was dealing with a general displacement of the stars, the amplitude of which varied according to the direction of the Earth's orbital motion. After much perplexity as to the origin of this strange phenomenon, he finally found the correct explanation: 'At last I conjectured,' he wrote in a letter to Halley, 'that all the phenomena hitherto mentioned proceeded from the progressive motion of light and the Earth's annual motion in its orbit. For I perceived that, if light was propagated in time, the apparent place of a fixed object would not be the same when the eye is at rest, as when it is moving in any other direction than that of the line passing through the eye and the object; and that when the eye is moving in different directions, the apparent place of the object would be different.'

Thus Bradley had not succeeded in observing stellar parallaxes but he had discovered an equally strong proof of the Copernican

heory and, at the same time, a confirmation of Römer's discovery
concerning the finite velocity of light (Fig. 7).

The angle of aberration, or *aberration constant*, is defined as the
emi-major axis of the ellipse apparently traversed by the star in
he course of a year as a result of the aberration of light, and is

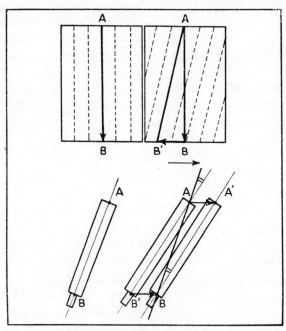

FIG. 7. THE ABERRATION OF LIGHT, AFTER BRADLEY.

Raindrops (*above*) which leave vertical marks AB on the window of a
stationary railway compartment (*left*) leave oblique marks AB' when the
coach is in motion (*right*) as a result of the combined displacements
AB, BB'.
Similarly, starlight (*below*) arriving along AB and seen in this direction
by a stationary observer (*left*) appears to an observer in transverse motion
AA' (*right*) to come from the direction AB' (or A'B).

about 20 seconds of arc. Numerous determinations of this constant
have been carried out since Bradley's discovery, because its precise
value is of great importance not only as a correction to be applied
to observed stellar positions, but also because it is directly related
on one hand to the velocity of light and on the other to the velocity

of the Earth—thus providing an independent estimate of the solar
distance, on which the Earth's orbital velocity depends.

Bradley's second great discovery, that of the *nutation of the
Earth's axis*, resulted from a further development of these same
observations from which the aberration of light had been deduced.
Even after the effects of aberration had been allowed for, Bradley
noticed that the polar distances of stars seemed subject to small
variations, and the law of distribution of these variations among
stars in different parts of the celestial sphere suggested to him that
this effect might be due to an oscillation of the Earth's rotational
axis under the Moon's influence: 'When I considered these circumstances and the situation of the Ascending Node of the Moon's
Orbit at the time when I first began my observations; I suspected
that the Moon's action upon the Equatorial Parts of the Earth
might produce these effects: for, if the Precession of the Equinox
be, according to Sir Isaac Newton's Principles, caused by the
actions of the Sun and Moon upon those Parts, the Place of the
Moon's Orbit being at one time above ten Degrees more inclined
to the Plane of the Equator, than at another; it was reasonable to
conclude, that the part of the whole annual Precession, which arises
from her action, would in *different years be varied* in its quantity
. . .' Now, as mentioned earlier, the line of nodes of the lunar orbit
completes a revolution over the celestial sphere in about eighteen
and a half years, the period of the Saros (I, 4). Therefore this
period is also that of the nutation of the Earth's axis, and this agreement was naturally an immediate proof of the correctness of
Bradley's hypothesis.

Bradley published the results of his observations in 1747, after
studies of the nutation ellipse which extended over more than an
entire period—from 1727 to 1747. Bradley's success in determining
an inequality only 10 seconds of arc in amplitude shows how much
progress had been achieved in measurements of position since
Tycho Brahe's time (II, 9). Towards the end of his life Bradley
devoted himself to the compilation of a great new catalogue of
stellar positions, for which he collected over 60,000 observations
in the course of his last twelve years. His catalogue was published
long after his death, in 1798 and 1805, in two large volumes. In

1818 the German astronomer Bessel (IV, 25) published a catalogue of 3,000 stars based on Bradley's observations. This catalogue has proved invaluable in modern investigations of stellar proper motions.

15. N. L. de la Caille (1713–1762) and J. J. de Lalande (1732–1807)

While, thanks to the succession of brilliant observers who worked there, Greenwich Observatory played the leading part in the astronomical developments discussed above, the Paris Observatory was allowed by Cassini's successors to fall into a state of virtually complete disuse during the eighteenth century. French astronomers were then devoting their main energies to the great geodetic operations in progress at the time (section 16). However, the tradition of positional astronomy was fortunately revived by an 'amateur', the Abbé Nicholas Louis de la Caille, who after having taken part in the work of the Paris Observatory from 1736 to 1740, then installed his own personal observatory at the Collège Mazarin (now the Institut de France) in Paris, where he accumulated an immense number of positional observations of the Sun and stars. His most remarkable investigations were, however, carried out from 1751 to 1753, during a stay at the Cape, where he determined the lunar parallax and compiled a large catalogue of southern stars much more extensive than Halley's. On this occasion he also carried out the first measurement of an arc of the meridian in the southern hemisphere.

His measurement of the lunar distance was the first one carried out by the trigonometric method and was effected in cooperation with his pupil Lalande, who observed from Berlin; Berlin is almost on the same meridian as the Cape and nearly 90° away in latitude, providing a base line longer than the Earth's radius (Fig. 8). Their observations were carried out simultaneously in 1752 and gave a parallax of 57 minutes of arc, very close to the value obtained from modern measurements. This result implies that the (mean) distance from the Earth to the Moon is some 60 times the Earth's radius.

However, La Caille's great star catalogue, which was published posthumously in 1763, was a still more important contribution. Whereas Halley had made determinations for 350 stars only, La Caille in fact managed in less than two years to obtain with a small telescope the positions of over 10,000 stars down to the seventh magnitude; thus for the first time a star catalogue was produced which contained a substantial number of stars invisible to the naked eye. His positions are, however, not very precise owing to

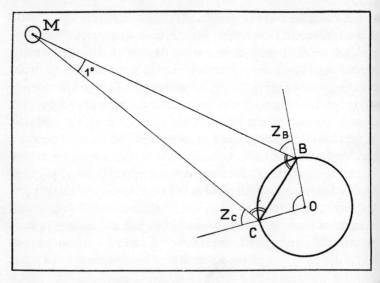

FIG. 8. MEASUREMENT OF THE LUNAR PARALLAX BY LA CAILLE

Simultaneous observation of the Moon's zenith distance Z during its meridian transit at the Points B (Berlin) and C (the Cape) permits a determination of the angles B and C of the triangle MBC; from this the angle M and hence the lunar distance may be deduced.

the small size of the instrument which he used. La Caille observed many southern stars for the first time and named 14 new constellations—names which are still in use. Finally, he returned from his journey with the first systematic list of nebulae, comprising 42 objects, which was published in 1755.

On his return to Paris he made further observations of position for over 500 stars distributed round the zodiac, which were published in 1763. He also calculated 'Celestial Ephemerides' for the period from 1745 to 1774, later extended by Lalande to 1800.

Joseph-Jérôme le Français de Lalande began his astronomical career at a very early age, since he was sent to Berlin to take part in the measurement of the lunar parallax when he was only nineteen. In 1759 it was he who carried out the calculations suggested by Clairaut to determine the perturbations of Halley's comet by the influence of Jupiter and Saturn (cf. section 13); as already mentioned these calculations were confirmed by observation to within a month, precisely the estimated margin of error of the theoretical prediction. He published numerous astronomical books, among them a large *Treatise on Astronomy* in 1764 and an imposing *Astronomical Bibliography* in 1801. In 1795 he was appointed director of the Paris Observatory and devoted himself to renewing its obsolescent equipment. Shortly afterwards, in 1801, he published his *Histoire Céleste Française*, inspired by Flamsteed's work (II, 12), but of much greater volume. In it are recorded observations of nearly 50,000 stars, down to the tenth magnitude, the positions of which had been determined at Paris between 1789 and 1799 by his nephew, Michel le Français de Lalande, and Michel's wife. These observations later enabled the English astronomer F. Baily to compile a catalogue of 47,390 stars, which was published in 1847.

16. The measurement of the Earth

As a result of the acceptance of the heliocentric system and of the need for measurements of the distances of celestial bodies, information on the Earth's dimensions became increasingly important. It has been mentioned that Picard had, in the seventeenth century, already obtained a reasonably accurate measurement of an arc of the meridian north of Paris, and that this had enabled Newton to confirm his ideas on universal gravitation.

After the foundation of the Academy and of the Paris Observatory, Louis XIV had entrusted his astronomers with a very important mission—that of measuring with the utmost possible accuracy the arc of a meridian crossing France from north to south, from Dunkirk to Perpignan, which was then to serve as a base line for the construction of a precise map of the kingdom. This vast operation was undertaken by J. D. Cassini and La Hire in 1683, but many difficulties were encountered, and it was not completed until about 1718. This meridian across France was checked in 1739 by J. D. Cassini's son, Jacques Cassini (1677-1756).

At about this time also, efforts were made to settle the question of the flattening of the Earth's figure (II, 11). In 1735 the Academy of Sciences instructed the geodesists Godin, Bouguer and La Condamine to repair to Peru, while another expedition, consisting of Maupertuis, Clairaut, Le Monnier and others, travelled to Lapland; it has already been mentioned that a comparison of the measurements obtained in the two regions proved that the Earth was flattened—as Newton had suggested. The length of a degree of latitude was in fact found to be 56,737 'toises' in Peru, compared with 57,419 in Lapland.

Unfortunately, however, although the flattening of the Earth's figure had now been qualitatively verified, the actual value obtained in these geodetic operations did not agree with the predictions of celestial mechanics as developed by Newton and his successors. The problem remained unresolved throughout the eighteenth century, until the adoption of the metric system came to be discussed by the French Constituent Assembly in 1790. Acting on the proposals of a commission consisting of Borda, Lagrange, Laplace, Condorcet and Monge, the Assembly made its well-known decision in 1791 to adopt as the unit of length one ten-millionth part of a quadrant of the Earth's meridian—the metre. It was therefore necessary to measure the terrestrial meridian with the highest possible accuracy, and to establish the relationship between the new metre and the old unit of length—the toise.

The operation of measuring the arc of the meridian from Dunkirk to Barcelona was entrusted to the French astronomers Delambre and Méchain. This operation took more than ten years, in consequence of numerous difficulties caused by the Revolution and the continual state of war, but resulted finally in a much more precise determination of the terrestrial meridian, which remained standard for a long time. The final results were published by Delambre in 1810; they gave a value of 57,025 toises for the mean degree of latitude in France. A comparison of this value with that found previously in Peru (the Lapland measurements having been proved to be inaccurate) gave a value of 1/334 for the degree of flattening of the Earth and 5,130,740 toises for the length of a quadrant of the meridian, which determined the new standard of length.[1]

Fundamental importance was attached not only to the dimensions of our planet, but also to a measurement of its mass. Until the seventeenth century the idea of 'weighing' the Earth would undoubtedly have seemed impossible, if not insane. But this was no longer so in the eighteenth century. Newton had in fact suggested that, if his law of universal attraction were correct, the attraction of a large isolated mountain should be sufficient to deflect a plumb line through an appreciable angle, which might be measured by astronomical observations of the zenith.

Some such observations had been attempted by the French academicians during their measurement of an arc of the meridian in Peru, but they had not been sufficiently accurate to give any clear results. It was the fifth Astronomer Royal, Nevil Maskelyne (1732–1811), who made in 1774 the first successful and conclusive observations on an isolated mountain in Perthshire (Fig. 9). By comparing observations of stellar positions carried out on the north and south sides of the mountain, he first determined the apparent difference in latitude between the two stations. Then he determined the geographic distance between the two parallels of latitude by a direct survey. He found that the difference in latitude deduced from astronomical observations was greater than that corresponding to the true separation of the two parallels; the former being 54″.6 and the latter only 42″.94. He concluded that the difference of 11″.6 could be attributed to the sum of the two forces of attraction, acting in opposite senses, exerted by the mountain. Finally, he determined the shape and dimensions of the mountain and deduced that the effect of the observed attraction might be explained on the assumption that the density of material in the mountain was about half the mean density of the Earth, or in other words that

[1] Approximate relations between the old and new units are 1 toise = 1·95 metre = 6 ft. 4¾ in. (Engl.).

the mean density of the Earth is double that of its outer layers. This result was of great importance, because on one hand it provided a direct and immediate proof of the law of universal attraction exerted by a mass of matter that was relatively trivial on the

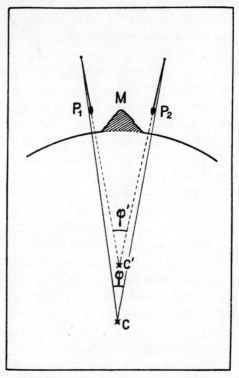

FIG. 9. GRAVITATIONAL ATTRACTION DUE TO A MOUNTAIN, after Maskelyne

Owing to the attraction of the mountain M, the plumb lines P_1, P_2 are deflected so as to converge to C′ instead of the centre of the Earth C. The apparent difference in latitude φ' is thus greater than the true difference φ.

astronomical scale, namely a mountain, and on the other hand it demonstrated that the density of the Earth increases inwards, showing that it is not a hollow sphere as some contemporary philosophers had still supposed. Finally, he drew attention to the importance in geodetic surveys of avoiding mountains, which might falsify the measurements of astronomical coordinates. This important point was taken into account in the great geodetic operations that took place at the end of the eighteenth century.

17. The distance of the Sun

Kepler's laws had given relative values for the distances of the planets. In fact they provided a 'scale model' of the solar system; but to obtain the actual scale in true measure it is necessary to know the value of the 'astronomical unit', the distance between the Earth and the Sun, in terms of some terrestrial standard of length—mile or kilometre.

Until the seventeenth century it was impossible, with existing instruments, to measure the distance between the Earth and the Sun accurately by the only method that was then known, the extension to the Cosmos of the methods employed by surveyors on the surface of the Earth. This method uses observations of a planet in the Earth's neighbourhood taken from two observatories sufficiently far apart, for example one in the northern and one in the southern hemisphere; alternatively the observations may be made from a single observatory first when the planet considered has just risen and then when it is nearly setting, in which case the base is constituted by the displacement in space provided by the Earth's rotation. From the small apparent angular displacement of the planet with respect to the stars the distance may be easily deduced. Orbital calculations then give the distance between the planet and the Earth at each instant in terms of the unit, the distance from the Earth to the Sun, so that the solar distance may be deduced from such observations. Astronomers usually express the results of these measurements not in terms of the actual distance of the Sun in miles or kilometres, but in terms of the angle subtended by the equatorial radius of the Earth at the mean distance of the Sun—known as the solar *parallax*.

The first applications of this 'trigonometric' method to the planets in the seventeenth and eighteenth centuries had already given results that were correct in order of magnitude, but still very rough. Observations of Mars by Cassini in 1672 had given a value of 9″.5; Maraldi in 1704 had obtained about 10″; Bradley in 1719 about 10″.5; and La Caille in 1751 about 10″.2.

The first results precise enough to be interesting were obtained by the method of observing transits of Venus, as suggested by Halley (III, 13) (Fig. 10). The application of this method had to await the transits of 1761 and 1769. Preparations were made in anticipation of these by a large number of astronomers and expeditions were despatched throughout the world in order that the transits of the planet might be observed under the best possible conditions. Unfortunately the actual phenomenon did not possess

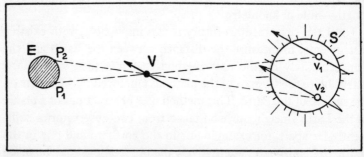

FIG. 10. MEASUREMENT OF THE SOLAR PARALLAX FROM TRANSITS OF VENUS, ACCORDING TO HALLEY

The planet Venus (V) in transit, seen at the same instant from two points P_1, P_2 on the Earth (E), appears in the positions V_1, V_2 respectively and crosses the solar disc along two parallel chords. Observation thus provides the angle P_1VP_2, from which the angle P_1SP_2 may be deduced; this is equal to the solar parallax if P_1P_2 is equal to the Earth's radius.

the geometric simplicity envisaged by theory; optical, instrumental and atmospheric effects conspired to make the observations highly uncertain and the results did not live up to expectations. In fact the observations obtained from the transit of 1761 showed a very large scatter ranging nearly from 7″.5 to 10″.5. Astronomers renewed their efforts in the hope of obtaining a more accurate value at the transit of 1769, in connection with which over two hundred memoirs were published. The values obtained still showed considerable scatter, but were already very much better, ranging mostly from 8″.5 to 8″.8. The French astronomer Pingré analysed all the material available at that time and in 1775 concluded that the solar parallax is very close to 8″.8. This choice, which now seems excellent, did not impress his contemporaries.

As the next transits of Venus after these two were not to take place until 1874 and 1882, astronomers were then reduced over a long period of years to rediscussing the transits that had already happened in an attempt to obtain the best possible value. Thus values obtained by various authors between 1786 and 1815 led to estimates ranging from 8″.56 to 8″.85.

The most complete discussion, however, was carried out by the German astronomer Encke in the early nineteenth century, and his result of 8″.57, published in 1824, was throughout the first half of the nineteenth century generally adopted as the most probable value of the solar parallax; it gave the distance from the Earth to the Sun as about 153 million km. (95 million miles), $3\frac{1}{2}$ million km. (2 million miles) in excess of the modern value.

18. The development of celestial mechanics

During the development of positional astronomy in the eighteenth and nineteenth centuries, the work of a whole series of mathematicians brought Newton's celestial mechanics to a high degree of perfection, capable of explaining in detail all the peculiarities of celestial motions revealed by the increasing accuracy of measurements. Among the chief astronomers and mathematicians who contributed to this development, mention must be made of the Frenchmen Clairaut (1713–1765), Maupertuis (1698–1759), D'Alembert (1717–1783), Lagrange (1736–1813), Laplace (1749–1827), Poisson (1781–1840), Cauchy (1789–1857), and of the Germans Euler (1707–1783) and Gauss (1777–1855).

The most important contributions, or at any rate those having the most considerable philosophical implications, were those of Lagrange and Laplace.

Joseph Louis Lagrange (born in Italy) worked for a long time in Berlin and was then called to Paris early in 1787 by Louis XVI; in the following year he published an immense treatise on *Mécanique Analytique* in which he systematized the results of his calculations on the stability of the solar system. It is not possible to enter here into the details of these results, but it may be mentioned that the basic object of Lagrange's investigations was to demonstrate that the progressive inequalities that had been observed in the motions of the planets, especially Jupiter and Saturn, were actually oscillatory variations of very long period due to the mutual perturbations of the planets. Far from leading to instability of the solar system and to its ultimate disintegration, as had been feared at the beginning of the eighteenth century, these perturbations are actually entirely periodic so that in the long run the system remains completely stable.

Newton's work certainly received its final crowning in the *Mécanique Céleste* of Pierre-Simon Laplace, which appeared in the form of five large volumes from 1799 to 1825. The purpose of this book was summarized by Laplace himself as follows: 'In the first part of this work we have given the general principles of the equilibrium and motion of bodies. The application of these principles to the motion of the heavenly bodies has led us by geometrical reasoning, without any hypothesis, to the law of universal attraction; the action of gravity and the motions of projectiles on the surface of the Earth being special cases of this law. We have considered a system of bodies subject to this great law of nature and we have obtained by analysis a general expression for their motion and shapes, and for the oscillations of the fluids with which they are covered. From these expressions we have deduced all the known phenomena of the ebb and flow of tide, the variations in the length of a degree of latitude and the force of gravity at the Earth' surface; the precession of the equinoxes; the libration of th Moon; the figure and the rotation of Saturn's rings. We have also indicated why these rings remain permanently in Saturn's equatorial plane. Furthermore we have deduced from the same theor of gravitation the principal equations of motion of the planets especially Jupiter and Saturn, the inequalities of which have period of over nine hundred years. The inequalities in the motion of Jupiter and Saturn first appeared to astronomers as anomalies the laws and causes of which were unknown, and for a long tim these inequalities appeared to be in conflict with the theory o gravitation; but a more detailed examination has shown that they may be deduced from this theory, and now these irregularities constitute one of the most striking proofs of the truth of the theory.' Thus Laplace affirmed the permanence and stability of the solar system with still greater certainty. Using the results of his calculations Laplace compiled considerably improved astronomical tables of planetary motions which continued in use until the middle of the nineteenth century.

Furthermore, in 1796, Laplace published his *Exposition du Système du Monde*, a popular work which was widely acclaimed because it expounds a cosmogonic hypothesis designed to account for the origin of the solar system. According to it, the solar system is supposed to have resulted from a primitive nebula which rotated about the Sun and condensed into successive zones or rings from which the planets themselves are supposed to have been formed. Laplace thus accounted for a large number of the facts known at his time. During the nineteenth century Laplace's cosmogonic hypothesis was generally accepted as an explanation of the origin of the solar system. Since then, however, it has been shown that it is impossible for planets to form in the manner suggested by Laplace. Furthermore, new phenomena were discovered later which could not be explained by Laplace's mechanisms.

19. The discovery of Uranus and of the minor planets

An examination of the map of the solar system (Fig. 11) immediately reveals a large gap, which appears anomalously between the orbits of Mars and Jupiter. Kepler, with his keen sense for proportions and harmony, had already noticed this gap and had supposed that some planet must move round its orbit in this region. This hypothesis, however, was contrary to a general prejudice concerning the number of the planets and attracted no attention.

The hypothesis was revived in a more precise way in the second half of the eighteenth century after 1772, when a regularity in the order of the planets noted some years earlier by J. D. Titius was taken up and widely publicised by the director of the Berlin Observatory J. E. Bode (1747–1826), so that the law is generally

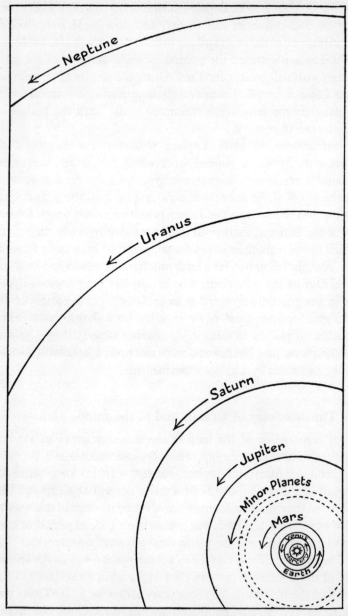

FIG. 11. PLAN OF THE SOLAR SYSTEM, drawn to scale—
1 inch = 500 million miles.

known as Bode's Law. According to this law the distances of the planets from the Sun are obtained by adding to the constant number 0·4 the products of the coefficient 0·3 with successive powers of 2, as shown by the following table:

Planet	Bode's Law	Observed
Mercury	0·4	0·39
Venus	0·7	0·72
Earth	1·0	1·00
Mars	1·6	1·52
—	2·8	—
Jupiter	5·2	5·20
Saturn	10·0	9·54
Uranus	19·6	19·18

It is clear that this series of numbers gives a remarkably accurate representation of the distances of the planets known at that time: Mercury, Venus, Earth, Mars, Jupiter and Saturn. Shortly after the announcement of Bode's Law, William Herschel, a German-born astronomer established in England, whose work will be discussed at length below (IV, 23), made, in 1781, a sensational discovery—that of a new planet beyond Saturn. This discovery was of great consequence, because it showed that the limits of the solar system, fixed since antiquity at the orbit of Saturn, were by no means final and that new objects remained to be discovered far out in space beyond these limits.

During a methodical survey of the sky, undertaken in the course of a different investigation, W. Herschel discovered on March 13, 1781 an object of unusual size for a star in the constellation of the Twins (Gemini). He saw it move from night to night and, in spite of its unusual appearance, described it as a 'comet', for it did not occur to him that a new planet could be discovered in this way. After various unsuccessful attempts to represent the orbit of the new comet by means of a parabola or a highly elongated ellipse it was finally realized that the orbit was actually very nearly circular and that the new body was in fact a planet rather than a comet. The calculations then showed that the orbital radius was nineteen times greater than that of the Earth, corresponding very well to the prediction of Bode's Law. From then onwards Bode's series seemed to be a true law of nature, perfectly verified from Mercury to Uranus, apart from the empty space between Mars and Jupiter corresponding to the number 2·8.

For this reason, at the end of the eighteenth century, a group of German astronomers undertook to search for a planet that might have an orbit in this region of the solar system. They had not yet had time to execute their plan when an Italian astronomer, G. Piazzi (1746–1826), accidentally discovered on January 1, 1801 a small speck of light moving among the stars. This was soon recognized as a new planet; its orbital elements were first calculated by the German mathematician C. F. Gauss, who applied to it the famous 'method of least squares' that he had just invented. It appeared that the mean distance between the Sun and the new planet was 2·77, very close to the number 2·8 predicted by Bode's Law. Success thus seemed to be complete and the empty gap in the series was filled.

Astronomers were therefore somewhat disconcerted when in 1802 the German astronomer Olbers (1758–1840) discovered another moving body, which was clearly another planet. After this, two further planets were discovered in the same region, in 1804 and in 1807. Thus, early in the nineteenth century, four planets had been found in the empty region of the solar system, Ceres, Pallas, Juno and Vesta. They were called 'Minor Planets' owing to their comparative minuteness and Olbers suggested that they were fragments of a planet that had disintegrated. No others were discovered until the middle of the nineteenth century (V, 29).

20. The discovery of Neptune

An examination of stellar observations of the eighteenth century soon revealed some observations of Uranus, which had at that time been taken for a star and observed as such. On the basis of these observations, and of observations collected from 1781 onwards, tables of the motion of Uranus were established.

In 1821 the French astronomer Bouvard published tables of the motion of Uranus which provided a good representation of the observations obtained between 1781 and the time of publication, but left some discrepancies in the older observations. Bouvard wondered whether these disagreements should be attributed to errors in the old observations or whether perhaps they might be due to some unknown perturbation influencing the course of the planet.

After 1830 this hypothesis became more and more plausible, for the observed positions of Uranus again began to differ from those predicted by the ephemerides, and the discrepancy continued to increase rapidly. Several astronomers, therefore, began to consider seriously the possibility that a new planet outside the orbit of Uranus might be responsible for the observed perturbations. However, while the problem of calculating the perturbations produced by known planets was now classical, it appeared extremely difficult to solve the inverse problem, that is to say to deduce the unknown perturbing planet from the perturbations.

This task was nevertheless undertaken almost simultaneously, in 1844–5, by a young English mathematician, J. C. Adams (1819–1892), and by an astronomer of the Paris Observatory U. J. J. Le Verrier (1811–1877).

Le Verrier studied the anomalies in the motion of Uranus in a series of memoirs which he presented to the Académie des Sciences and finally, on August 31, 1846, produced his last note entitled 'On the Planet Producing the Anomalies Observed in the Motion of Uranus. Determination of its Mass, Orbit and Present Position', in which he gave the final calculated elements for this planet. The planet was actually observed a few weeks later, on September 25, 1846, by the German astronomer J. G. Galle of Berlin—less than one degree away from the position predicted by Le Verrier.

The extraordinary success of this prediction of the position of a new planet by pure calculation aroused the just enthusiasm of contemporaries. F. Arago, then director of the Paris observatory, who had suggested this investigation to Le Verrier, said: 'Astronomers have sometimes accidentally come across a moving point, a planet, in the field of their telescopes, while M. Le Verrier perceived the new body without having to cast a single glance towards the sky: he saw it at the tip of his pen. By the power of calculation only he determined the position and size of a body situated well beyond the limits of our planetary system as known hitherto, a body more than 1,200 million leagues away from the Sun—which hardly produces a visible disc in our most powerful telescopes.'

It is only fair to add that the same calculations were carried out at the same time in England by Adams, and led to practically identical results; unfortunately for him he was still very young at the time and the calculations that he had presented to Airy, who was then Astronomer Royal, aroused only mild interest. A visual search for the planet undertaken in the summer of 1846, under J. Challis, at the Cambridge observatory, was still in progress when Le Verrier's results and Galle's observations were announced.[1]

This striking success of celestial mechanics was the crowning glory and final justification—if this were needed—of Newton's theory. Celestial mechanics seemed complete. However, new difficulties were soon to arise.

21. Lunar theory and the motion of Mercury

In several places mention has been made of the inequalities successively discovered in the motion of the Moon and the part that their explanation played during the seventeenth and eighteenth centuries in testing Newton's theory. This complicated problem of the lunar motion has always been a preoccupation of astronomers and the establishment of tables of the Moon has continued to be one of the major problems of positional astronomy and celestial mechanics.

From the beginning of the eighteenth century it had been clear that Newton's purely theoretical calculation did not provide an adequate representation of the observations: Halley had therefore recognized the necessity of introducing empirical corrections, deduced from observation, and he compiled a set of tables in 1719 that were published posthumously in 1749. Nevertheless these

---

[1] For modern accounts of the events and controversies surrounding the discovery of Neptune, see L'Astronomie, **60**, 1946, 255–278.

tables were still very poor; they were soon replaced by new tables compiled in 1753 by the German astronomer Tobias Mayer (1723–1762), and which were used in calculations of ephemerides throughout the second half of the eighteenth century.

However, this was not a satisfactory solution from the theoretical point of view. Following a proposal of Laplace in 1820, the French Académie des Sciences offered a prize for the calculation of lunar tables based entirely on theory. Theoretical investigations of the motion of the Moon were then resumed first by Damoiseau of France and then by Plana of Italy, whose respective tables appeared in 1824 and 1832; they were continued in the middle of the nineteenth century by the German astronomer Hansen, whose lunar tables were published in 1857 by the British Government and were at that time considered to afford a complete solution of the problem. Unfortunately the Moon persisted in departing from the positions calculated by the tables for future epochs, and it had to be conceded that, although the short-period inequalities had been calculated with success, those of long period continued to defy the theory. This problem was to occupy many an astronomer until the present time (VII, 41).

The theory of planetary motions was also to reveal strange discrepancies. After the investigation of the motion of Uranus that had led him to the discovery of Neptune, Le Verrier undertook a complete revision of the entire theory of planetary motions, taking into account the existence of the new planet and the observations that had been collected since Laplace's time. In this way he established tables for the various planets which were used until the end of the nineteenth century. These, however, still did not represent planetary motions perfectly; the most serious disagreement occurred in the motion of the perihelion of Mercury. According to perturbation theory, the influence of the other planets should cause a slow rotation of the major axis of Mercury's orbit; the observations showed that this movement was greater than provided for by the theory when the masses of all known planets were taken into account—the perihelion was advancing 38″ too much per century. Encouraged by the precedent of the discovery of Neptune, Le Verrier announced in 1859 that this discrepancy could be explained by the existence of a planet as yet unknown, moving in an orbit within that of Mercury. In the same year (1859) a French amateur astronomer observed a black point in transit across the Sun; it was then thought that this was really the expected planet, which was christened 'Vulcan'. Le Verrier immediately computed its orbit and announced the dates of its future transits across the Sun; unfortunately the expected body did not appear on any of the expected dates and has never been seen since, despite a thorough search from all quarters for over twenty years.[1]

The motion of the perihelion of Mercury remained unexplained it was to continue thus until the Theory of Relativity, over half a century later (VII, 41).

[1] The story of Vulcan was summarized by O. J. Eggen in Leaflet No. 287 (1953) of the *Astronomical Society of the Pacific*.

PLATE V. THE OUTER LAYERS OF THE SUN

(A) A PROMINENCE ON THE SUN'S LIMB, photographed in light of the K line of ionized calcium by means of the spectroheliograph of the Meudon Observatory.

These enormous gas jets that the Sun emits in its active regions stretch out like enchanted luminous fountains many hundreds of thousands of miles in length. They emit a bright-line spectrum in which the radiations of hydrogen, ionized calcium, iron and helium are particularly prominent. After the eclipse of 1868 Janssen of France and Lockyer of England independently conceived the idea of isolating these bright radiations in order to observe the prominences at any time in monochromatic light. Such observations became still easier to carry out after the invention of the 'spectroheliograph' (see below), which permit automatic photography of the solar disc or its surroundings in monochromatic light.

(B) THE UPPER LEVELS OF THE SOLAR CHROMOSPHERE, photographed in light of the K line of ionized calcium by means of the spectroheliograph of the Meudon Observatory.

The rarefield gaseous atmospheric layer above the photosphere was named the 'chromosphere' by Lockyer in 1868; it is from this layer that the prominences appear to come. Detailed study of the chromosphere became possible after the introduction of the 'spectroheliograph' in 1891 by G. Hale in America and H. Deslandres in France. In this instrument, which is based on Janssen and Lockyer's method of observing prominences (see above), light from one of the 'dark' lines of the Fraunhofer spectrum is isolated by a slit and used to photograph the image of the Sun in monochromatic light by continuous scanning.

By isolating a single portion of a broad line, such as those of hydrogen and ionized calcium, it is even possible to photograph separately different layers of the solar atmosphere. Images taken in light of the centre of the K line (or K_3) show the highest level of chromospheric calcium vapour; in particular the characteristic network of bright 'flocculi' is visible which join together to form the 'plages faculaires' above the sunspots or active areas. The K images show also dark 'filaments' which are nothing but prominences seen in projection against the brighter disc.

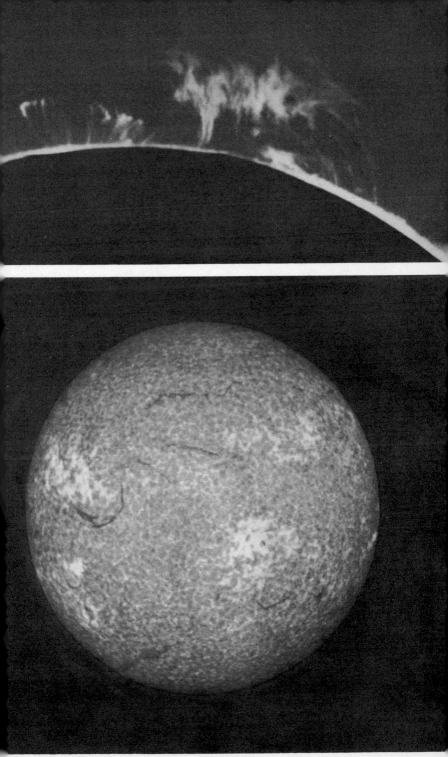

PLATE VI. THE GREAT COMET OF 1882

A historical photograph of comet Finlay 1882 taken by D. Gill t the Cape Observatory on 19 October, 1882 by means of a small amera and an exposure of 30 minutes.

This bright comet, visible to the naked eye, was among the irst to be successfully recorded by photography; the many star mages recorded in the emulsion together with the image of the :omet inspired Gill to undertake the first large photographic :atalogue of stars, the 'Cape Photographic Durchmusterung', and ater to become one of the promoters of the international 'Carte lu Ciel'.

In the past, comets were taken to be signs of celestial wrath and or a long time inspired primitive peoples with irrational terror; .ven after Halley had shown that comets describe regular orbits ubject to the laws of universal gravitation and that their return :ould be predicted, they were still believed capable of producing a worldwide catastrophe. Modern studies have shown the absurdity)f these fears and the soundness of the remark of the French)hysicist Babinet that comets are 'visible nothings'. Several imes the Earth has passed through cometary tails without the)ccurrence of anything of note to mark these passages. Only a lirect encounter with a cometary nucleus, which is highly impro-)able, could present any danger, and even then the damage would)e very limited and probably of the same order as that which is)roduced from time to time by the fall of large meteorites.

While the gases of a comet's tail, repelled by the radiation pres- ~ure of the Sun's light, as was shown by the Russian astronomer 3redichin in the closing years of the last century, may extend over ens of millions of miles, their solid nuclei are very small on the :osmic scale, at most a few miles across. Comets appear to consist)f the same light elements, hydrogen, carbon, nitrogen and)xygen, that are as common on the Earth as in the Heavens, both n inorganic and organic matter.

* IV *

The Beginnings of Modern Astronomy from the End of the Eighteenth Century to the Middle of the Nineteenth Century

I. THE STELLAR SYSTEM

22. The precursors

Until the eighteenth century, astronomers had taken only littl
interest in the stars themselves, considering them merely as object
for the measurement of coordinates and the compilation of eve
more comprehensive catalogues.

Following the discoveries of Huygens and Halley which hav
been mentioned, it became clear in the middle of the eighteent
century that the stars were other suns at immense distances; fron
this time on some bold minds began to take an interest in thei
distribution through space and to consider the nature of the stella
system. Three names deserve mention in this context: those of th
Englishman Thomas Wright, of Durham (1711–1786), of th
illustrious philosopher Immanuel Kant, of Königsberg (1724
1804), and of the Alsatian physicist J. Lambert (1728–1777). A
three independently reached the conclusion that the stars might b
organized in an enormous system of finite extent.[1]

The first of these, chronologically speaking, was Thomas Wrigh
who in an essay entitled *An Original Theory of the Univers*
published in 1750, discussed the appearance of the Milky Way, tha

[1] Similar views had been advanced earlier by the Swedish schol
E. Swedenborg (1688–1772) in his *Principia rerum Naturalium* (172
1734).

uminous band which girdles the celestial vault, and interpreted it
or the first time in terms of a theory that agrees in its broad out-
ines with our present ideas. In order to explain the accumulation
of stars in the direction of the Milky Way he supposed that all stars
n the sky were grouped in a highly flattened lenticular formation

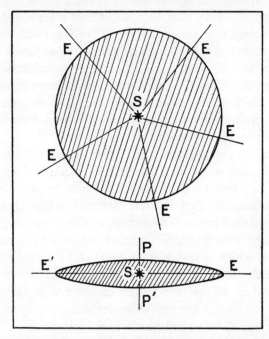

FIG. 12. EXPLANATION OF THE APPEARANCE OF THE MILKY WAY, ACCORDING TO WRIGHT AND KANT

The distribution of stars in an extended, flattened system enveloping
he Sun produces the appearance of the Milky Way through the accu-
nulated effect of distant stars in all directions SE in the equatorial plane,
vhile the number of stars visible towards the poles PP′ is relatively very
small.

imilar to a wheel or pancake, in which the Sun was located (Fig. 12).
He clearly explained that such a distribution, as seen by us, would
give rise to the appearance of the Milky Way, and it even occurred
o him that the irregularities in the outline of the Milky Way on
he celestial sphere were due to the non-central position of the Sun

in the system; this last, most remarkable piece of intuition has only been confirmed in the last few decades.

The same idea was taken up by Kant in his *Universal Natural History and Theory of the Heavens*, published in 1755. Kant, however, pushed the same line of reasoning further: he realized that if the stellar system was arranged in an isolated group of finite size constituting the Milky Way, there must exist other island systems of stars far away in space outside the Milky Way; with a stroke of genius he identified the few nebulae known at that time with these exterior stellar universes. Using thoroughly sound reasoning he showed how the Milky Way, seen from an immense distance, must appear in the form of a small, feebly luminous disc, completely analogous to the appearance of the nebulae when seen in a telescope. Here are his own words:

'It is far more natural and conceivable to regard these nebulae as being not such enormous single stars but systems of many stars whose distance presents them in such a narrow space that the light which is individually imperceptible from each of them, reaches us on account of their immense multitude, in a uniform pale glimmer. Their analogy with the stellar system in which we find ourselves, their shape, which is just what it ought to be according to our theory, the feebleness of their light which demands a presupposed infinite distance: all this is in perfect harmony with the view that these elliptical figures are just universes and, so to speak, Milky Ways, like that whose constitution we have just unfolded.'

It must, however, be mentioned that in Kant's time diffuse objects of all kinds were classed in the same category; many of these were not what we now call 'island universes', objects outside our Milky Way. A large number of these faint objects were actually either simply clusters of stars or masses of diffuse matter in space. None the less Kant's intuition was remarkable and his general conception has now been entirely confirmed (VIII, 44).

To Kant we owe other ideas of astronomical interest. He was the first to show that the Sun is slightly to the north of the median plane of the Milky Way, and he also originated the idea of a very slow retardation of the rotational movement of the Earth by the frictional effect of tides due to the Moon's attraction. Finally he as the first to put forward a cosmogonic hypothesis to explain the origin of the planetary system; this was the nebular hypothesis that was taken up and developed by Laplace (III, 18).

Finally, the idea of a hierarchy of systems embracing larger and larger numbers of stars was again taken up by Jean Lambert in his *Cosmologischen Briefe*, which appeared in 1761. He gives the following summary:

'The law of gravitation extends universally over all matter. The fixed stars obeying central forces move in orbits. The Milky Way comprehends several systems of fixed stars; those that appear out of the tract of the Milky Way form but one system which is our own. The Sun being of the number of fixed stars, revolves round a centre like the rest. Each system has its centre, and several systems taken together have a common centre. Assemblages of these assemblages have likewise theirs. Finally, there is a universal centre or the whole world round which all things revolve. Those centres are not void, but occupied by opaque bodies.'

Although these last ramifications are somewhat fantastic, they are none the less quite remarkable in their anticipation of the 'local cluster' of stars surrounding the Sun and of the rotation of the Galaxy (VIII, 43).

Thus, as early as the middle of the eighteenth century, several independent thinkers had been led by way of analogy to recognize the fundamental fact that the stars are organized in a stellar system of finite extent and that other stellar systems exist outside. It was not until the end of the eighteenth century, however, that these speculations were supported by observational results founded on systematic measurements and star counts.

3. William Herschel (1738–1822)

While Copernicus, in his pioneering study of planetary motions in true perspective, is to be considered the founder of classical planetary astronomy, William Herschel's pioneer investigations of the stars in their natural framework entitle him to be regarded as the originator of modern stellar astronomy.

After difficult early years in his native Hanover, William

Herschel migrated to England in 1758. There, after another long strenuous period as an organist and musician, Herschel was attracted by the study of the heavens and undertook the task of constructing with his own hands much more powerful reflecting telescopes than those used previously. In 1776, after innumerable trials, he finally succeeded in constructing a Newtonian reflector of 7 ft. focal length (aperture 6 in.), with which he began his first survey of the heavens, assisted by his sister Caroline Herschel (1750–1848).

It was in the course of these systematic observations that he discovered Uranus in 1781. Thanks to this startling discovery, which attracted attention all over Europe and in particular earned him a pension from King George III, Herschel from then on was able to devote his entire energy to the construction of larger telescopes and to studies of the sky carried out with their aid. He successfully constructed a telescope of 20 ft. focal length in 1787, followed by a 40-ft. telescope in 1789, which latter remained the largest in existence for half a century. Its aperture was 48 in. However, Herschel's most interesting observations were carried out with the intermediate, less cumbersome telescope of 20 ft. focal length (aperture 20 in.).

Herschel made many observations of the Sun, Moon and planets; he discovered two satellites of Saturn and two of Uranus (V, 29). But it was in the course of his investigations in the field of stellar astronomy that Herschel made his greatest and most significant discoveries.

His first discovery in this field was, in 1783, that of the intrinsic motion of the Sun. It has been recalled how Halley had in 1718 discovered the proper motions of some stars. Bradley in 1748 and Lambert in 1761 had pointed out that this apparent displacement of the stars was very probably due to a combination of the intrinsic movement of the Sun with those of the stars, and Mayer had even attempted to detect this intrinsic solar motion from a list of stellar proper motions, but had not been successful.

In 1783 Herschel examined the proper motions of seven bright stars—Sirius, Castor, Pollux, Procyon, Regulus, Arcturus and Altair—which had been thoroughly established by Maskelyne, and showed clearly that these motions contained a systematic trend

ccording to their position on the celestial sphere, which could only
be a reflection of the Sun's own movement through space. From a
detailed discussion of the motions of these different stars, he
showed that the Sun must be moving through space towards the
constellation Hercules. He added:

'We know that the sun, at the distance of a fixed star, would
appear like one of them; and from analogy we conclude the stars
to be suns. Now, since the apparent motions of these seven stars
may be accounted for, either by supposing them to move just in
the manner they appear to do, or else by supposing the sun alone
to have a motion in a direction, somehow not far from that which
have assigned to it, I think we are no more authorized to suppose
the sun at rest than we should be to deny the diurnal motion of the
earth.'

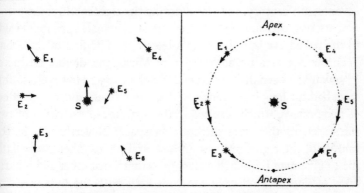

FIG. 13. THE PROPER MOTION OF THE SUN, ACCORD-
ING TO W. HERSCHEL (1783)

The intrinsic motion of the Sun through space towards the Apex
(left) is shown by the tendency of the apparent motion of the stars on the
celestial sphere to converge towards the point diametrically opposite—
the Antapex (right).

Herschel showed further that his discovery was confirmed by a
study of the proper motions of twenty-seven stars, the values of
which had been given by Lalande, and he deduced from the complete analysis that the Sun moves through space towards the star
Lambda Herculis, an excellent result which agrees within 10° or
less with modern determinations of the Sun's motion. This point

of the celestial sphere towards which the Sun is travelling is called the *apex* (Fig. 13).

It should be added that the astronomers of the early nineteenth century still for some time doubted Herschel's results and his conclusion. However, it was finally confirmed in a highly convincing and more elaborate fashion by the German astronomer Argelander in 1837 (section 27).

Thus, just as Copernicus had destroyed the dogma of the Earth's immobility and proved that it moves just as the other planets, so had Herschel freed astronomy from the hypothesis of the immobility of the Sun, and demonstrated that it too moves through space just as the other stars.

Another fundamental discovery made by Herschel was that of *double stars in relative orbital motion*. Already in the middle of the seventeenth century, then later during the eighteenth, some astronomers had occasionally come across stars which appeared single to the naked eye but double in a telescope. The first of these had been the star zeta Ursae Majoris, or Mizar, the double character of which had been discovered by Riccioli in 1650. However, double stars had for long been considered as mere freaks due to the effect of perspective, which resulted in the fortuitous association of two stars seen in the same direction in space. Nevertheless, in the middle of the eighteenth century, several philosophers, especially the Englishman J. Michell, had noticed that the number and separations of double stars were not consistent with the hypothesis of fortuitous optical proximity and that these double stars must be physically associated in some way. However, the first systematic investigation involving the measurement of double stars was undertaken only by Herschel. In 1782 he had compiled a catalogue of 269 stars, 227 of which he had himself discovered, and he published a second list of 284 new pairs in 1784.

The reason for Herschel's interest in double stars was his hope that he might be able to use them to demonstrate stellar 'parallaxes' which had defied all the efforts of astronomers. In fact he thought in terms of a method that had already been suggested by Galileo, imagining that by a careful measurement of the separation of the components of a double star, one of which might be far away in

he depths of space while the other was relatively very close, he
might be able to demonstrate the small parallactic displacement of
the near component relative to the distant one, which latter would
constitute a convenient fixed reference point. It was for this reason
that he undertook regular measurements of the relative positions
of the components of a certain number of double stars. Herschel

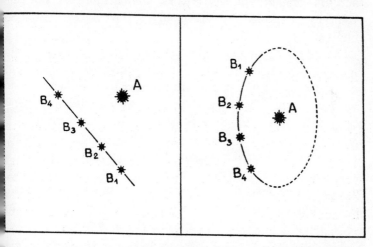

FIG. 14. OPTICAL AND PHYSICAL PAIRS, ACCORDING
TO W. HERSCHEL (1802)

Optical double stars (*left*) are brought together by a chance coincidence of perspective and may be identified by their uniform relative
motion in a straight line resulting from the combination of their respective
proper motions.

Physical pairs (*right*), which are actually associated together in space,
are identified by their elliptic orbital motion, which is superimposed
on their common proper motion.

This difference is illustrated in the figure by the successive positions
of star B relative to star A (regarded as fixed).

did not succeed in his attempt to measure a stellar parallax, but he
was led in 1802 to a discovery of equal importance, namely that of
the existence of relative orbital motion in a certain number of
binary stars. In that year he finally established the fact that chance
optical approaches could not account for the large number of
double stars observed and he announced further that, since the

beginning of his observations, the relative positions of the com
ponents of some of the double stars had changed in a progressiv
fashion—indicating a periodic revolution of one component abou
the other. In 1804 he returned to this discovery in order to make
more definite and showed that double stars are for the most par
not apparent pairs or 'optical' pairs, as they are called, but tha
they are genuine 'physical' pairs, combinations of two star
physically connected by the bond of their mutual attractio
(Fig. 14).

This discovery was of the greatest importance, for it showed tha
Newton's law of gravitation was really 'universal' as had alway
been asserted, but no proof of this had ever been available outsid
the solar system. The study of the motions of double stars, whic
was greatly developed after Herschel's time, has permitted a
exact verification of the validity of Kepler's laws and more generall
of Newton's law in stellar systems out to enormous distances fror
the Earth. This was therefore a considerable advance in astronomy
which was thus assured of the applicability of its calculations a
least to large parts of the entire Universe. In fact we shall see tha
it was not until the twentieth century that astronomical exploratio
reached distances where Newton's law becomes inadequate t
account for observation (VIII, 44, 45).

However, Herschel devoted his most important observation
work throughout his life chiefly to the problem of the stellar system
the 'structure of the heavens', as he called it. His counts of star
extending systematically over the entire celestial sphere visibl
from England, had been undertaken from the beginning of hi
career for this purpose. In 1785 these 'gauges' had led him to adop
the theory of the structure of the Milky Way put forward b
Wright, Kant and Lambert, and had given a solid statistical founda
tion to the hypothesis of a flattened stellar system. To explain th
appearance of the Milky Way, with its great bifurcation fron
Cygnus to Sagittarius, Herschel had supposed the Sun to be in th
neighbourhood of the centre of the Galactic System, which h
thought to be doubled over a part of its periphery as shown i
Fig. 15. As regards the dimensions of the system, Herschel had n
means available for a precise determination in view of the complet

ack of knowledge of the true distances of stars at that time: he attempted to circumvent this difficulty by taking as an arbitrary unit the 'mean' distance of the stars of first magnitude; in terms of this he estimated the total diameter of the Galaxy[1] at about 950 units and its total thickness at about 150 units. His attempt was actually premature for two reasons: first, Herschel wrongly supposed that his 20-ft. telescope enabled him to see the outermost stars of the Milky Way; however, he soon realized his error when his 40-ft. telescope revealed new stars that were still fainter; second, the idea of the 'mean distance' of the stars of first magnitude is almost entirely devoid of meaning owing to the enormous differences in intrinsic stellar luminosities established by modern

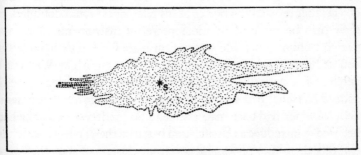

FIG. 15. CROSS SECTION OF THE MILKY WAY, ACCORDING TO W. HERSCHEL (1785)

investigations, so that distance is far from being the principal factor in a star's apparent brightness. Furthermore, other factors play a part of which Herschel could have had no idea at that time (VIII, 12).

In any case Herschel later realized that the structure of the Milky Way is more complex than he had thought at first and he came to the conclusion that its true depth was 'unfathomable'.

On the basis of his own observations Herschel also revived Kant's hypothesis that the faint nebulous objects visible in various parts of the sky were actually other stellar systems—other galaxies

[1] The name 'Galaxy' (from the Greek *galaxias*=Milky Way) is now usually applied to the stellar system in space, while the name of 'Milky Way' is reserved for its appearance on the celestial sphere.

too far away for their individual stars to be distinguishable. The number of recorded objects of this kind had greatly increased since Kant's time, owing partly to the observations of the French astronomer Ch. Messier (1730–1817), but chiefly to those of Herschel himself. Messier was an active observer of comets (V, 30) and had been annoyed by nebulous objects fixed on the celestial sphere which looked like faint comets and had led him astray several times. He therefore compiled a list of 103 of these objects that he had incidentally encountered, which was published in 1781. By this time Herschel had begun his exploration of the heavens and he discovered to his surprise that in his most powerful instruments the 'nebulae without stars' of Messier were frequently resolved into a swarm of faint stars; he soon concluded from this that those objects that resisted the power of his telescopes would doubtless in their turn be resolved by more powerful instruments. This appeared to him to provide a very firm basis for Kant's hypothesis and he himself did not hesitate to assert that our Milky Way was a nebula of a particular type fitting in his classification system. Indeed Herschel had seen in his telescopes a large number of faint nebulae which had been inaccessible to his predecessors and he had been led to introduce a classification based on their appearance while entering them into his catalogue—from clusters of stars that were fully resolved down to diffuse pale objects with no trace of structure. We now know that this classification is mainly illusory and groups together an extremely heterogeneous and incompatible collection of objects. In particular the 'nebulae without stars' of Messier that Herschel resolved, far from being galaxies outside our own, are in fact 'globular' clusters of stars closely associated with our own Galaxy (cf. VIII, 43); the actual external stellar system analogous to the Galaxy passed unnoticed among the true 'nebulae' formed by diffuse matter.

In the course of his observations Herschel himself came to modify his initial views and to recognize that certain nebulae must be 'non-resolvable' in nature, composed 'of a luminous fluid the nature of which is totally unknown to us'; examples of such nebulae are the diffuse nebulae, such as that in Orion, and the nebulae which Herschel called 'planetary' merely because the present small luminous discs having apparent sizes of the same order as those of planetary discs.[1] Finally, in 1791 Herschel came to consider that this diffuse matter might condense progressively to form stars; but it was not until 1811, in a study based on the 2,500 nebulae that he had himself catalogued, that Herschel put forward this idea in a systematic manner, showing that among the objects he had observed there occurred all intermediate forms from a diffuse irregular mass to a perfectly condensed star. We now know that this classification is to a large extent illusory and that stars are not formed through the series of stages suggested by Herschel, but his work is nevertheless the beginning of a long series of speculations on the origin of stars that has continued until our own time. William Herschel's work was soon to be taken up again and continued by his son.

24. John Herschel (1792–1871)

In 1816, at the age of twenty-four, John Herschel began his first observations of double stars, no doubt at the suggestion of his father, who was then seventy-eight. In 1820, following his father's instructions, he constructed a telescope of 20 ft. focal length (18-in. aperture), with which he was to carry out most of his future observations.

His observations of double stars, carried out in collaboration with an English amateur—J. South—confirmed the existence of orbital motions discovered by William Herschel, and in 1827 the Frenchman Savary showed for the first time that the motion of the star Ksi Ursae Majoris could be represented by an elliptic orbit swept out according to Kepler's Laws with a period of fifty-eight years. In 1831 John Herschel showed that with the relatively poor accuracy of double-star measures graphical methods were sufficient for the determination of orbits. Since then many astronomers have improved these graphical or semi-graphical methods, permitting rapid reduction of the enormous mass of accumulated measures.

In 1825 John Herschel undertook with his telescope a complete revision of the nebular discoveries made by his father. He published

[1] This unfortunate designation has been sanctioned by usage.

the results of this investigation in 1833 in the form of a catalogue of 2,306 nebulae and star clusters, including 525 new ones; furthermore, in the course of his explorations of the sky he discovered 3,347 new double stars. His observations were made in England and naturally only covered the part of the southern hemisphere visible from northern latitudes. Herschel realized the interest that would attach to an extension of his investigation to the whole of the southern sky, providing complete and uniform data over the entire heavens. He therefore decided, as Halley and La Caille had done earlier, to repair to South Africa with his instrument; he spent there the three years from 1834 to 1837, not far from the Cape of Good Hope. The results of his work were not published until 1847; he had observed over 2,000 double stars and over 1,700 nebulae, including 300 new ones. In particular he paid much attention to a detailed description of the two Magellanic clouds, these diffuse-looking nebulae visible to the naked eye in the southern hemisphere, where they appear as fragments detached from the Milky Way. Herschel's great telescope revealed to him the incredible richness of these 'clouds' in which he counted no less than 919 different objects in the Large Cloud (among them 278 nebulae and clusters) and 244 in the Small Cloud. He concluded from this study that 'the nubeculae are to be regarded as systems *sui generis*, and which have no analogues in our (northern) hemisphere'; with some qualification this opinion has received remarkable confirmation from the investigations of modern astronomers (VIII, 43, 44).

During his stay at the Cape, Herschel also made the first systematic observations designed to determine the relative brightnesses of stars by actual measurements, using for comparison the light of the Moon reflected by a distant prism. Crude as these measurements were, they nevertheless provided the relative luminosities of 191 stars using as a standard the bright star Alpha Centauri; finally he compared the latter with the full Moon, which he found to be 27,408 times as bright. Since the relative brightnesses of the Moon and Sun were already approximately known at that time, and the distances of some stars had just been determined (section 25), his measurements now made it possible for the first time to compare the absolute luminosity of the Sun with that of some stars. Naturally the later progress of astronomical photometry has resulted in a great increase in the accuracy of such comparisons (VIII, 42).

During the course of his stay at the Cape there also occurred a remarkable phenomenon, still unique to this day: the brightening of the star Eta Argus (now Eta Carinae). This star, which had been estimated to be of the fourth magnitude by Halley in 1677 during his stay at St. Helena, then of the second magnitude by La Caille in the mid-eighteenth century, and later again of the fourth magnitude early in the nineteenth century, had been observed to be of the second magnitude by John Herschel on his arrival in South Africa: he was therefore amazed to see it rival the brightness of the most brilliant stars of the first magnitude in December 1837 and January 1838. The star increased in brightness still further after Herschel's departure and in 1843 it attained almost the brightness of Sirius, the brightest star in the sky. It then progressively faded, became invisible to the naked eye in 1870 and has been more or less stable since then at about the eighth magnitude.[1] This phenomenon drew attention to 'temporary' and variable stars, which had attracted little notice since the eighteenth century.

Although he made no fundamental discovery comparable in importance with those of his father, John Herschel did a greal deal to confirm and complete his work; we have already seen what he achieved from this point of view in the field of double stars and nebulae. He also did much to complete William Herschel's 'gauges' in the southern hemisphere. In this way he explored 2,300 star fields, counting 70,000 stars; the result of these counts completely confirmed the results obtained in the northern hemisphere and he concluded from them that 'the plane of the Galaxy is to stellar astronomy what the ecliptic is to planetary astronomy—a basic reference plane, the fundamental plane of the stellar system'. All later investigations and developments have reinforced this conclusion and confirmed its correctness (VIII, 43).

After his return from the Cape, John Herschel abandoned celestial observation; he devoted his time to collating, editing and

---

[1] The story of η Carinae was summarized by the author in Leaflet *Ast. Soc. Pacific* No. 281 (1952) following its recent brightening (IX, 49).

publishing the data accumulated by his father and himself. Thus, besides the account of his observations at the Cape, which appeared in 1847, he published a general catalogue of nebulae containing 5,079 objects, which appeared in 1864, and he compiled a list of over 10,000 double stars which was published after his death.

Thus, at a time when the investigations described in Chapter IV had brought planetary astronomy to such a high degree of perfection that it seemed practically complete, the investigations of the Herschels opened an immense new field of a vastness greatly surpassing the limited solar system and revealed a much less rigorous order than that to which astronomers had become accustomed by the planetary motions. William Herschel, by his discoveries of the double stars and of the motion of the Sun, by his invention of stellar statistics and his counts of nebulae, had opened the path to all the principal branches of modern stellar astronomy. And at the very moment when John Herschel was giving up observing, on his return from the Cape, other astronomers were almost simultaneously about to win a final decisive success in the development of this new field: the measurement of stellar distances.

25. F. W. Bessel (1784–1846)

The achievement of determining the first stellar parallax was that of the German astronomer Friedrich Wilhelm Bessel. Bessel became Director of the Königsberg Observatory at the early age of twenty-six on account of his exceptional ability (at the age of twenty-one he had by himself recalculated the orbit of Halley's comet from observations going back to 1607) and was responsible for a considerable development in positional astronomy.

Before his time, admittedly, several other astronomers had already devoted much effort to the development of star catalogues; those of Bradley, La Caille and Lalande have been mentioned earlier. These catalogues, however, contained only the raw data of observation, i.e. were uncorrected for precession, nutation and aberration, so that they were not of immediate use in the determination of, for example, stellar proper motions. It had thus become necessary to 'reduce' this enormous mass of observations to a predetermined 'epoch' under well-defined conditions so that different sets of observations might be compared with one another.

Bessel undertook this task for the oldest and most accurate catalogue, that of Bradley, for which, in 1818, he published the results for 3,222 stars reduced to the equinox of 1760. After this Bessel began to repeat and extend these observations, determining directly stellar positions for his own epoch. This immense task took him twelve years, from 1821 to 1833, during which he obtained over 76,000 accurate observations of stellar positions and compiled a catalogue giving the coordinates of over 63,000 stars. This work was afterwards still further extended by his assistant and successor Argelander (section 27).

Encouraged, no doubt, by the precision of his absolute measurements of stellar positions, Bessel began an attack on the still unsolved problem of stellar parallaxes (Fig. 16), shortly after the completion of his catalogue. For this purpose he naturally resorted to 'differential' measures, more precise than absolute ones, by means of which he compared the position of the star under investigation with those of several nearby stars used as reference points. The instrument used in these investigations was the *heliometer* of the Bavarian optician Fraunhofer, to whom optics and astrophysics owe so many advances (VI, 32). The discussions arising from the vain quest for stellar parallaxes had at least had the merit of giving a precise definition of the conditions which stars must fulfil if they were to be successfully examined: they must be either very bright, or endowed with a high apparent proper motion, or physical pairs with widely separated components—and should preferably fulfil all these conditions simultaneously. Now, as early as 1812, Bessel had noticed that the star 61 Cygni fulfilled the last two conditions (consisting as it does of two components some $25''$ apart and having a common proper motion of $5''.2$ per year, the highest known at that time); he therefore decided to examine this star in 1837. His undertaking was rewarded with remarkable success and in December 1838, after one year's observation, he was already able to announce that the star presented a perceptible parallax perfectly measurable by his instrument, and amounting to $0''.31$. Further observations in 1840 gave him the value of $0''.35$, which confirmed the accuracy of

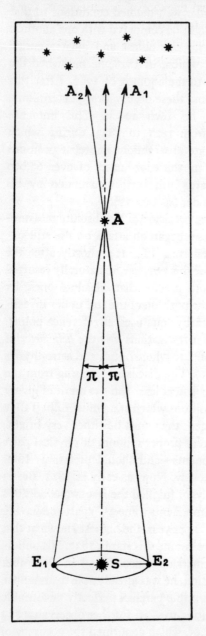

FIG. 16. PARALLACTIC
DISPLACEMENT OF
A NEARBY STAR

A nearby star (A) appears
displaced relative to more
distant reference stars when
the Earth moves from E_1 to
E_2 in the course of its
orbital motion. The star's
apparent position shifts from
E_1A_1 (when the Earth is at
E_1) to E_2A_2 (when the
Earth is at E_2) and the
angle π is the parallax.

his first result.[1] Thus the actual distance of a star, one of those closest to the Earth, had been determined for the first time. Almost at the same time two other stellar distances were announced; one was that of alpha Centauri by the English astronomer Henderson, the other that of alpha Lyrae by W. Struve, of whom we shall have more to say later.

First, however, a further very remarkable contribution of Bessel must be mentioned: the prediction of the future discovery of 'invisible' stars revealed purely by their gravitational action. As early as 1834 his precise measures of stellar positions, and those of his predecessors that he had reduced, had seemed to him to indicate irregularities in the proper motion of Sirius (Fig. 17); in 1840 he was led to the same conclusion with regard to Procyon and, after new measures of great precision, he announced in 1844 his conclusion that these irregularities must be due to the perturbing action of invisible bodies accompanying these bright stars along their course and affecting their motion. He wrote: 'I am convinced that Procyon and Sirius form true binary systems composed of one visible and one invisible star. There is no reason to suppose that luminosity is an essential characteristic of the heavenly bodies. The visibility of a multitude of stars is no evidence against the invisibility of a multitude of others.'

Thus Bessel was led to infer the existence of invisible stars in the same way as the existence of Neptune had been inferred from perturbations of the motion of Uranus. Bessel himself had been interested in the problem of Uranus' motion and doubtless it was only his death that prevented him from taking a leading part in the discovery of Neptune. However, the ideas that he expressed with such clarity on the causes of the perturbation of stellar movements received only little attention at the time, so difficult it is for new ideas to obtain credence. It was only after his death, in 1851, that the problem was taken up again by the German astronomer C. A. J. Peters (1806–1882), who showed that the observed motion of Sirius could be completely explained on the hypothesis that it described a fifty-year orbit—the elements of which he specified—about an

---

[1] This has been thoroughly confirmed by modern results, which lead to a parallax of 0″.30 for 61 Cygni.

invisible companion (or rather about their mutual centre of gravity).
The suspected star was actually discovered visually and observed
in 1862 by the American optician Alvan Clark (1832–1897), while
testing a new objective of 18 in. aperture, the largest that had been
successfully constructed until that time. Beside the dazzling image
of Sirius as seen in this large instrument there appeared a tiny speck

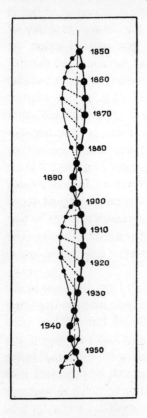

FIG. 17. THE SINUOUS MOTION
OF SIRIUS, due to the combination
of its rectilinear proper motion with
its orbital movement, led Bessel to
predict the existence of its faint
companion.

of light in the exact position that the calculations had predicted!
The complete success of this prediction led to the acceptance of
Bessel's views and resulted in the rise of a new branch of astronomy
that is sometimes picturesquely called 'the astronomy of the
invisible' and which has developed considerably in our time.

Encouraged by the observation of the companion of Sirius, the
German astronomer G. F. A. Auwers in 1862 immediately under-

took a study of the perturbed motion of Procyon—the second of the stars pointed out by Bessel—and published the orbital elements of the invisible star responsible for the perturbations. The latter was discovered visually in its turn in 1892—in the position predicted by the calculations—by Schaeberle, who employed the great 36-in. telescope of the Lick Observatory, then the largest in the world. These two faint bodies which thus accompany Sirius and Procyon on their course were subsequently shown to be of remarkable interest from the physical point of view and will be discussed later (VIII, 1).

26. W. Struve (1794–1864)

Friedrich Georg Wilhelm Struve also began his astronomical career at a very early age, being appointed director of the Dorpat Observatory in Estonia in 1815, at the age of twenty-two. This observatory was poorly equipped at the time, but in 1824 he was able to purchase a telescope of 10 in. aperture mounted by Fraunhofer. This instrument was the first to be provided with an equatorial mounting driven by a clock, making it possible to follow automatically the movement of the stars across the sky; the Dorpat refractor has become famous not only through the achievements of Struve in his use of it but also because it was the prototype of the later great refractors, which continued to increase in aperture throughout the nineteenth century—culminating in 1897 with the 40-in. telescope of the Yerkes Observatory.

With this refractor Struve had in his possession an instrument of unparalleled quality for the accurate micrometric measurement of double stars. Indeed, while Herschel had achieved the discovery of a large number of double stars, his measures of them had still been very crude and had consisted rather of estimates than of true measurements. Struve on the other hand attached a travelling wire micrometer to his equatorial telescope and was thus the true founder of 'double-star astronomy'—a branch of sidereal studies which is of fundamental importance because it provides us with measurements of stellar masses. Struve immediately achieved in his measurements an accuracy that has not been surpassed until our own time, after the introduction of new techniques.

Apart from introducing precise measurement into the study of double stars, Struve also discovered a very large number of new ones. In the years 1825–1827 he conducted a complete survey of the sky from the north celestial pole down to 15° southern declination, in which he observed 120,000 stars and collected about 2,200 new double stars en route. He then devoted ten years to the precise measurement of the most interesting double stars; the results of his work were published in 1837 in an enormous volume, his *Mensures Micrometricae* (the beginning of the Latin title of the work), which contains data for 3,112 double or multiple stars and remains a model of its kind. For more than half a century, the efforts of his successors in the field of double stars were concentrated on further observations of 'Struve's stars' in order to determine the orbits of an ever-increasing number of binaries.

After this monumental work on double stars and, no doubt, in view of the accuracy of his measurements, Struve turned to the problem of stellar distances; his choice of the star Vega (Alpha Lyrae) as an object although logical was not a happy one and the parallax which he deduced in 1840 from observations carried out between 1834 and 1837 was 0″.26, which differs considerably from the value now accepted (0″.13). Nevertheless, the attempt had been successful in so far as detecting a measurable parallactic displacement was concerned, then a great achievement.

In 1839 Wilhelm Struve was appointed director of the new observatory at Pulkovo near St. Petersburg, which the Emperor of Russia, Nicholas I, wished to make the best-equipped astronomical institute in the world.[1] The main instrument was a telescope of 15 in. aperture, enormous for its time, which was not to be surpassed until nearly a quarter of a century later. At Pulkovo Struve devoted most of his research to the structure of the Milky Way, but his views were not well received and have not been confirmed. He supposed that the Galaxy extended to infinity in its

[1] The 'Central' Observatory at Pulkovo was destroyed by German artillery fire during World War II at the siege of Leningrad; it has since been rebuilt and restored in its original architecture and layout by the Soviet Government; it was formally reopened in 1954.

own plane, but that its distant regions are hidden from us by the progressive absorption of light in space; we shall see later that, while modern research has partly confirmed the second point, it has clearly demonstrated the falsity of the first.

Wilhelm Struve did not altogether abandon his work on double stars; assisted by his son Otto Struve (1819-1905), he continued to search for them and measure them with the aid of the large refractor, which revealed 514 new pairs inaccessible to the Dorpat instrument. In 1861 he resigned his position as director and was replaced by his son Otto, who was also an excellent astronomer and to whom we are indebted, if not for great discoveries, at least for an important series of miscellaneous observations, particularly measurements of double stars supplementing those of his father.

27. Argelander (1799-1875)

Friedrich Wilhelm August Argelander also took up astronomy at a very early age, under the influence of Bessel, whose assistant he became in 1820. Shortly afterwards, in 1823, he was appointed director of the Åbo Observatory and then in 1827 of the Observatory of Helsinki—the new capital of Finland. He equipped this observatory on the model of Bessel's institute and carried out measurements of stellar positions there according to his principles. However, he did not share Bessel's incredulity as to the Sun's motion discovered by Herschel, and in 1837 he published a major investigation of it based not merely on a dozen proper motions, but on 390 motions—deduced from a comparison between Bradley's catalogue (reduced by Bessel) and his own observations in Finland; he showed that Herschel's results were completely confirmed by this massive material and from that time on the reality of the Sun's intrinsic movement was universally accepted. It may be added that shortly afterwards, in 1842, Otto Struve in turn confirmed this conclusion.

However, the great achievement which was to immortalize Argelander's name among astronomers was the task that he undertook from 1837 onwards, when he was appointed director of the new observatory at Bonn. Here he completed the most immense of all star catalogues, greatly surpassing in comprehensiveness all works of the kind that had been published before. In twenty-five years of continuous work he observed all stars in the northern hemisphere visible in his modest telescope, a refractor of 4 in. aperture, with which he determined the positions and approximate brightnesses of over 324,000 stars. This immense work was published in 1863 and is known as the *Bonner Durchmusterung*; for nearly a century it has been of incalculable value to astronomers, the more so because with his catalogue Argelander published a detailed Celestial Atlas in which the 324,000 stars of the catalogue were entered in their exact positions. One may judge the extraordinary importance of this work from the simple fact that, at the request of the International Astronomical Union, the Bonn Observatory has recently published a reissue of Argelander's Celestial Atlas and Catalogue, which even at the present time still constitute an indispensable tool in research of all kinds.[1]

In particular, Argelander's great catalogue has remained the basis of all modern investigations of the distribution of bright stars (it is practically complete down to the eleventh magnitude), because it was progressively extended over the whole sky by his successors. His assistant Schönfeld (1828–1891), who had already taken a considerable part in the completion of the *Bonner Durchmusterung*, succeeded Argelander in 1875 and began to extend the catalogue as far as possible into the southern hemisphere with a more powerful instrument; in less than ten years, between 1875 and 1884, he observed in this way over 133,000 stars, constituting the *Südliche Durchmusterung* which was published in 1886. Later still, this time with the aid of photography, the catalogue was extended to the south celestial pole by the Cordoba Observatory; this catalogue, the *Cordoba Durchmusterung*, includes 580,000 stars and was published in 1914.

After 1863 various German observatories undertook the re-observation of the stars of Argelander's catalogue under the auspices of the German Astronomical Society which distributed the work among various observatories (the Astronomische Gesell-

[1] For the history of the 'B.D.', see Leaflet *Ast. Soc. Pacific* No. 271 (1951) by C. G. Burwell.

schaft Catalogue); parts of this long-drawn-out operation were not successfully completed until our own time.[1]

This series of investigations carried out as a sequel to Angelander's work and more or less along the same lines bears eloquent testimony to its fundamental importance to stellar astronomy.

However, there is also another important branch of astronomy in which Argelander initiated a movement that has continued to develop since his time and has been greatly extended in our own: the observation of *variable stars*. Until then, in fact, these bodies had received attention only on exceptional occasions and a very small number of them had been recognized; after the variability of Mira Ceti (p. 63) that of Algol (Beta Persei) had been discovered in the seventeenth century. Towards the end of the eighteenth century an English amateur—J. Goodricke (1764-1786)—had discovered the variability of two further stars, Delta Cephei and Beta Lyrae. William Herschel had also come to suspect as a result of his painstaking and repeated comparisons of the apparent brightnesses of stars visible to the naked eye that certain stars might be variable. But it was Argelander who in 1844 drew general attention to these bodies, only six of which were then known. He described a simple method—based on that of Herschel—for the visual comparison of the brightnesses of variable stars with those of unchanging stars serving for reference, and personally undertook such observations with great persistence. Argelander's 'step method' was immediately adopted by German and British amateurs such as Heis, Pogson and Schmidt and the study of variable stars began to develop very rapidly. Now, a century later, it has become one of the most important fields of physical astronomy (VIII, 42; IX, 49).

8. Lord Rosse (1800-1867)

William Herschel had immediately increased the aperture of reflecting telescopes to the limits of the technical potentialities of his time; he had perhaps even exceeded them, because his largest

[1] A newer, still more precise revision carried out by photographic methods was undertaken in 1924 by the Yale University Observatory, at New Haven, U.S.A., and is now being extended to the southern hemisphere in collaboration with the Cape and Sydney observatories (IX, 47).

telescope of 48 in. aperture had been of only little use to him. All his main discoveries and those of his son had been made with a telescope of 18 in. aperture.

In the middle of the nineteenth century a wealthy British amateur, William Parsons, third Earl of Rosse, undertook the construction of a much larger instrument than those of Herschel. In 1845, after more than ten years of toil and experiments, he finally succeeded in setting up a telescope with a bronze mirror 6 ft. in diameter, which was to remain the largest in the world (though not the most useful) for over three-quarters of a century. Between 1845 and 1850, Rosse discovered with this instrument a class of object which was to become of outstanding significance: the spiral nebulae. Until then the nebulous objects discovered by the Herschels had shown forms which were either irregular or globular or elliptic without much structural detail. However, in the giant instrument, some of these nebulae showed the unexpected form of spiral vortices, the appearance of which filled astronomers with amazement (cf. Plate XII).

This discovery was confirmed some years later by another British amateur astronomer W. Lassell (1799–1880), who had set up a telescope of 48 in. aperture at Malta and also discovered some new nebulae. However, visual observation was incapable of revealing the nature of these objects or their generality. The latter was not to be in evidence until the end of the nineteenth century, with the progress of photography and the development of the silver-on-glass mirror (VI, 32, 37).

PLATE VII. THE SERIES OF STELLAR SPECTRA

From photographs taken by D. Barbier and D. Chalonge at the Scientific Station of the Jungfraujoch, Switzerland.

These photographs show the spectral region from the blue (*left*) to the near ultra-violet; identifications are given of the principal lines of hydrogen (H beta, H gamma, etc.), ionized calcium (H and K lines) and of some molecular bands (G-band and cyanogen bands).

Spectra are classified from class B to class M in order of decreasing temperature, according to a series that has been established since 1885 at the Harvard College Observatory (Henry Draper Catalogue). Note the progressive change in the intensity of certain lines, notably of hydrogen and calcium, with diminishing temperature from about 20,000° C. for type B1 to 3,000° C. for type M2, and the appearance of molecular bands (G, CN) in the cooler stars of types K and M. These variations in intensity are governed as much by physical conditions prevailing in stellar atmospheres, such as temperature and pressure, as by the abundance and intrinsic properties, such as electronic structure of the atoms concerned.

Investigations in the past thirty years, begun in 1920 by the Indian physicist Meg Nad Saha, have led to a considerable degree of understanding of the formation of stellar spectra and of their interpretation. Analysis of the shapes or profiles of stellar absorption lines led to the discovery of stellar rotation by O. Struve in the U.S.A. and G. A. Shajn in the U.S.S.R. about 1928, and still more subtle observations to the discovery of stellar magnetic fields by H. D. and H. W. Babcock, of the Mount Wilson and Palomar observatories, in 1948.

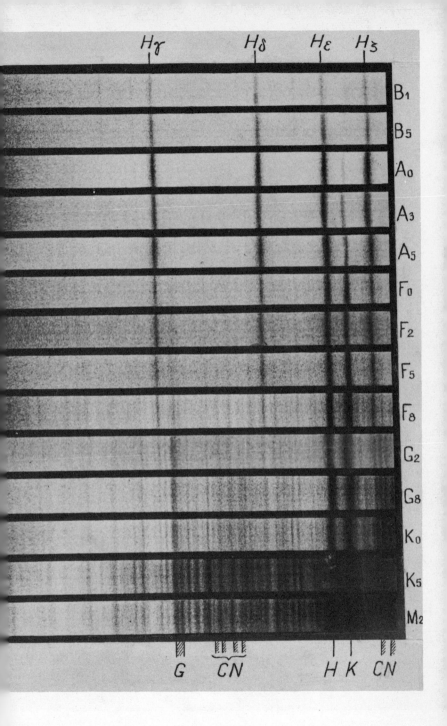

Plate VIII. THE GREAT NEBULA IN ORION

Photograph taken with the 24-in. reflector of the Yerkes Observatory, near Chicago.

This nebula was discovered by Huygens in 1656 and is at a distance of about 1,000 light-years from the Earth. It is a splendid example of the ultra-rarefied gaseous masses that are scattered in interstellar space and are illuminated by bright stars of high temperature (Type B); the intense ultra-violet radiation of these stars is the source of the fluorescence of the gas.

The spectra of gaseous nebulae of this type show a number of bright lines, especially the hydrogen lines and two green lines that were discovered in 1864 by the British amateur astronomer Huggins and first attributed to an unknown element, 'nebulium'. The non-existence of this element was established in 1928 by the American astrophysicist I. S. Bowen, who was able to demonstrate that the mysterious radiations were actually due to ionized atoms of oxygen and nitrogen which, in the extraordinarily rarefied medium which constitutes the nebula, emit lines that are 'forbidden' under the normal conditions of laboratory experiments.

* V *

The Beginnings of Modern Astronomy from the End of the Eighteenth Century to the Middle of the Nineteenth Century

II. THE SOLAR SYSTEM

29. Lunar and planetary observations

As has been seen in earlier chapters, astronomers in the seventeenth and eighteenth centuries took relatively little interest in the detailed observation of the surfaces of the Moon and planets; the motions of the heavenly bodies interested them more than their physical constitution. The reason for this was to a considerable extent the fact that early instruments, until the invention of achromatic objectives by the English optician J. Dollond (1706–1761), in the middle of the eighteenth century, gave optical images that were too blurred to enable many details of most planets to be distinguished.

Nevertheless Cassini, Huygens and Hooke in the seventeenth century, and Maraldi at the beginning of the eighteenth, had been able to recognize certain details quite clearly, particularly on Mars and Jupiter, which enabled them to determine the periods of rotation of these planets. But it was not really until the end of the eighteenth century, after the introduction of reflecting telescopes and achromatic objectives, that the physical aspect of the planets began to attract attention.

Herschel made the first good observations of Mars with his telescopes and recognized the analogy between the white polar spots on this planet and the polar ice caps of the Earth. His discovery of the planet Uranus and of two of its satellites as well as that of two satellites of Saturn, may be recalled here.

However, it is chiefly Herschel's compatriot and emulator, the German amateur astronomer J. Schröter (1745–1816), to whom we owe the first systematic observations of the various planets. He began his work about 1785 with a small telescope constructed by Herschel and was actively engaged in making drawings of the appearance of the Moon and planets. Unfortunately hardly any of his conclusions has survived the test of later progress; he thought he could distinguish large mountains on Mercury and Venus and attributed to these planets rotational periods in the neighbourhood of 24 hours which have not been confirmed; he thought that Mars was surrounded by an atmosphere laden with clouds, whereas they are in fact very rare. Thus astronomy has derived only very little benefit from his industry; it should, however, be mentioned that Bessel at the beginning of his career was his assistant for some years. Schröter's observatory was destroyed and burnt in 1813 in an act of vandalism by retreating French troops.

After Schröter, lunar and planetary observations were taken up in a much more effective manner by the German astronomer J. H. von Mädler (1794–1874). In collaboration with a Berlin banker, W. Beer (1797–1850), who possessed a private observatory with a modest refractor of 4 in. aperture, he carried out remarkably precise observations of the surfaces of the Moon and Mars, establishing the first topographic map of the latter and making an accurate redetermination of its rotational period. However, it was chiefly his work on the Moon which attracted attention at the time; this consisted of a large general map of our satellite which was much more complete than any that had been published before. In a large volume—*The Moon: General and Comparative Selenography*, which appeared in 1837—the main characteristics of the physical nature of the lunar world were established for the first time: an airless waterless world, frozen and lifeless; this idea was a great advance at a time when Schröter's mistaken ideas on the habitability of the Moon were still accepted.

This book drew attention to Mädler, and in 1840 he was offered the post that Struve had vacated at the Dorpat Observatory.

Here he abandoned planetary observation and devoted himself to less fortunate speculations on the structure of the stellar system. His hypothesis of the 'central sun' which attracted much attention in the mid-nineteenth century, deserves only passing mention.

The German astronomer J. Schmidt (1825–1884) took up the subject that Mädler had abandoned and made further advances in lunar studies which cast doubt on Mädler's doctrine of the immutability of the lunar surface. Schmidt was interested in the study of the lunar mountains from his earliest years and carried out observations of our satellite throughout his life. After working in various German observatories and acting as assistant to Argelander at Bonn, Schmidt was appointed director of the Greek National Observatory at Athens in 1858. There he successfully completed a gigantic lunar Atlas in twenty-five sections (incorporating earlier work of his compatriot Lohrmann), which was published in 1878 and recorded no less than 32,856 lunar craters. Only photography has recently permitted a more complete representation of the lunar surface.

In 1866, in the course of these studies, Schmidt came to announce a sensational discovery: the disappearance of a small lunar crater called Linné which was some five miles in diameter on Mädler's map, but had apparently changed into a tiny excavation less than a mile across—leaving an encircling whitish halo. The question of this change in Linné raised a long controversy; modern studies have shown that the apparent dimensions of the crater and particularly of the halo vary markedly with the angle of incidence of sunlight, so that the reality of the change announced by Schmidt is no longer believed. However, his observation had the merit of attracting attention to the subtle play of light and shade that often changes the appearance of the lunar landscape. It was also the first of a series of innumerable investigations patiently carried out in the hope of establishing the reality of changes in the lunar surface, and there is no proof that these studies may not one day finally succeed.

The planet Mars again attracted the attention of observers when it returned to a favourable position for observation in 1862 and

1864.[1] On these two occasions excellent observations were obtained by the Dutchman F. Kaiser at Leyden and by the Englishmen W. R. Dawes (1799–1868) and N. Lockyer (1836–1920). A comparison of these observations with those of Beer and Mädler established the permanence of the planet's appearance, the usual but not universal clarity of its atmosphere and the analogy between its seasons and those of the Earth. On the basis of these observations another English amateur, R. A. Proctor (1837–1888), established in 1869 a map of Mars considerably superior to that of Mädler; it shows bright reddish regions which were regarded as continents and dark bluish zones that were then thought to be extended oceans. However, all these studies were soon to be surpassed by the work of Schiaparelli, which will be discussed later (VI, 34).

Beyond Mars the once empty gap in the solar system was filled in an unexpected fashion during the nineteenth century; after the discovery of four planets in rapid succession at the beginning of the century (III, 19), no other had been added to the group in the forty years succeeding. The question might have been considered settled. Great was the surprise of astronomers, therefore, when in 1844 an obscure German amateur, K. L. Hencke (1793–1866), who had been looking for new planets since 1830, announced the discovery of a new asteroid (Astraea), and then of another (Hebe) in 1847. Shortly afterwards other astronomers joined in the search, which became more and more methodical, so that the number of minor planets has continued to increase since that time. In 1847 the Englishman J. R. Hind (1823–1895) discovered two (Iris and Flora), bringing the total of known minor planets up to 8; the number reached 13 in 1850, 88 in 1866, 172 in 1876 and 264 in 1887. It has risen still more rapidly since the introduction of photography in the search for these small bodies (VII, 39).

The distribution of these minor planets in space shows the dominating influence of the heavy major planet Jupiter on their motion; in particular, the American astronomer D. Kirkwood

---

[1] Owing to the very considerable eccentricity of its orbit the successive oppositions of Mars, which occur every two years, are unequally favourable and it returns to its minimum distance from the Earth with a period of approximately fifteen years.

(1815–1895) showed in 1866 that there are gaps in the asteroid belt at distances from the Sun for which the periods of revolution would be in a simple ratio to that of Jupiter. This observation offers an interesting analogy with one that may be made in connection with the divisions in Saturn's rings.

In spite of its great distance, the planet Jupiter—ten times bigger than the Earth in diameter—shows a visible disc with an apparent diameter sometimes reaching 48″. Certain characteristic features of this planet had been known since the seventeenth century: namely changing belts parallel to the equator, which were soon generally recognized as cloudy in nature. The physical character of these clouds was less clear. However, towards the end of the eighteenth century and then with greater clarity in the course of the nineteenth under the influence of Laplace's cosmogonic theory (III, 18), it came to be thought that the enormous globe of Jupiter had a constitution intermediate between that of the solid, cold planets such as the Earth or Mars and that of the incandescent Sun. It was held that Jupiter had not yet entirely cooled down; the activity of its belts seemed to indicate an internal source of heat, intrinsic to the planet and independent of the Sun's radiation; it was even suggested that this giant planet might perhaps have a feeble intrinsic luminosity. These opinions more or less survived until our own time and only recent astrophysical investigations have led to their final abandonment (VII, 39).

On the other hand, painstaking observation of Jupiter's satellites had very early shown an interesting peculiarity in their rotation. In 1797 Herschel had already noticed that the brightness of these satellites varies systematically during their revolution and he correctly concluded that a simple explanation of this fact was that there are spots on the surface of these small globes and that they always turn the same face towards Jupiter during their orbital motion, as the Moon does to the Earth. This conclusion has been amply verified since. Furthermore, from the middle of the nineteenth century onwards, instrumental progress enabled the presence of surface features to be recognized on their tiny discs.[1]

---

[1] The largest, Ganymede, is less than 2″ in apparent diameter.

The planet Saturn has attracted the main attention of observers because of a unique peculiarity—its ring, the shape and appearance of which had been recognized and explained by Huygens as early as the mid-seventeenth century (II, 12). Through the development of celestial mechanics it was realized towards the end of the eighteenth century that its existence and stability presented a special problem. Trusting in its telescopic appearance it was then still believed that the ring was a flat solid body, but it was difficult to understand how this could be the case in view of Kepler's Laws, which require a decrease in the angular velocity of rotation with increasing distance from the centre of attraction—in this case the globe of Saturn.

The question became urgent in 1850 when the American astronomer William C. Bond (1789–1859), using the great 15-in. equatorial of the newly established Harvard College Observatory, Cambridge, Mass., discovered a smoky, faintly luminous ring inside the bright ring that was already known (cf. Plate II, c). This discovery, which was also made independently in the same year by Dawes in England, led astronomers to reconsider the problem of Saturn's ring, or *rings*, taking into account the divisions that had been discovered by Cassini (II, 12) in the seventeenth century and by the German astronomer Encke early in the nineteenth. Therefore George P. Bond (1825–1865), who was to succeed his father as director of Harvard College Observatory, declared in 1851 that the ring could not be considered as a continuous solid body.

The problem was taken up again in 1856 in a celebrated memoir (published 1859) by the great English mathematical physicist, James Clerk Maxwell (1831–1879) who proved formally from the laws of celestial mechanics that the ring could not be solid but must consist of a multitude of small satellites revolving independently about Saturn like so many tiny moons. The difference in brightness of the various parts of the ring was then explicable as a result of the different numbers of small bodies in each zone.[1]

[1] The French mathematician E. Roche of Montpellier had already reached this conclusion in 1849 by showing that the ring is at a smaller distance than the minimum where a satellite could remain stable (Roche limit). But his work, published in some obscure provincial University Annals, does not appear to have then attracted the attention of astronomers.

At about the same time much discussion took place concerning a possible secular variation in the radius or width of Saturn's ring which seemed to have changed appreciably since Cassini's time. Later measurements, however, have not confirmed this supposed variation, which must therefore be attributed to the inaccuracy of the old drawings.

Finally, from his observation of the very considerable variation in brightness of one of Saturn's satellites—Iapetus—Herschel had also been able to deduce a rotation of the same kind as the Moon's which has also been confirmed since then.

As regard Uranus, the circumstances under which it was dis covered (III, 19) have already been discussed and also the dis covery of its satellites, two of them by Herschel in 1787 (in fact he thought he had discovered in 1797 four more satellites of this planet, but these have not been confirmed) and two further in 185 by Lassell, who also identified a satellite of Neptune within a few weeks of its discovery. Further discoveries in this field were no made until recent years (VII, 39).

30. Studies of comets and meteors

Towards the end of the eighteenth century, following the brilliant success of Halley's prediction of the return of his comet in 1759, the study of comets became a sufficiently important branch in itself to occupy a considerable part of astronomers' activities. They began to search for them systematically instead of waiting for the chance apparition of a bright comet to study.

The French astronomer Charles Messier (1730–1817), who had discovered Halley's comet independently on its return in January 1759, was the first to undertake this systematic search; the King of France, Louis XV, had even nicknamed him 'the ferret of comets'. In the course of his long career he actually discovered as many as twenty-one and observed forty-six. All his discoveries and ob servations were carried out in the middle of Paris with a small instrument installed on top of a tower, where an observatory was maintained by the Navy at the time.

Shortly afterwards Caroline Herschel discovered eight comets

However, it was the German astronomer Heinrich Olbers (1758–1840) who mainly introduced the physical study of these objects into the realm of astronomical practice. Already in 1779 he had devised a new method for the calculation of cometary orbits—a problem that had hitherto been solved by long and complicated procedures. However, he did not publish it until much later, in 1797, when he was already a recognized authority in the field. He made all his observations with a small instrument of only 4 in. aperture mounted on the roof of his house; these observations were begun in 1781. His contribution to the discovery of the first minor planets has been mentioned earlier (III, 19); but his main interest was always in comets, many of which he studied with great care. In particular, after the appearance of the great comet of 1811, he put forward the first reasonable theory of cometary tails (cf. Plate VI); he suggested that these tails are formed of minute particles thrown out into the direction opposite the Sun by a repulsive force' which he supposed to be electric in nature. This was a revival of Kepler's ideas (page 53) and was a genuine advance, although the nature and mode of action of this force still eluded him—which is not surprising in view of the inadequacy of physical knowledge at that time. In 1815 he discovered a long-period comet period seventy-two years) belonging to the same family as Halley's, which still bears his name; Olbers' comet was seen again in 1887 and is expected to return in 1959.

Shortly after the discovery of the second long-period comet by Olbers, another German astronomer, this time a professional, J. F. Encke (1791–1865)—then assistant at the Göttingen Observatory —made a new important contribution to cometary astronomy: the discovery of a short-period comet. In 1818 a faint comet had been discovered at Marseilles by the French astronomer J. L. Pons 1761–1831), who from janitor of the observatory had become a skilful comet-hunter (he discovered thirty-six altogether); Encke computed the orbit of this comet and found to his surprise that it corresponded to a very short period, barely three and a half years, but confirmed his result by identifying it with objects observed previously by Méchain in 1786, Caroline Herschel in 1792 and Pons himself in 1805. Thus Encke predicted the return of the comet in 1822, a prediction which was confirmed with perfect accuracy. This was the second example of the return of a comet in accordance with prediction and was quite sensational; furthermore it established the existence of a new class of comets—those of short period.

Since then Encke's comet has been regularly seen at each of its returns, the last perihelion passage observed—the 44th—having taken place in 1954.

This comet has been of great value in improving our knowedge of these bodies: observations of it established clearly in 1828 a fact that had previously been only suspected—that the extent of comets heads diminishes as they approach the Sun; this peculiar feature was accounted for by subsequent theories. Its successive returns also gave rise throughout the nineteenth century to long debates on the existence of matter dispersed through interplanetary space as its motion appeared to be accelerated at each revolution; this phenomenon has more or less continued in our century and was not explained until recent years (IX, 48).

Shortly after Encke's comet there was discovered another short-period comet which was also to make a large contribution to our understanding of these objects. A comet discovered in 1826 by the Austrian Biela was recognized by him (and also by the French observer Gambart, who had come upon it independently) as being identical with comets observed in 1772 and 1805 with period a little over six years. It was actually seen again in 1832, but was missed in 1838. When it was seen once more on its following return, at the end of 1845, it showed at first its normal appearance of a diffuse nebulosity; but the following month astronomers were amazed to find it split into two twin comets sailing through space in convoy! This appearance continued throughout the observations, although the two nuclei receded from each other progressively. The two bodies were seen yet again at a still greater distance apart at the new return of the comet in 1852; but it was impossible to identify it again at any subsequent return in spite of precise knowledge of its orbit and a thorough search carried out by many astronomers. Thus the disintegration and disappearance of a comet had been seen while actually in progress. Finally, another effect, which will be discussed later (page 162), was to result from this disintegration and to contribute to a further advance in our knowledge of comets.

After the comet of 1811, other great comets were observed in the nineteenth century beginning with the return of Halley's comet in 1835; then in 1843 an extraordinarily brilliant comet (it could be seen in broad daylight) had a tail with the record length of over 80 million miles! Its head approached within 30,000 miles of the surface of the Sun itself, sweeping round it in a mere two hours.

The observations made at the perihelion passages of these various comets showed the extreme tenuity and fragility of these bodies; it relegated to the realm of outdated superstitions the fears that they had aroused up to that time, as well as the ideas maintained until the end of the eighteenth century by scientists such as Buffon and Laplace who still believed in the possibility of cosmic catastrophes caused by comets. By the middle of the nineteenth century their small dynamical importance had been well established which the French physicist Babinet summarized in the neat formula: 'Comets are visible nothings.'

The early nineteenth century also saw considerable progress in the understanding of shooting stars and fire-balls, those luminous meteors that appear unexpectedly in the night sky, streak across it rapidly and disappear without trace. Until the end of the eighteenth century the most fantastic ideas had prevailed on the subject; it was generally believed that shooting stars were due to terrestrial exhalations which spontaneously burst into flame in the atmosphere. Furthermore, scientists categorically denied that there might sometimes be 'stones falling from the sky' as was asserted by popular belief. It was only after some well-authenticated cases of falling meteorites, the most famous of which occurred in 1803 near the small village of Laigle, in Normandy, that the reality of this phenomenon was definitely accepted; but the origin of these meteors remained a mystery for a considerable time. However, as early as 1794, the German Chladni (1756–1827) had suggested that these bodies were of celestial origin and approached the Earth while travelling along their orbits, being heated to incandescence by friction in the atmosphere; but in 1802 Laplace still declared that they were merely stones ejected by lunar volcanoes and that in any case the subject did not deserve the attention of scientists!

Nevertheless, astronomers were obliged to pay attention to them when on the night of 12–13 November 1833 a prodigious 'shower' of shooting stars surprised observers on the American continent. Several remarkable facts forced themselves on astronomers' attention: first it was noticed that all these meteors appeared to diverge from the same point in the celestial sphere and that this point or 'radiant' was carried round along with the rest of the celestial sphere by the diurnal motion, or, in other words, remained fixed among the stars. It was soon realized that this fact proved that meteors were cosmic and not terrestrial in origin and that they followed parallel orbits in space the apparent divergence of which resulted from an easily understood effect of perspective. It was also noticed that the phenomenon was a periodic one, for a similar shower of shooting stars had been observed on 12 November 1799 by the German naturalist and traveller F. von Humboldt (1769–1859), while secondary showers of lesser importance had also been noticed on the same date of the year, particularly in 1834 and 1837.

Shortly afterwards the Belgian astronomer J. Quetelet (1796–1874) also demonstrated the annual return of shooting stars on 10 August, known popularly as 'the tears of St. Lawrence' and now as the 'Perseids', owing to the position of their radiant in the constellation Perseus. These observations showed that there are actually currents or closed rings of meteoric matter, moving through space and describing regular orbits about the Sun.

Thus towards the middle of the nineteenth century the nature of shooting stars and their importance in the solar system began to become apparent and a new branch of astronomy was founded—meteoric astronomy, which has held the attention of a large number of specialized observers ever since.

However, the decisive advances regarding the physical nature of comets and meteors and the relations between them were not to come about until somewhat later (VI, 35).

31. Solar studies

Knowledge of the Sun made practically no progress from the time of the discovery of sunspots by Galileo until the end of the eighteenth century; at this time, following the opinion of the greatest astronomers, theories were generally accepted which now seem extravagant.

It was then thought that the Sun's globe was rocky in nature—like those of the planets—and that the spots were mountains or volcanoes that emerged at certain places through an incandescent ocean. However, already in 1774 the British astronomer A. Wilson (1714–1786) of Glasgow had concluded from his observations of the successive appearances of a large spot in transit across the Sun's disc that the phenomenon was actually a depression rather than an elevation in the solar surface.

As a result of these observations, William Herschel had put forward a 'theory' of the Sun which (relying on his great authority) was to be generally accepted until the middle of the nineteenth century. He supposed that the internal globe of the Sun was cold and solid like that of a gigantic planet on which he did not hesitate to place vegetation and even inhabitants! The luminous surface, according to him was only a thick atmosphere covered with dazzling clouds, which Schröter called the 'photosphere', a designation which has survived. The cloudy structure was inspired by the granular appearance of the photosphere, which was already known at that time. Thus the spots were openings through which the dark underlying regions became visible. These ideas should occasion no surprise if one recalls that the science of heat was not yet in existence; it was not to be developed until the first half of the nineteenth century with the investigations of Fourier, Carnot and Mayer—only then did the absurdity of current ideas on the nature of the Sun become apparent (VI, 32, 33).

Nevertheless, once the atmospheric nature of the luminous envelope was accepted, certain advances could be made even if the other ideas were mistaken. Thus, in the course of observations carried out during his stay at the Cape, John Herschel came to the conclusion that the spots might be due to disturbances of the same nature as tornadoes or cyclones in the Earth's atmosphere, an idea which has more or less survived with the advance of knowledge (VII, 38).

At about the same time, however, a discovery of fundamental importance for the progress of solar research was made by a German amateur H. S. Schwabe (1789–1875), an apothecary who devoted his spare time to a methodical study of the Sun. In 1826, with a very small telescope, he had begun to count the number of sunspots every day, in the hope that one day he would discover some intramercurial planet in transit across the solar disc. In this way, with remarkable patience and assiduity, he counted sunspots day after day for forty-three years in succession. He did not find an intramercurial planet but what he did discover was a still more important reward. In 1843, after seventeen years of observation, he noticed that the number of spots visible on the Sun showed a systematic variation from one year to the next and this in a cyclic manner, the period being ten or eleven years. The announcement of his result attracted hardly any attention at the time, but in 1851 his further observations accumulated over now more than two complete cycles were published by Humboldt and removed all doubts on the subject; so that the surprised astronomical world was forced to submit to the evidence.

In the same year a set of independent observations of a completely different character was added to these investigations and confirmed them. For some fifteen years stations had been established at Humboldt's suggestion to take daily records of the variations in the Earth's magnetism (using Gauss magnetometer), in particular in the angle between the magnetic and geographic meridians (the magnetic declination). It had been known for a long time that this declination undergoes a slight periodic variation in the course of a day. In 1851 the Scottish astronomer J. Lamont working in Munich, noticed to his surprise that the amplitude of the daily variation changes from year to year and shows a periodic cycle of about ten years' period. In the same year Sir Edward Sabine found that the number of magnetic perturbations or 'storms' during which the magnetic needle shows an abnormal departure from its usual position also went through a periodic variation with a period of about ten years, reaching a high frequency and considerable amplitude in some years and becoming weaker and less frequent in the intervening periods.

However, at this time Schwabe's results were known and Sabine was then able to establish the fact that the two curves showing the respective variations in magnetic and solar activity were completely parallel—the maxima and minima of the two effects being in perfect correspondence.

This unexpected correlation, which was announced in 1852 and immediately confirmed by other astronomers, showed that sunspots exert a mysterious influence on the magnetism of our globe, the first sign of solar-terrestrial relationships which were to be recognized in ever increasing number afterwards and in our day form the subject of a new branch of astronomy. At that time, however, the nature and cause of these relationships remained a complete mystery. At least they showed how mistaken was the opinion of the French astronomer J. B. Delambre (1749–1822), who declared at the beginning of the nineteenth century that sunspots were 'more curious than really useful', and brought out the importance of an attentive and systematic study of them.

This was immediately taken up on all sides; among others the Swiss astronomer R. Wolf (1816–1893) examined the few observations quoted in earlier astronomical literature and compiled a list of the maxima and minima of solar activity going back to the first observations of Galileo; however, the data before 1750 are very uncertain and the variation curve is well established only after that date (Fig. 18). He also laid down the principles of a statistical treatment of sunspot counts which has always been accepted since then apart from slight improvements and is still extensively used as an index of solar activity (Wolf-Wölfer numbers) published each year by the Zürich Observatory.

Wolf undertook a comparison of all kinds of terrestrial phenomena with his curve of solar activity, in the hope of detecting new correlations. In the field of local meteorology he reached only questionable results and a century later the question of the Sun's influence on the weather still remains in great confusion—all kinds of mutually contradictory results having been obtained. On the other hand he was more successful when he came to consider the appearances of polar aurorae mentioned in the ancient chronicles of the city of Zürich; furthermore, it was already known at the time that the appearance of the aurora coincides with particularly strong disturbances of the magnetic needle, as had been established by the French astronomer F. Arago (1786–1853) in the first quarter of the nineteenth century.

The first systematic and consistent series of sunspot observations inspired by Schwabe's discovery was undertaken by the English amateur R. C. Carrington (1826–1875), in 1853 and he was led to a new and important discovery in 1859. Carrington was concerned with the positions of spots on the solar disc rather than

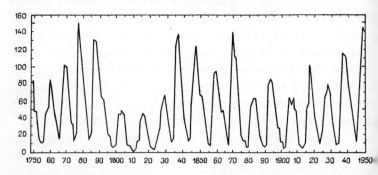

FIG. 18. THE CURVE OF SUNSPOT ACTIVITY FROM 1750 TO 1950, according to spot statistics established at the Zürich Observatory (Wolf numbers).

with their numbers, since he was trying to determine the exact period of rotation of the Sun, still not too well known at the time, and the displacements of individual spots on the photosphere. His systematic observations revealed that the reason why the period of solar rotation had not yet been well determined is that it does not have a well-defined unique value, but varies according to the latitude of the spots used in deriving it. In other words, he found that the Sun rotates not as a rigid body (at least in those parts of it visible from the outside) but in a 'differential' fashion as a fluid medium would. He also noticed that the mean latitude of spots varies systematically through the course of the solar cycle: the first spots appear at the beginning of the cycle at mean latitudes of about 35° while they are still few in number and descend progressively towards the equator, until finally, at the end of the cycle, they are concentrated very close to it at about 5°; the passage through a maximum of activity shows no outstanding feature in this respect. Similar results had also been discovered independently by a German amateur, G. Spörer (1822–1895), shortly after Carrington; Carrington's name is usually associated with the law of solar rotation and Spörer's with that of the latitude variation of spots.

All these results made increasingly untenable the old theory of a solid dark Sun; this theory was to receive its fatal blow during the same period, from 1859 to 1861, when the historic researches of the German physicist Kirchhoff—creating the new science of astrophysics—established the gaseous nature and chemical composition of the Sun (VI, 32).

While these investigations prepared the ground for the emergence of the modern conception of the Sun, others also helped to further its development in different ways. In particular observations carried out during eclipses of the Sun should be mentioned. Here again, until the end of the eighteenth century, the passage of the Moon's disc in front of the Sun had hardly been considered otherwise than from the point of view of celestial mechanics and positional astronomy; the observations carried out were designed to determine the moments of contact of the two discs in order to verify the tables of the motions of the two bodies and improve the lunar ephemerides.

During total solar eclipses, observers had not failed to observe the bright ring and pale 'glory' surrounding the black disc of the Moon, but very little interest had been taken in establishing its origin; the cause was a lunar atmosphere according to some, a solar atmosphere according to others, while a third opinion held that it was merely a peculiar optical effect. Not until the total eclipse of 1842, which was visible in Europe, was the attention of astronomers finally directed in a more systematic manner to the interpretation of these strange luminous effects. This time the objective existence of a red luminous ring surrounding the eclipsed Sun, large red flames or 'prominences' suspended above it and finally an enormous whitish halo or 'corona' extending to considerable distances in all directions (cf. Plate III) was clearly recognized. The observations carried out on this occasion and repeated at the eclipse of 1851 (when the first photograph of the inner corona was obtained) established the fact that these bright appendages were an outward extension of the Sun, a kind of distended atmosphere in front of which the Moon visibly changed its position in the course of the eclipse, proving that the extensions are not connected with the lunar globe. A final irrefutable proof which led to general agreement was provided by the eclipse of 1860 during which photography was first systematically applied to the study of eclipses (VI, 33).

Thus was prepared the revolution in ideas on the constitution of the Sun and the inauguration of a new branch of astronomy: solar physics, the importance of which has never ceased to increase from that time till our own.

Plate IX. DETECTION OF FAINT EMISSION NEBULOSITIES

Photographs taken by C. S. Gum with a 4-in. $f/1$ Schmidt camera at the Commonwealth Observatory on Mount Stromlo, near Canberra, Australia.

The brightest gaseous nebulosities such as the Orion nebula (Plate VIII) have been known for a long time, but fainter and often more extensive emission areas have only been detected in recent years by refined techniques. In 1936 Otto Struve discovered by means of a specially designed spectrograph that the red H-alpha line of hydrogen was faintly glowing over vast areas of the Milky Way. Later these weak-emission areas were directly photographed by means of suitable combinations of colour filters and red-sensitive photographic emulsions isolating the hydrogen line.

Here two photographs of a southern Milky Way field measuring $3° \times 4°5$ (centre 16h 30m, $-48°$) show the effect of plate-filter combinations (a) including, or (b) excluding the H-alpha line. The emission regions strongly brought out on (a) are virtually invisible in (b). Exhaustive surveys of northern and southern emission regions along the Milky Way have been made in recent years in the United States, the Soviet Union, France, South Africa and Australia.

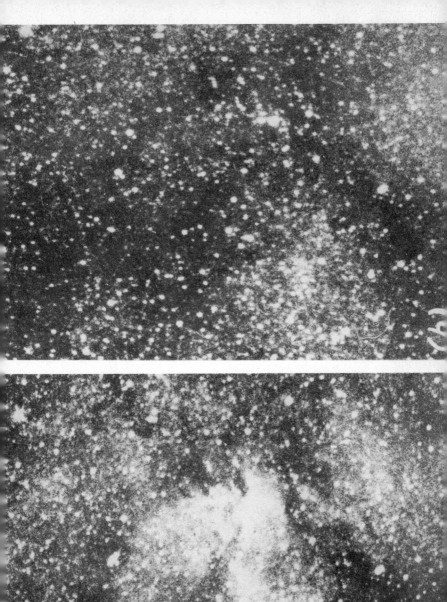

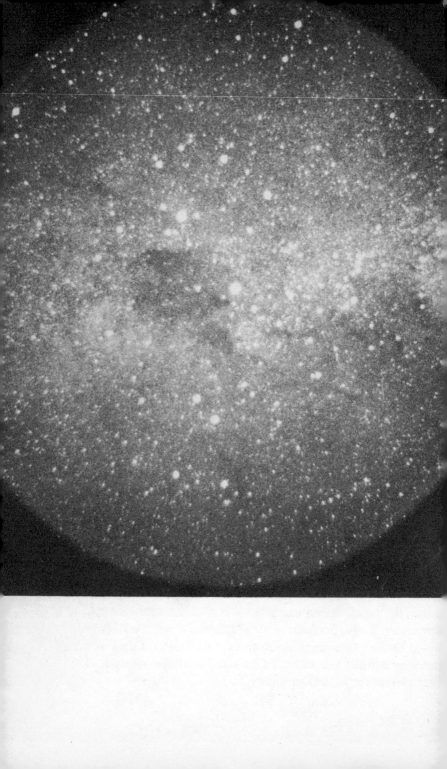

PLATE X. THE SOUTHERN CROSS AND THE COAL
SACK

Photographed from Mount Stromlo, Australia, with a miniature
camera.

This section of the southern Milky Way extending from Carima
to Centaurus through Crux includes the most striking dark nebula
in the sky, the 'Coal Sack'. It is visible here near the centre of the
8 degrees field marked by the first-magnitude star Alpha Crucis.
The other stars of the Southern Cross can be recognized above it.
At the left edge of the field is Beta Centauri.

The distance of the Coal Sack is of the order of 550 light-years
and its diameter about 50 light-years. It is one of the nearest
well-defined clouds of interstellar dust, but it is by no means
outstanding in size or density. A dark patch in the northern
Milky Way between Cygnus and Lacerta is almost as remarkable.
Prominent dark clouds mark only regions of higher density in the
all-pervading medium of gas and dust which fills interstellar
space.

The presence of obscuring clouds of diffuse matter in space
first suspected during the nineteenth century by the Italian
astronomer A. Secchi was demonstrated in the early years of this
century through wide-field photographs of the Milky Way, such
as this, by the German astronomer Max Wolf and the American
astronomer E. E. Barnard. The widespread absorption effects
caused by the less condensed substratum of interstellar dust were
finally established and measured by the Swiss astronomer R. J.
Trumpler, at the Lick Observatory, in 1930.

* VI *

The Rise of Modern Astronomy and the Beginnings of Astrophysics during the Second Half of the Nineteenth Century

32. The precursors of astrophysics

Astrophysics, or the 'new astronomy' as it used to be called fift years ago, was born from the conjunction of three physical method applied to the study of the stars: spectroscopy, photometry an photography. It is primarily through the application of these tech niques that the detailed constitution of the heavenly bodies ha become an object of scientific study while until then it had re mained a subject for arbitrary speculations.

The extent of the ground covered since the development astrophysics in the past century may be realized if one recalls tha in 1825 the French philosopher Auguste Comte in his *Cours Philosophie Positive* offered the chemical composition of the star as a perfect example of knowledge permanently inaccessible to mar In 1840 the French astronomer Arago still asserted his convictio that the Sun was habitable and in 1860, in his book on *La Plurali des Mondes Habités* the great French apostle of astronomy Camill Flammarion discussed the probable climates on the other plane in the following terms: 'To solve the problem of heat at the surfac of these worlds we would require data that we shall probably alway lack.' In less than a century all these mistakes have been swep away, these insoluble problems solved, these unknowables knowr thanks to the extraordinary progress of modern astronomy and th development of astrophysics.

.) SPECTROSCOPY

The creation of astronomical spectroscopy was the achievement
the Bavarian optician Josef Fraunhofer (1787–1826), to whom
tronomy owes so much for his improvements in achromatic tele-
opes. It is true that, as early as 1666, Newton had demonstrated
e decomposition of the Sun's light by the prism and the forma-
on of a 'spectrum' showing the colours of the rainbow. In 1802
e English physicist W. H. Wollaston (1766–1828), observing a
ng slit through a prism, had noted the existence of some dark
nes across the spectrum; but it was Fraunhofer who first made
systematic study of these lines in the light of the Sun and
ars.

By combining a prism with the small viewing telescope of a
eodolite and observing a distant narrow slit through this com-
ination, he created the first spectroscope and discovered in the
un's spectrum: 'an almost countless number of strong or weak
ertical lines which are darker than the rest of the coloured image;
ome appeared to be almost perfectly black'. He made this dis-
overy in 1814 and announced it in 1817; he added: 'I have con-
inced myself by numerous experiments and by varying methods
at these lines and bands are due to the nature of sunlight and do
ot arise from diffraction, optical illusion, etc.' and he published a
rawing on which several hundred lines were already marked. To
e principal lines he assigned letters: A, B, C, D ... which have
een retained since then and the dark lines of the solar spectrum
e still called 'Fraunhofer Lines' (cf. Plate VII).

Fraunhofer then turned his spectroscope on to the Moon and
e planets Venus and Mars, observing that the same lines that
ere visible in the Sun's spectrum also appeared in the same posi-
ons in the spectra of these bodies: 'the light of the Moon gave
e a spectrum which showed in the brightest colours the same
xed lines as did sunlight and in exactly the same places'.

Then, turning a more powerful telescope on to the bright stars,
e observed that some presented the same lines as the solar spec-
rum while others showed different ones. He was particularly struck
y the presence in almost all the spectra that he studied of a strong
ne in the orange region which he designated by the letter D. This

D-line appeared even in the spectrum of the flame blown from torch—this time as a bright line against a background that wa otherwise continuous: 'The prismatic spectrum of the light comin from the flame of a lamp does not show the dark fixed lines whic are present in the spectrum of sunlight; instead of them there is i the orange a bright line which is prominent above the rest of th spectrum, is double, and is at the same place where in sunlight th double line D is found.'

This orange line, now known to be due to sodium, had alread been observed in the eighteenth century by the Scottish physicis Melvill in the spectra of various flames, and its ubiquity was t delay for a long time the recognition of the fundamental laws o spectra by physicists.

Fraunhofer had also observed that the refrangibility of the ligh of the Sun and stars by a prism is precisely the same for any give colour, a fact which proved that the light coming from variou bodies was all of the same kind. At the same time it established tha atmospheric refraction has precisely the same value for all stars a the same altitude,[1] a fact of which astronomers were not yet quit sure at the time.

An explanation of these lines was completely lacking. Physicist discussed it in vain and made contradictory experiments on th subject until the middle of the nineteenth century. The myster was not solved until 1859 as a result of the historic investigation of the German physicist Kirchhoff and the chemist Bunsen, wh conclusively established the fundamental laws of spectroscopy.

But we must first mention the work of the precursors of astro nomical photometry and photography.

(B) PHOTOMETRY

Already in the seventeenth century Huygens had attempted t compare the light of the Sun with that of a candle and the latte with Sirius (II, 12). But it is the Frenchman Bouguer who deserve to be regarded as the real founder of photometry, the first principle of which he set out in a treatise on *The Gradation of Light*, pub

---

[1] In fact one must specify for all stars 'of the same colour'.

shed in 1760; at about the same time the physicist Celsius of
weden had carried out some crude measurements of the compara-
ve brightnesses of a few stars. However, it is not until the middle
f the nineteenth century that the first series of measurements still
etaining some value were obtained by John Herschel with his
strometer' during his sojourn at the Cape (IV, 24). At about the
me time some observations were carried out at Munich by the
ptician Steinheil with a somewhat better stellar photometer. But
was the German astronomer Zöllner who introduced in 1859 the
rst modern photometer that has continued to be used until the
resent, with only minor improvements.

Parallel to these developments of devices for photometric
easurement, an extremely simple technique for the comparison
f stellar brightnesses was put into operation first by William
erschel, then by Argelander (IV, 6)—which has for the past cen-
ry made possible an enormous number of observations of variable
ars at small cost. Its full value was realized when genuine photo-
etric measures had made it possible to determine the brightnesses
f non-variable stars on a well-defined scale which served for com-
arison. The elaboration of this scale gave rise in particular to the
vestigations of the German physiologist Fechner, who inferred
om the first measurements of John Herschel and Steinheil that
ue brightnesses of stars of successive magnitudes were almost in a
onstant ratio to one another—close to 2·5. In other words, the
ale of stellar 'magnitudes' forms an arithmetic progression while
ue corresponding luminosities form a geometric progression; from
us Fechner deduced his famous psychophysical 'law' according
which 'sensation varies as the logarithm of the stimulus'. It is
ow known that this law is only an approximation valid in a limited
nge. Nevertheless, it had the advantage of giving a well-defined
nysical significance to the scale of stellar 'magnitudes' which until
en had been purely subjective and arbitrary. In 1857, using these
vestigations as a basis, the Englishman Pogson laid down the
ndamental relation that has since then been adopted as the defini-
on of the stellar magnitude scale. Stellar photometry was thus
idowed with a solid foundation on which it could now be erected
id perfected.

(C) PHOTOGRAPHY

In 1839, at the very time when he communicated to the Frenc
Chamber of Deputies the invention of Niepce and Daguerre, Arag
had shown singular penetration in emphasizing the great benei
that astronomy could derive from it: 'One is entitled to hope th:
it will be possible to make photographic maps of our satellite. Th:
is to say that in a few minutes it will be possible to carry out or
of the most lengthy, precise and delicate tasks of astronomy.' Bett
still, he clearly described the possible applications to astronomic
photometry and even to spectroscopy; thus in truly prophet
fashion he immediately outlined the studies from which the ne
astronomy was to arise.

However, photography was still in the very rudimentary state
the 'daguerreotype' and some time was to elapse until its applic:
tion began to result in genuine astronomical progress. The fir
successful photograph of the Sun was obtained in 1845 at the Par
Observatory by the French physicists Fizeau and Foucault;
showed some spots. The granulation of the photosphere and i
bright areas or 'faculae' were not recorded until later; but as alread
noted the German astronomer Busch—director of the Königsbe
Observatory—assisted by a photographer named Berkowski, su
ceeded in obtaining an excellent daguerreotype photograph of tl
solar corona during the total eclipse of 1851. In spite of its compar:
tive faintness, the Moon was also photographed as early as 18
by the American physician J. W. Draper and much better :
1849, at Harvard College Observatory, by W. C. Bond—assist
by the photographer Whipple—using the large 15-in. refractor.[1]
the following year they also succeeded in photographing for tl
first time the image of the first-magnitude star Alpha Lyrae (Veg
and that of the double star Alpha Geminorum (Castor).

However, it was not until the discovery by Scott-Archer, in 185
of the wet collodion process—ten to a hundred times more sensiti
than the primitive technique of Daguerre—that photography beg:

[1] The fascinating early history of astronomical photography was told I
D. Norman, in *Osiris,* V, 1938 (Harvard Reprint 1953). See also *Sor
firsts in Astronomical Photography* by D. Hoffleit, Harvard College, 195

bout 1858 to produce the first results that really contributed to
stronomical progress.

Indeed the instruments of the time, designed for visual observa-
on, left much to be desired in photographic applications and
everal years had to pass before existing instruments were adapted
o their new application or new ones were specially built for the
urpose.

After this, results accumulated rapidly: in 1858 the first daily
hotographic observations of the Sun, suggested by J. Herschel in
847, were made at the Kew Observatory near London, using the
photoheliograph'; at the solar eclipses of 1858 and 1860 the first
ear photographic records of prominences were obtained (section
3); in 1857 and 1859 the English amateur astronomer W. De La
ue (1815–1889) succeeded in taking the first fairly detailed photo-
raphs of the Moon and it was also in 1857 that the American
stronomer G. P. Bond (1825–1865), who had succeeded his father
s director of the Harvard College Observatory, obtained the first
hotographic measures of a double star, Zeta Ursae Majoris
Mizar).

Finally, again in 1857, the French astronomer and physicist
éon Foucault (1819–1868) constructed the first telescope with a
lvered glass mirror; this type of instrument is ideally suited to the
eeds of spectroscopy and photography because of its high reflect-
g power and perfect achromatism and it rapidly replaced first the
ewtonian reflectors with bronze mirrors and then refractors them-
lves as a tool of physical astronomy.

Thus by a remarkable coincidence all the elements required for
e growth of the new astronomy were provided at virtually the
me time in the years 1857 to 1859. This conjunction was to lead
the explosive development of modern astronomy and particularly
astrophysics, which we shall now survey.

. Solar studies

The foundations of astrophysics were laid by the investigations
f the German physicist Gustav Robert Kirchhoff (1824–1887),
ho discovered the interpretation of the Fraunhofer Lines. In

1859, in collaboration with the chemist Bunsen, he carried ou studies of the spectra of flames and metallic vapours in the electr. arc, which led him to consider in more detail the famous D-line i the solar spectrum:

'In order to test in the most direct manner possible the truth the frequently asserted fact of the coincidence of the sodium line with the D lines, I obtained a moderately bright solar spectrum, an brought a flame coloured by sodium vapour in front of the slit. then saw the dark D lines change into bright ones. The flame of Bunsen's lamp threw the bright sodium lines upon the sola spectrum with unexpected brilliancy. In order to find out the exter to which the intensity of the solar spectrum could be increase without impairing the distinctness of the sodium lines, I allowe the full sunlight to shine through the sodium flame upon the sli and, to my astonishment, I saw that the dark D lines appeared wit an extraordinary degree of clearness. I then exchanged the sunligl for Drummond's or oxyhydrogen limelight, which, like that of a incandescent solid or liquid bodies, gives a spectrum containing n dark lines. When this light was allowed to fall through a suitab. flame coloured by common salt, dark lines were seen in the spec rum in the position of the sodium lines. . . . The phenomenon i question is easily explained upon the supposition that the sodiu flame absorbs rays of the same degree of refrangibility as those emits, whilst it is perfectly transparent for all other rays.'

After similar experiments with the salts of lithium, potassiun etc., Kirchhoff concluded that the 'spectrum of every incandescer gas must be reversed, when it is penetrated by the rays from source of light of sufficient intensity giving a continuous spec trum'.

Shortly afterwards he announced the two fundamental laws spectroscopy which since then have been named after him:

(1) To each chemical species there corresponds a characterist spectrum.

(2) Every element is capable of absorbing the radiation which is able to emit; this is the phenomenon of the *reversal* of th lines.

Furthermore, it was stated that an incandescent solid or liquid emits a continuous spectrum while gases emit discrete line spectra.[1]

Kirchhoff was thus able to attribute the dark lines in the solar spectrum to the absorption by vapours in the solar atmosphere of the continuous spectrum emitted by the photosphere; the name 'reversing layer' was given to this region of the solar atmosphere where reversal of lines was supposed to occur. By comparing these lines with the spectra of various elements observed in the laboratory, Kirchhoff was also able immediately to identify a large number of these lines and to announce the presence in the Sun of numerous well-known chemical elements such as sodium, iron, calcium, nickel, etc. This discovery was at the same time of considerable philosophical importance, since it demonstrated that the same familiar chemical elements were found in the heavens as well as on earth, a result which all later studies have confirmed and extended.

The study of the solar spectrum immediately underwent considerable development. As early as 1860, the Englishman D. Brewster (1781–1868) recognized the fact that certain dark bands observed in the spectrum of the setting Sun were due to absorption by the gases in the Earth's atmosphere ('telluric' bands) and in 1865 the Frenchman J. Janssen verified experimentally that these telluric lines are due to the oxygen and water vapour of our atmosphere, since he was able to detect them in the spectra of distant lamps observed through a long column of air. In 1866 the British amateur astronomer Norman Lockyer (1836–1920) undertook a detailed study of the different parts of the Sun's surface by projecting an image of the Sun on the slit of the spectroscope; the spectra of spots in particular showed him that these are dark not merely because the general emission of light in them is reduced, but also because the absorption lines are more numerous and stronger than in the normal photospheric spectrum—two clear signs of a reduction in temperature.

The study of the normal solar spectrum—the Fraunhofer Spectrum—was developing at the same time chiefly through the

[1] It was discovered later that gases under high pressures also emit continuous spectra.

efforts of physicists. In 1869 the Swedish physicist A. J. Ångström (1814–1874) published the wavelengths of 1,000 lines of the solar spectrum expressed in terms of the unit of length to which his name has been given (1 Ångström = 1 ten-millionth of a millimetre); this work was successively developed by H. Draper (1837–1882) in the U.S.A., by W. de W. Abney in England and by M. A. Cornu in France. Finally, the American physicist H. A. Rowland (1848–1901) published between 1886 and 1895 new tables and a much more detailed and complete atlas giving the precise wavelengths and approximate intensities of 14,000 solar lines, from the ultra-violet to the red; this solar atlas has remained the basis of all modern investigations of the solar spectrum. At the same time the number of chemical elements identified in the Sun continued to increase and 39 of them had already been identified in Rowland's time.[1]

At the same time, Kirchhoff's discovery completely overturned the old solar theory; indeed it proved on the one hand that the solar atmosphere was at a high temperature, since the metals in it were in the gaseous state, and on the other hand that the photosphere, which emits a continuous spectrum, was at a still higher temperature (since the spectral lines appear in absorption), so that the temperature of the Sun must increase inwards. Finally sunspots had to be interpreted as regions of lower temperature which Kirchhoff compared to some kind of clouds. These views were set forth by Kirchhoff in 1861 in his historic memoir *On the Solar Spectrum*.

Shortly afterwards these views were developed and organized in the framework of a new solar theory proposed in 1865 by the French astronomer Hervé Faye (1814–1902). In this theory Faye tried to account for all the facts revealed by the new investigations. For the first time a theory was put forward which considered the entire solar mass as gaseous, radiating to the outside the heat emerging from its interior. As regards the mechanism of transfer of this energy, Faye supposed that it consisted of ascending and descending convection currents mixing the entire solar mass and transporting to photospheric level chemical substances which

[1] The number has been increased to 57 in 1928 by the Revised Rowland Tables listing 20,000 lines and to 67 in 1952 when 26,000 lines had been recorded between 2,935 and 13,495 A.

reacted violently and produced a strong incandescence at this level; they then condensed and fell back to be dissociated again by the high temperatures of the interior. This idea, though consistent with the knowledge available at the time, was abandoned later in consequence of the theoretical investigations of our century. Nevertheless, this theory of Faye was a considerable advance and opened the gateway to modern ideas of the Sun.

The regular photography of the Sun's surface, taken up in 1858 at Kew Observatory and continued until 1872, provided the first systematic and objective records of the Sun's surface, spots and rotation. This series was followed in 1873 by the inauguration of a similar permanent service at the Greenwich Observatory through the initiative of the British astronomer E. W. Maunder (1851–1928); the long series of daily photographs of the Sun, continued without interruption until the present time at Greenwich, later supplemented by the establishment of a similar service at Kodaikanal, India, and in several other places, has made it possible to determine accurately the variations in the area covered by spots, their motions and in particular their latitude variations in the course of the cycle of solar activity; these observations have been an important contribution to solar studies.

However, the most spectacular results of this period in the realm of solar photography were obtained by the French astronomer J. Janssen (1824–1907) at the Meudon Observatory, of which he became the first director in 1876. Using a small telescope (less than 6 in. in aperture) specially designed for this purpose and giving through a magnifying lens solar images of large diameter (up to 20 or even 28 in.), he was able to obtain some remarkably clear pictures—that have hardly been equalled since—of the granular structure of the photosphere, the 'rice grains', not exceeding a few seconds of arc in diameter (Plate IV). These rice grains were regarded as the visible manifestation of convection currents emerging from the solar mass at photospheric level and this view has more or less continued to be held up to the present.

The application of spectroscopy to the study of eclipses also led to tremendously rapid advances in solar physics. On 18 August 1868 a total eclipse of the Sun was observed by several French and

British expeditions; they demonstrated that the 'pink flames', the prominences visible around the black disc of the Moon, give a spectrum containing a few bright lines among which two particularly conspicuous ones—one red and one blue—were soon attributed to hydrogen, and also an orange-yellow line close to the D-line. This observation showed definitely that the prominences really belong to the Sun and furthermore that they are gaseous eruptions. However, the most important result that Janssen obtained from these observations was 'the discovery of a method the principle of which was devised during the eclipse itself, that permits a study of the prominences and of the circumsolar regions at any time without the necessity of having recourse to the interposition of an opaque body in front of the solar disc'.

Janssen was greatly impressed by the intensity of these bright lines and it occurred to him that it would be possible to observe them even outside an eclipse: 'Immediately on the day after the eclipse the method was successfully applied and I was thus able to observe these phenomena by a new kind of eclipse that lasted throughout the day.' For, by using a spectroscope with very high dispersion, the continuous background of sunlight scattered by the atmosphere is spread out and therefore weakened, while the light of the prominences—concentrated in a small number of monochromatic lines—is unreduced. Thus, by placing the slit of the spectroscope tangentially to the limb of the Sun and moving it progressively, it is possible to trace a general contour of the prominences systematically by following the extent of the bright lines of hydrogen.

Now by a curious coincidence the British astronomer Lockyer had thought of the possibility of this technique as early as 1866 and in October 1868, when Janssen was announcing this discovery in France, he was making the same observation independently. Furthermore, Lockyer found that the prominences emanated from a gaseous envelope close to the solar surface to which he gave the name 'chromosphere', since universally adopted.

The following year, at the eclipse of 7 August 1869, Lockyer observed further that the orange-yellow line emitted by prominences did not correspond to the lines of any element known at the time and he suggested that it should be attributed to an unknown element peculiar to the Sun which for this reason he called 'helium'. The new element was not found on the Earth until twenty-five years later, in 1895, by the British chemist W. Ramsay.

Meanwhile the study of prominences, which could now be carried out on any day, progressed rapidly; as early as 1869 the British amateur astronomer W. Huggins (1824–1910) showed that instead of studying them in sections it was possible to obtain a complete view of one all at once by opening wide the slit of the spectroscope and the same idea was described almost at the same time by the German astronomer Zöllner. In the following year, 1870, the application of this method made it possible to recognize two chief types of prominence, 'quiescent' prominences in the form of clouds, and 'eruptive' prominences in the form of flames. From then on the daily mapping of the distribution of prominences all round the solar disc was undertaken systematically in the same way as that of sunspots. The first observers who devoted themselves to this task were chiefly the Italians A. Secchi (1818–1878), L. Respighi (1824–1889) and P. Tacchini (1838–1905). The accumulated observations soon showed that the number and activity of the prominences visible round the Sun also varied in very close synchronism with the cycle of spot activity. They showed further that there are two special zones in which prominences chiefly appear, one close to the spots and the other in the polar regions of the Sun where no spot has ever been observed.

At the eclipse of 22 December 1869, the American astronomer C. A. Young (1834–1908) made a new observation of the greatest importance: 'Just previous to totality, I had carefully adjusted the slit tangentially to the sun's limb at the point where the second contact would take place. . . . As the crescent grew narrower, I noticed a fading out, so to speak, of all dark lines in the field of view, but was not at all prepared for the beautiful phenomenon which presented itself when the moon finally covered the whole photosphere. Then the whole field was at once filled with brilliant lines, which suddenly flashed into brightness and then gradually faded away until, in less than two seconds, nothing remained. . . .'

Young immediately perceived that: '(This observation) . . .

tends to make tenable the original theory of Kirchhoff as to the constitution of the sun and the origin of the dark lines in the ordinary solar spectrum.'

Young had indeed observed the emission lines due to the vapours in the reversing layer which normally produce the absorption lines of the Fraunhofer spectrum. This transitory spectrum which is emitted by the reversing layer of the solar atmosphere in agreement with Kirchhoff's theory is called the *flash spectrum*.

During these same eclipses the solar corona was also examined by spectroscopic methods. It was observed that it chiefly emits a green line first observed by the American astronomer W. Harkness in 1869 and the position of which was measured at the eclipse of 1870 by Young. Since it could not be attributed to any known chemical element this line was later considered as a sign of a new unknown chemical element present in the Sun, which was called 'coronium'. However, unlike helium, coronium was never found on the Earth for the good reason that it does not exist and it has only been in the course of the last decade that the green line of the solar corona has been successfully explained (VII, 38).

At the same time, the systematic photography of the corona, successfully carried out at eclipses from 1869 onwards, provided a new important testimony to the fundamental influence of the cycle of sunspot activity on the entire behaviour of our central star. In particular, at the eclipse of 1871, when the Sun was in a phase of great activity, the corona extended all round it 'like the petals of an enormous dahlia' as Janssen said (Plate III). At the eclipse of 1875, which occurred in a declining phase of solar activity, the corona appeared in the general form of a rectangle less extended near the poles. Finally, at the eclipse of 1878, which coincided with a minimum of solar activity, the corona extended almost entirely along the equatorial belt of the Sun and in the polar regions showed only a faint extension of fine bundles of rays.

This spectacular systematic variation in the form of the coronal jets as a function of phase in the cycle of solar activity has always been observed and confirmed at every eclipse since that time.

Until the beginning of the nineteenth century the amount of heat emitted by the Sun was unknown. It was only in 1837 that the first determinations, made by the French physicist Pouillet and by John Herschel, showed that at the top of the atmosphere the Earth receives from the Sun about two calories per square centimetre per minute. This result was confirmed at least as an order of magnitude by later studies; although until the end of the century considerable uncertainty prevailed as to the exact value of this quantity that has since been called the 'solar constant'.

Knowledge of the value of the energy flux reaching the Earth was not sufficient to determine the temperature of the Sun; it was also necessary to know the law relating the total radiation of a body to its temperature. This law was still unknown in the middle of the nine-teenth century and estimates of the solar temperature were then quite arbitrary; thus, while Pouillet estimated the Sun's temperature at about 1,500°, others like Secchi spoke of 5 to 10 million degrees.

Only after the Austrian physicist J. Stefan had announced in 1879 the law that bears his name, according to which the total radiation increases as the fourth power of the temperature, was it possible to obtain the correct result, close to 6,000° C. Progress in knowledge of the laws of radiation has since made it possible to refine and confirm this value. However, uncertainty in the solar constant continued to delay the establishment of a precise value for a considerable time.

The first investigations undertaken to determine this quantity accurately were due to the French physicist Violle, who, observing from Mont Blanc, found in 1875 a value of 2·54 cal./cm.^{2}/min., and more especially to the American physicist Langley, who, in 1881, obtained with the 'bolometer' (which he had just invented) detailed records of the Sun's radiation throughout the spectrum from the ultra-violet to the infra-red; unfortunately Langley over-estimated the absorption of the atmosphere and deduced from his observations a value (3 cal.) considerably in excess of the solar constant. However, his investigations marked the beginning of the modern phase in studies of solar radiation, which were continued by his successors at the Astrophysical Observatory of the Smithsonian Institution.

The sources of the Sun's heat still remained a complete mystery until the middle of the nineteenth century; at that time physics had not yet advanced sufficiently to provide an explanation for it. However, as early as 1848 the German physicist R. Mayer, one of the founders of thermodynamics, put forward the idea that the Sun's heat could be provided by a continual fall of meteorites on to the Sun; this source was soon recognized to be totally inadequate, first because meteorites do not fall on to the Sun, but revolve round it in closed orbits, and secondly because the required amount would have caused an appreciable change in the Sun's mass during the last two thousand years and this possibility is excluded by the study of planetary motions.

The first plausible scientific theory was put forward in 1854 by the German physicist H. von Helmholtz (1821–1894). He drew attention to the fact that a gaseous mass radiating like the Sun must tend to cool down and hence to contract. As the molecules fall towards the centre of the Sun in the course of this contraction, their potential energy is changed into kinetic energy, i.e. heat; in this mechanism he saw a method of making up for the heat losses of the Sun. His theory had the advantage of agreeing with Laplace's cosmogonic hypothesis (III, 18), which was generally accepted at the time. Assuming that the Sun originated from an infinitely extended nebula, calculation showed that the energy produced by contraction would have been sufficient to maintain the solar radiation at its observed value for some 20 million years and held promise for a similar period in the future; at this time geologists had only the vaguest notion of the age of the Earth[1] and this source was considered adequate until the turn of the century. Not until the beginning of the present century was it realized that this hypothesis still fell far short of requirements and the solution of the problem was not found until our own time (VIII, 42).

Until the middle of the nineteenth century the value of the solar parallax obtained by Encke from transits of Venus in the eighteenth century (p. 83) had been generally accepted. But at this time some doubts arose as to the accuracy of this value.

First, the development of celestial mechanics had provided new

---

[1] In 1897 Lord Kelvin still thought the age of the Earth to be between 20 and 400 million years, but probably less than 40 million. This estimate was 100 times too small.

ndirect methods for the determination of the solar parallax from he inequalities in the lunar and terrestrial motions, the details of which will not be discussed here. Thus, between 1855 and 1860, Le Verrier and Hansen obtained values close to $8''.95$, considerably larger than that of Encke ($8''.57$).

Then laboratory measurements of the velocity of light on the Earth's surface carried out simultaneously by Foucault and Fizeau, combined with the value of the aberration constant obtained from a great many stellar observations, at Pulkovo by W. Struve, provided a further determination of the Sun's distance (III, 14). Foucault thus obtained a solar parallax of $8''.86$ in 1862. In the same year new observations of Mars by various astronomers led to values ranging from $8''.93$ to $8''.96$. Finally, in 1864, a new discussion of the 769 transit of Venus by the German astronomer Powalky gave a parallax of $8''.86$, and in 1865 the American astronomer Newcomb published a value of $8''.85$ derived from a general discussion of the then available data.

Thus for some twenty years early in the second half of the nineteenth century a value of $8''.86$, considerably higher than Encke's value, was generally adopted for the solar parallax.

Finally, after much anticipation, the transits of Venus of 1874 and 1882 took place. Immense preparations had been made in many countries in the hope of obtaining the best possible results from these events; unfortunately, however, difficulties of observation again introduced serious errors. From the 1874 transit, various astronomers had obtained values ranging from $8''.76$ to $8''.91$. The 1882 transit led to values in the range $8''.80$ to $8''.85$. However, Newcomb in a renewed discussion of the four transits of Venus of the two preceding centuries obtained in 1895 a final value of $8''.797$—in excellent agreement with the value of $8''.794$ he had deduced from the velocity of light, using the aberration method. In spite of this, the use of transits of Venus in the determination of the solar parallax has since then been completely discredited and it is quite certain that the next transits—due in the years 2004 and 2012—will not be used by astronomers for this purpose. In the meantime other more accurate methods have been devised, which will be discussed later (VII, 41; IX, 47).

34. Lunar and planetary studies

This field derived hardly any benefit from the rise of astrophysics until the end of the nineteenth century.

The leading observer at this time was the Italian astronomer G. Schiaparelli (1835–1910), who was director of the Milan Observatory from 1862 onwards. After making an important contribution to the study of meteors (section 35), he turned his attention to planetary studies in 1877. In that year the planet Mars passed through a favourable opposition[1] and he undertook a detailed study of it with a $9\frac{1}{2}$-in. telescope. This study enabled him to produce a map of Mars which was greatly superior to any previously published; it was particularly remarkable for a large number of delicate, narrow, more or less straight lines connecting the dark areas across the bright regions—lines which Schiaparelli called 'canali' (cf. Plate II, *a*). At the next opposition, in 1879, Schiaparelli saw his 'canals' again and discovered still more of them; he drew them to look quite straight and artificial, which led him to the idea that the term 'canal' might represent more than merely a convenient label. The strangeness of these Martian appearances increased still more in 1881, when he discovered some of the canals to be doubled at certain times: at a place where he had seen only a single canal there appeared often on the same or the following day two parallel lines apparently some hundreds of miles apart; this he called 'gemination' (or doubling) of the canals.

These discoveries, confirmed with more or less difficulty by other observers, were greeted with considerable scepticism; they gave rise to passionate debates which were to continue for many years and that have not completely ceased to this day (VII, 39).

Schiaparelli also devoted himself to the observation of Mercury and Venus and announced in 1889 and 1890 that these planets were endowed with a rotation of the lunar type, the period of rotation being equal to that of their orbital revolution; they always turn the same face towards the Sun. These observations were confirmed for Mercury by later studies, but for Venus

[1] During which the American astronomer A. Hall (1829–1907) discovered at the Washington Observatory two tiny satellites to the planet.

the conclusion still seems somewhat doubtful. Shortly afterwards the English mathematician G. H. Darwin (1845–1912) attributed this peculiarity of the inner planets to the damping of their rotation by the effect of internal tidal phenomena due to the Sun; the effect is analogous to the slow braking of the Earth's rotation by lunar tides which contributes to a secular acceleration in the apparent motion of the Moon (III, 13).

In 1879 it was Jupiter's turn to attract attention after the discovery of its 'Great Red Spot', which was very strong in that year and has always been observed since then although with very variable intensity. Indeed an examination of earlier drawings soon showed that this spot was not new, since it can be traced back to some of Cassini's drawings made in the seventeenth century. At the time of its rediscovery, it was considered in the light of Zöllner's ideas (according to a hypothesis revived by him in 1865 that the major planets had not yet cooled down completely) as a sign that the planet was beginning to solidify. This idea has, however, been abandoned although at present the nature of the spot is still something of a mystery (cf. Plate II, b).

The photometric, spectroscopic and photographic results obtained at that time were often very crude and not always consistent; they are not worthy of recall. The first real progress along these lines was not made until the twentieth century.

35. Studies of comets and meteors

Interest in the study of comets and meteors was considerably revived around 1860 as a result of the successive passages at perihelion of several large comets in 1858, 1861, 1862 and 1864. The comet of 1861 was noteworthy for its demonstration of the harmlessness of comets, for on 30 June in that year the Earth passed through its tail without any noticeable effects. The 1862 comet was more important because of the parental relationship which was to be established between it and the shooting stars visible in August.

The question of meteor streams was taken up again in 1864 by the American astronomer H. A. Newton, who made a detailed study of historical records relating to the November stream and predicted the return of an intense shower on 13–14 November 1866; and Adams in England showed that these meteors describe an elongated elliptic orbit with a period of thirty-three years and a quarter. This prediction was triumphantly verified and people were regaled with the spectacle of a magnificent repetition of the 1833 shower in Europe this time.

The interest excited by this phenomenon was to lead to a new advance of the utmost importance for our knowledge of meteors as well as of comets: the recognition of the fact that these two kinds of object are related. Shortly afterwards, at the end of 1866, Schiaparelli made the surprising announcement that the August meteors—the Perseids—describe the same orbit in space as the bright comet of 1862. Immediately afterwards, at the beginning of 1867, the German astronomer Peters corroborated this discovery by announcing the identity of the orbital elements of the November meteors—the Leonids—calculated by Le Verrier, with those of Comet Tempel 1864, and this was immediately confirmed by Schiaparelli. Several other coincidences of the same kind were noticed afterwards, the most important of these was that of the path of the 'Andromedids', observed at the end of November, with the orbit of the defunct Biela Comet, which was announced by several astronomers early in 1867.

These astronomers did not hesitate to announce that as a consequence a particularly copious shower of meteors would appear in 1872, the year when the lost comet would have been due to return to perihelion. The event brilliantly confirmed the prediction and a fine meteor shower was observed in Europe on the evening of 27 November. It occurred again in 1885. Here was final proof that comets disintegrate progressively into particles which disperse along their orbits and continue to pursue their path round the Sun through the ages. As a result of planetary perturbations these streams of dust are progressively dispersed and their orbital elements undergo a slow variation; thus, little by little, the showers become less abundant and finally cease when the Earth no longer crosses their orbit. On the other hand, new meteoric currents may come to hit the Earth. At present the meteors from Biela's comet can still be observed each year about 20 November, but they no longer produce the spectacular showers of the past.

Since then, other examples of cometary disintegration have been observed, and sometimes it has been possible to demonstrate that such disintegrations follow the passage of the comet through the immediate vicinity of one of the major planets, such as Jupiter.

The physical knowledge of comets and meteors made no less important progress during this period, thanks to the application of the spectroscope to the problem. The first comet studied from this point of view was Tempel's Comet in 1864, which was examined by the Italian astronomer Donati. He observed that the light of the comet was resolved by the spectroscope into three widely separated bands on a dark background. This observation proved that comets do not shine predominantly with reflected solar light, as had been supposed till then, but that they are self-luminous after the style of a luminescent gas.

This was confirmed by Huggins's observations of three faint comets in 1866, 1867 and 1868; during 1868 a new bright comet appeared and Huggins was able to make more exact observations, when he saw to his surprise that the three bands emitted by the comet coincided with those in the spectrum of hydrocarbon flames: 'The comet bands, as I had seen them on the previous evening, appeared to be identical in character in this respect as well as in position in the spectrum, with the flutings as they appeared when I took the spark in a current of olefiant gas.[1] I immediately filled a small holder with this gas, arranged an apparatus in such a manner that the gas could be attached to the end of the telescope, and its spectrum, when a spark was taken in it, seen side by side with that of the comet. . . . The expectation which I had formed from my measures was fully confirmed. The comet's spectrum when seen together with that from the gas agreed in all respects precisely with t. The comet, "though subtle as Sphinx", had at last yielded up its secret.'[2]

[1] Ethylene, C_2H_4, and its dissociation products.
[2] Shortly afterwards Huggins observed that the spectrum of the gases discharged by a meteor was similar to that of the comet, thus establishing on a physical basis the connection between the two kinds of objects, already known from the coincidence of the orbits of meteor showers and comets.

These identifications, which were confirmed and extended in 1874, showed that the luminosity of comets was due not to solid incandescent particles, but to a luminescence that was supposed to be electrical in nature; it was also believed that some electric action was responsible for the repulsion of cometary tails.

The theory of cometary tails was put into more elaborate form in 1877 by the Russian astronomer T. Bredichin (1831–1904); he determined mathematically the forms of cometary tails corresponding to various ratios of the force of repulsion to the attraction of the Sun. He thought he could classify cometary tails into three main categories according to the value of this ratio and thought that these three particular values corresponded to the presence in the comets of three main substances having atomic or molecular weights in the same ratios, namely hydrogen, hydrocarbons and iron. Although the details of Bredichin's theory have since been largely abandoned, it has nevertheless formed the original basis of modern theories of the structure of comets.

The study of comets made a further advance at the appearance of the bright comets of 1881 and 1882. Indeed it was in 1881 that photography was successfully applied for the first time in the recording of the spectrum as well as of the direct image of a comet. In June 1881, Tebbut's Comet was photographed simultaneously by Janssen in France and by Draper in America; Janssen used a special telescope of very short focus and succeeded in recording a detailed image of the head and of the beginning of the tail of the comet with an exposure of only half an hour, while Draper, using an ordinary objective, photographed some 10° of the tail. Draper also obtained an image of the spectrum. In England Huggins, however, did still better: he not only photographed the ultra-violet spectrum of the comet for the first time, but found further that the nucleus showed a continuous spectrum interrupted by the Fraunhofer lines, proving that it shone by reflected sunlight.

In 1882, Comet Wells provided a new observation; it passed extremely close to the Sun and astronomers were surprised to observe that its spectrum was entirely different from those of other comets. It consisted almost uniquely of the bright D-line of sodium vapour emitted by the nucleus under the influence of the Sun's heat. This effect has been observed again on several subsequent occasions; it is characteristic of all comets passing sufficiently close to the Sun.

However, still more important consequences were to follow the appearance of another large comet in 1882 which for several days was visible to the naked eye in broad daylight. It passed in front of the Sun before the eyes of astronomers and its entire invisibility during its transit provided a proof of the very small size of cometary nuclei—furthermore, comparison of its positions before and after its passage at perihelion close to the Sun's surface definitely established the tenuity of the medium surrounding the Sun. This comet was also of importance for the progress of stellar photography, for it was photographed, when it became visible at night, by the British astronomer D. Gill, then H.M. Astronomer at the Cape, with a small camera hastily mounted on a telescope; simultaneously with the comet a large number of faint stars left their imprint on the emulsion (Plate VI, p. 95). Gill was so struck by this result that he there and then decided to undertake a systematic photographic survey of the Southern sky, and later was also a strong advocate of the International Map of the Sky (section 36).

36. Stellar studies

The publication of Kirchhoff's results on the Sun rapidly inspired astronomers to apply the spectroscope to the examination of stars. This was undertaken almost simultaneously in 1863 and 1864 by the Italian Jesuit Father A. Secchi (1818–1878), at the observatory of the Roman College, and by the English amateur W. Huggins (1824–1910). Fortunately, the investigations that they undertook were complementary in character; while Secchi observed a large number of stars with low dispersion, with a view to classifying their spectra, Huggins concentrated his attention on the spectra of a few bright stars taken with high dispersion, with the object of analysing their composition in detail.

Thus Secchi published in 1868 a catalogue of 4,000 stars divided into four classes according to the appearance of their spectra (cf. Plate VII): white stars, like Sirius or Vega, in which only four dark lines of hydrogen appeared; yellow stars, such as Capella or Arcturus, giving a spectrum like that of the Sun; orange and reddish stars, such as Betelgeuse or Antares, which show in their spectrum a row of 'columns' consisting of alternate bright and dark bands; finally, some faint red stars formed a fourth class. Secchi considered that this series must be related in some way to the stellar temperatures; but he was not interested in identifying the elements responsible for the lines and bands that he had observed.

Huggins on the contrary extended to the stars the work of identification that Kirchhoff had carried out on the Sun; as early as 1863, he identified the lines of sodium, iron, calcium, magnesium, bismuth, etc., in the spectra of certain bright stars such as Betelgeuse and Aldebaran.

In 1868 Huggins succeeded in carrying out an observation of crucial importance: the determination by means of a spectroscope of the line-of-sight velocity of a star, by application of the Doppler-Fizeau effect. In 1842 the Austrian physicist Christian Doppler of Prague had pointed out that the apparent pitch of a note must be altered by relative motion of the source and he had suggested that, in the same way, the colour of a star in motion might be changed according to its velocity of approach or recession relative to the observer; this idea, though correct in principle, was mistaken in practice as the changes in wavelength are too small to cause any appreciable change in star colours—the velocity of light being enormously greater than any stellar velocity. However, in 1848, the French physicist H. Fizeau (1819–1896) pointed out that spectral lines constitute very well-defined fiducial marks which should permit the detection of the very small changes in wavelength to be expected.

Nevertheless, the observation of the effect remained of an extreme delicacy: 'It would be scarcely possible, even with greater space,' wrote Huggins, 'to convey to the reader any true conception of the difficulties which presented themselves in this work . . . and of the extreme care and caution which were needful to distinguish spurious instrumental shifts of a line from a true shift due to the star's motion.' However, Huggins overcame these difficulties and was able to announce in 1868 that Sirius was endowed with a velocity of recession of some 29 miles per second; shortly afterwards he measured the radial velocities of approach or recession of a number of other stars of the first magnitude.

This achievement was of incalculable importance, since from then on it enabled astronomers to measure the motions of heavenly bodies not only according to their projection on the celestial sphere (proper motion)—i.e. the *tangential* component of their velocity—but also the *radial* component along the line of sight. The field of application of this method has permeated every field of modern astronomy from the measurement of the solar parallax to the discovery of the expansion of the Universe (VIII, 44).

The reality of these results and the validity of the method were fully confirmed in 1871, when the German astronomer H. Vogel (1842–1907) succeeded in measuring the speed of rotation of the Sun by comparing the positions of spectral lines on the East and West limbs of the solar disc, one of which is approaching and the other receding owing to the Sun's rotation. However, the application of the Doppler effect remained highly delicate and the results somewhat uncertain until the use of photography made it possible to record spectra in detail.

Shortly afterwards, Vogel turned his attention to stellar spectroscopy. Taking up an idea previously put forward by Zöllner in 1865, according to which the yellow and red stars were more 'advanced' or later stages in the evolution of white stars, considered to be cooling down, he proposed in 1874 a classification more detailed than that of Secchi, based on this evolutionary sequence. Then he undertook a systematic classification of all stars down to the seventh magnitude; in 1883, in collaboration with the Swedish astronomer N. C. Duner (1839–1914), he published a first catalogue of 4,051 stars, while Duner in 1884 published a special catalogue of 352 red stars with banded spectra—the origin of which was then still a mystery. However, visual classification of stellar spectra was coming to an end; in 1885 the American astronomer E. C. Pickering (1846–1919) obtained the first plate of the Pleiades photographed through an *objective prism* and thus ushered in the modern period in the spectral classification of stars (VIII, 42).

In 1887 Lockyer put forward a theory of stellar evolution, based on Vogel's classification, which marked both the culmination and the conclusion of the visual investigations of stellar spectra and provided the first clue to later discoveries on the complexity of spectral classification. In short, instead of considering a linear or one-dimensional evolutionary series from hot white stars to cold red stars, Lockyer introduced the idea of a two-dimensional classification following a 'temperature curve'; one branch of this curve corresponded to evolution through increasing temperatures accompanied by progressive condensation while the other corresponded to a later evolutionary progression through decreasing temperatures leading to the final extinction of the stars. White stars with simple spectra were placed at the top of the curve; yellow and red stars with complex spectra on the two branches. Lockyer also explained the simplicity of the spectra emitted by stars of high temperature by a hypothesis that he had introduced in 1878 in connection with his work on the Sun; he supposed that the normal chemical elements are dissociated under the influence of a higher temperature into simpler elements or 'proto-elements'—the existence of which he thought he had established by a series of comparative experiments on the solar spectrum. Although Lockyer's theory has not survived the test of subsequent advances, it may be regarded as the first suggestion of the idea of the *ionization* of elements, which is the key to present-day spectral classification (VIII, 42).

The modern period in stellar photometry began in 1861 with the publication of the first photometric catalogue of 226 bright stars by the German astronomer F. Zöllner (1834–1882). In his photometer Zöllner compared the brightnesses of stars seen through a small telescope with an 'artificial star' consisting of the reflected image of a small hole illuminated by a lamp, the brightness of which could be changed at will through a known amount by rotating a polarizer and an analyser (Malus' Law). Zöllner's photometer, gradually improved, has remained in use until the present time. Shortly afterwards, at the Harvard College Observatory, Pickering constructed polarizing photometers of other types with which—from 1879 to 1882—he established the first great photometric catalogue,

he *Harvard Photometry* published in 1884, in which the measured
magnitudes of 4,260 stars were given. For the first time a comprehensive series of accurate data on the brightnesses of a large
number of stars down to the seventh or eighth magnitude became
available. In the following year, 1885, the English astronomer
C. Pritchard (1808–1893), of Oxford, published a catalogue of
2,784 stars visible to the naked eye, measured with his 'wedge
photometer'—in which the brightness of the stars was determined
by the position given to a photometric wedge to make the star disappear from view. Although this rather crude procedure has not
continued in use, it marks the introduction of the photometric
wedge into stellar photometry; such a wedge has frequently been
used since then in place of polarizers in the Zöllner-type photometers.

After this considerably larger projects were started—particularly
at Harvard College, under the leadership of Pickering, and in
Potsdam, at the initiative of the German astronomers G. Müller
(1851–1925) and P. Kempf (1856–1920)—for the determination of
the magnitudes of a great number of stars. This work culminated
in the publication, in the early years of this century, of the *Harvard
Revised Photometry* and of the *Potsdamer Durchmusterung*.

The compilation of these catalogues provided a solid basis for
the observation of variable stars, the study of which was developing
rapidly. Thus, as early as 1880, at a time when the number of known
variable stars hardly exceeded one hundred, Pickering had proposed
a classification of variable stars into five groups which has in part
survived; in particular, he took up an idea previously put forward
by Goodricke in 1782—at the time of the discovery of the periodicity
in the variation of Algol (Fig. 19)—and suggested that the regular
light variations of this star were due to the periodic interposition
of a dark satellite revolving around a bright star, and calculated
its orbit and dimensions. This hypothesis was directly and
triumphantly verified some years later, in 1888, by Vogel, who
discovered the periodic oscillations in Algol's radial velocity (VIII,
1). The study of this class of variables—known as 'eclipsing
variables'—has since then led to remarkable advances in our
knowledge of the physical constitution of stars.

After Bond's experiments in 1857, other attempts to photograph the stars were made in the 1860's by the British amateur astronomer W. De La Rue (1815–1889) and in 1865 by the American L. M. Rutherfurd (1816–1892), who obtained the first good photographs of star clusters such as the Pleiades. However, the first astronomer

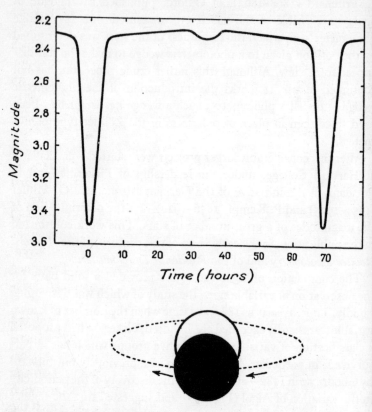

FIG. 19. LIGHT CURVE OF ALGOL (*above*) and principle of the explanation of the light variations of eclipsing binaries (*below*).

to obtain an important series of stellar photographs was the American B. A. Gould (1824–1896), then working at the Cordoba Observatory, where between 1875 and 1882 he took over 1,000 good plates of star clusters in the southern sky. Nevertheless, not until the development of gelatin-silver bromide emulsions did the photographic plate begin to have enough sensitivity first to compete with and then to replace visual observation of the stars.

It has already been mentioned how Gill had been struck by the large number of faint stars recorded on his photographs of the 1882 comet; he then decided to apply photography to the execution of a photographic map of the southern sky. This project was energetically carried out and completed in less than six years, from 1885 to 1891, with a small objective 6 in. in diameter, which recorded stars down to the tenth magnitude in an hour's exposure. The reduction of the stellar positions was undertaken at once with the cooperation of the Dutch astronomer J. C. Kapteyn (1851–1922) and, in the years 1896 to 1900, the first great photographic catalogue of stellar positions—the *Cape Photographic Durchmusterung*—including over 450,000 stars was finally published. It has remained a standard reference catalogue for southern stars.

About the same time, Pickering at Harvard was making his first experiments in stellar photography and photographic photometry: shortly afterwards he instituted at the Harvard Observatory—and later at its southern station in Peru—a continuous photographic 'patrol' of the entire celestial sphere with the aid of small large-field cameras; this photography has been constantly continued since then and constitutes the most complete uninterrupted document in existence for the history of stellar variations.

Also at about the same time the French astronomers Paul and Prosper Henry, at the Paris Observatory, carried out some experiments which resulted in the most grandiose undertaking of celestial photography of the nineteenth century: the international *Carte du Ciel*. At this time the search for minor planets engaged the attention of a large number of astronomers and to facilitate the search the Henry brothers had been commissioned to establish detailed sky maps of the region round the Zodiac. Their enterprise, begun by visual observation in 1873, was already well advanced in 1880 when they arrived in the region of the Zodiac crossing the Milky Way; here they found themselves confronted with such an enormous crowd of faint stars that it seemed impossible to carry out their task adequately by mere visual observation. They therefore decided to resort to photography. After constructing a $5\frac{1}{2}$-in. objective for this purpose they obtained in 1884 such striking plates that they immediately undertook the construction of a photographic objective of 13-in. aperture and 11 ft. 6 in. focal length, which was installed at the Paris Observatory in 1885. The results which they then obtained surpassed their highest hopes: on one of their first plates of the Pleiades taken at the end of 1885 they recognized the existence of a vast nebula associated with the stars and completely invisible to the eye; this was the first nebula to be discovered by photography. The Pleiades cluster itself immediately showed twice as many stars as the best previous maps, which had taken years of work to establish by visual observation. Admiral Mouchez, then Director of the Paris Observatory, became so enthusiastic over these results that he decided the time had come to call an international conference to prepare the way for the execution of a photographic map of the sky by observatories distributed over the whole world and equipped with instruments similar to the one in Paris. Other astronomers, in particular D. Gill, were consulted and supported the project. The congress met at Paris in 1887 and distributed the work among twenty-one observatories; it was then decided that the *Carte du Ciel* proper, which was to show several tens of millions of stars down to the fifteenth or sixteenth magnitude, should be supplemented by an *Astrographic Catalogue* giving the positions and magnitudes of about 3 million stars brighter than the eleventh magnitude. This immense task has taken two generations of astronomers more than half a century and its completion is only now in sight. Its value will not be completely manifest until the future, when a repetition of the plates will make it possible to determine the proper motions of a large number of faint stars.

The organization of the *Carte du Ciel* established photography officially as a means of studying the sky. It conveniently marks the beginning of the contemporary period in astronomy.

This new phase was also prepared in a parallel line of development by the first attempts to apply photography to the study of spectra.

As early as 1863, Huggins had attempted to photograph the spectra of bright stars on a collodion plate, but he had only obtained threadlike images with no dark lines. However, in 1872, he American amateur astronomer Henry Draper (1837–1882), by placing a prism a little way in front of the plate at the focus of his 28-in. telescope, succeeded in recording a spectrum of Vega which showed four dark lines of hydrogen; but it was only after the development of the gelatin-bromide process that more decisive results were obtained. The first to use the new emulsion was Huggins, who obtained a spectrum of Vega with seven dark lines by using a spectrograph placed behind his 18-in. telescope; in 1879 he obtained a spectrum extending further in the ultra-violet which showed some fifteen lines. Draper, for his part, obtained the spectra of some fifty bright stars between 1879 and 1882. In 1881 Huggins photographed for the first time the spectrum of a comet, showing the superposition of a continuous background due to reflected sunlight and bright bands due to the intrinsic emission of the comet. In 1882 he succeeded in photographing the spectrum of the Orion nebula and found a new line hitherto unknown—in the ultra-violet portion of the spectrum.

Shortly afterwards, in 1885 and 1886, Pickering at Harvard carried out some experiments in another direction: instead of trying to obtain the spectrum of one star by placing a prism behind a telescope, he placed a large prism in front of a photographic objective so as to record low-dispersion spectra of all the stars in the field of view at the same time (the method had already been used visually by Secchi). Thus, in January 1886, he obtained the spectra of forty stars in the Pleiades and with characteristic energy immediately undertook to photograph the spectra of all stars accessible to his instrument. This undertaking was to be greatly extended thanks to a donation in 1886–7 by H. Draper's widow, which permitted the development at Harvard of her husband's spectroscopic investigations. The inauguration of the 'Henry Draper Memorial' marked the success of the photographic recording of spectra and the beginning of the modern phase in stellar spectroscopy.

Finally, in 1887, Vogel achieved an advance of no less importance: the first photographic determination of a star's radial velocity, followed in 1888 by the discovery of the variable radial velocity of Algol, which proved its binary character (VIII, 42).

37. Study of nebulae

In the middle of the nineteenth century visual observations of nebulae had not yet made it possible to reach agreement on the nature of these objects. As a result of Herschel's observations the existence of true nebulae that could not be resolved into stars had been generally accepted; but doubt had again been cast on this by the observations of Lord Rosse (IV, 28), who had thought that with his large telescope he had succeeded in resolving into stars nebulae of all kinds.

It was Huggins in 1864 who provided the beginnings of a solution to this problem through the application of the spectroscope:

'On the evening of the 29th of August, 1864, I directed the telescope for the first time to a planetary nebula in Draco. . . . I looked into the spectroscope. No spectrum such as I expected! A single bright line only! At first I suspected some displacement of the prism . . . then the true interpretation flashed upon me. The light of the nebula was monochromatic, and so, unlike any other light I had as yet subjected to prismatic examination, could not be extended out to form a complete spectrum. . . . A little closer looking showed two other bright lines on the side towards the blue, all the three lines being separated by intervals relatively dark.

'The riddle of the nebulae was solved. The answer, which had come to us in the light itself, read: Not an aggregation of stars, but a luminous gas.'

Later observations enabled the identification of some of the lines observed in the nebulae with those of hydrogen; but the principal line—a green one—could not be attributed to any known element: Huggins suggested that perhaps there was a special element in gaseous nebulae, later christened 'Nebulium'; not until our time has the mysterious element been identified—its rays are merely due to a particular kind of radiation from common elements (VIII, 43).

Huggins then extended his investigations to other nebulae and was thus able to establish that all the 'planetary' nebulae and the large diffuse nebulae—such as that in Orion (Plate VIII)—present a bright-line spectrum, indicating that they are gaseous in nature. However, when he turned his spectroscope to the great nebula in

Andromeda (Plate XI), he found to his astonishment that this presented a continuous spectrum like those of the stars. However, the extreme faintness of the light dispersed through the prism did not enable him to observe whether this spectrum was interrupted by bright or dark lines. The discovery of significant details in these spectra had to await the first application of photography to the problem at the end of the century (VIII, 44).

Nevertheless, it was immediately clear from Huggins's results that nebulae must be divided into two classes that are essentially different: 'green' nebulae with bright-line spectra which are gaseous in nature, and 'white' nebulae with continuous spectra presumed stellar in nature. The latter group clearly had to include the external galaxies—the 'island universes'—the existence of which had been assumed since the middle of the eighteenth century; but the question was still far from solved and, towards the end of the nineteenth century, many astronomers thought rather that the Milky Way constituted the entire Universe.

In 1885, however, the appearance of a 'new' star near the nucleus of the Andromeda Nebula provided a new argument in favour of its stellar character; but it was far from decisive, since it was possible to suppose that the flare up of the star was due to its encounter with gaseous matter, somewhat as meteors vanish in a brilliant flash when they meet the Earth's atmosphere, a theory of 'novae' which was put forward in 1892 by the German astronomer H. von Seeliger (1849–1924).

Actually it was only when photography was applied to the study of nebulae that rapid progress was achieved. What the eye does not see in a fraction of a second it will never see; on the other hand, what a photographic plate cannot record in 1 second or 1 minute can be made to appear by prolonging the exposure to 1 hour, 10 hours or more if necessary.

It was Henry Draper who in 1880 first succeeded in obtaining a photographic image of the Orion Nebula (Plate VII); better plates obtained in 1881 and 1882 already showed all the stars that had been observed visually in the largest instruments available at the time. The following year the Englishman A. A. Common (1841–1903) obtained a still better result with a large telescope of 36-in.

aperture and 1 hour's exposure; his plate already showed star completely invisible to the eye. Common wished to do better still and undertook the construction of a 60-in. reflector specially adapted to photography; this instrument was finished in 1891 and, though it was little used, served as a prototype of all the large modern photographic reflectors, the vital instruments of twentieth-century astrophysical research.

In the same period another British amateur, I. Roberts (1829-1903), installed a 20-in. photographic reflector with which, in 1885 he began a long series of photographs of nebulae and star clusters which may be considered to mark the beginning of the modern phase in nebular studies. His first results in 1886 were plates of the Orion Nebula and of the nebulae in the Pleiades—much stronger and more extensive than those of Common and of the Henry brothers—and, in 1888, the discovery on a plate exposed for 3 hours of the spiral structure of the great Andromeda Nebula which is quite inaccessible to the eye (Plate XV).

From then on the photographic study of spiral nebulae continued to develop and has now become one of the most important branches of astronomy (VIII, 44; IX, 51).

In this respect the end of the classical period of the visual observation of nebulae and the beginning of the modern period characterized by the photographic study of them are marked by the publication in 1888 of the New General Catalogue of nebulae and clusters compiled by the British astronomer J. L. E. Dreyer (1852-1926) who worked most of his life in Ireland, first as assistant to the Fourth Earl of Rosse, then at the Dunsink and Armagh observatories. This new catalogue was based on John Herschel's General Catalogue of 1864, but included many later discoveries and listed 7,840 objects. It was followed by two supplements or Index Catalogues, which appeared in 1895 and 1908, bringing the total of objects catalogued to over 13,000. Since then the N.G.C. (as it is usually abbreviated) has been universally adopted as the standard catalogue of nebulae and is still in constant use. The N.G.C. was reprinted in 1954 by the Royal Astronomical Society, a clear testimony to its lasting value even after more than fifty years.

*

Thus as the second half of the nineteenth century came to its close an extraordinary revolution in the means employed in the study of the Universe had been completed and an enormous new field of investigation had been thrown open. Uninterrupted progress was to continue and develop ever more rapidly through a series of spectacular advances until the present time.

Plate XI. THE GREAT NEBULOUS COMPLEX
AROUND ETA CARINAE

Photographed with the 30-in. reflector of the Commonwealth Observatory, on Mount Stromlo, near Canberra, Australia.

This great complex of dark and bright nebulosities surrounding the nova-like variable Eta Carinae (cf. Fig. 27) was discovered by Sir John Herschel during his expedition to the Cape of Good Hope in the years 1834 to 1838. It was often called, during the nineteenth century, the 'Keyhole nebula' from the shape of the dark marking silhouetted against its brighter part, here just above the centre. The luminosity of this great glowing mass of hydrogen is excited by the ultra-violet radiation of the numerous O and B type stars immersed in it. The star Eta Carinae itself does not contribute to the illumination of the nebulosity, which did not appear perceptibly brighter during or after the great flaring up of the nineteenth century.

The distance of the nebulous complex and the associated star groups is of the order of 4,000 light-years. This is a typical example of the galactic formations called 'associations' by the Russian astronomer V. A. Ambartsumian and it must constitute a conspicuous 'knot' in the spiral arm of the Galaxy between us and the inner regions of our system. Similar formations are observed in many external galaxies (cf. Plate XIII).

PLATE XII. THE GLOBULAR CLUSTER OMEGA
CENTAURI

Photograph taken with the 60-in. telescope of the Southern
tation of the Harvard Observatory at Bloemfontein, South
frica.

This cluster, which is visible to the naked eye in the southern
emisphere, is one of the nearest and largest of the hundred or so
ar clusters that accompany our Galaxy like so many satellites.
s light takes about 22,000 years to reach us and it certainly
ontains several hundred thousands of stars. It was by a study
f the 'cepheid' variables in globular clusters that the American
stronomer H. Shapley determined their distances and thus
btained in 1918 a first idea of the total extent of our Galaxy and
e peripheral position of the Sun inside it.

The origin of the globular clusters, their perfect symmetry, and
e law of condensation governing the increase in star density
wards the centre present difficult problems of cosmogonic
eory first studied by the German astronomer H. von Zeipel
bout 1912 and later by the English theorists J. Jeans and A. S.
ddington.

Investigations of the distribution of colour and luminosity
mong the brighter stars in globular clusters by the American
stronomers at the Mount Wilson and Palomar Observatories
ave led to great advances in our knowledge of stellar populations
nd stellar evolution.

* VII *

The Rise of Astrophysics in the Twentieth Century and the Development of Contemporary Astronomy up to the Second World War

---

I. THE SOLAR SYSTEM

38. Solar studies

The present period in solar research began in 1891 with the invention of the 'spectroheliograph' by the American astronomer G. E. Hale (1868–1938). In this instrument the light of one spectral line selected by a slit is used to photograph by continuous scanning either the solar disc or the prominences. At the same time a very similar instrument—the 'spectro-enregistreur des vitesses' or 'spectral velocity recorder'—was constructed by the French astronomer H. Deslandres (1853–1948), this instrument made it possible to observe the appearance and displacement of a spectral line in a series of narrow strips covering the entire solar disc and thus to obtain the distribution of velocity over the whole of the Sun's surface through the Doppler effect.

These instruments were first set into operation at Hale's private observatory at Chicago, and later at the Yerkes Observatory which he established in the vicinity of Chicago in 1896, and in France by Deslandres at the Meudon Observatory; they have played a vital part in solar studies for half a century.

The new method of observing the Sun not only permitted much more efficient study of the prominences visible at the limb (Plate V, *a*), but also revealed the characteristic structure of the solar surface itself on which luminous clouds—especially of calcium and hydrogen—form an irregular network of condensations which Hale called 'flocculi'; these are particularly dense above spots and faculae, near which they form regions called 'plages faculaires' by Deslandres, the number and size of which vary according to the general degree of solar activity. Furthermore, a judicious selection of different portions of broad lines, such as the K-line of calcium, permits a refined analysis of successive levels in the solar atmosphere from the reversing layer up to high levels in the chromosphere (Plate V, *b*). In this way, images relating to the high levels revealed dark 'filaments' which were soon identified as images of the prominences when seen in projection on the disc. Maps of the distribution of these filaments over the disc are published monthly by the Meudon Observatory.

The increasing importance of solar work led Hale, with the support of the Carnegie Institution of Washington, to found in 1905 a second large observatory specially equipped for this purpose. This observatory was installed on Mount Wilson, in Southern California, where the greatest and most famous observatory of our time has gradually developed. Hale and his collaborators W. S. Adams (1876–1956) and Ch. St. John—in association with the spectroscopist A. S. King—soon made immense advances in our knowledge of the Sun. In 1905 a comparison of the spectra of sunspots with those of electric arcs or furnaces in the laboratory enabled them to demonstrate the presence of titanium oxide and of various other molecules (oxides, hydrides, etc.) in spots, and they also were able to prove finally that the temperature in spots is lower than in the surrounding photosphere.

In 1906 Adams undertook a systematic study of the Sun's rotation by the spectroscopic method, which had been originated by Vogel and extended in 1891 to the polar regions by the Swedish astronomer N. C. Duner; these studies showed that the decrease in the angular velocity of the Sun's rotation with increasing latitude —first observed in the spot regions by Carrington (VI, 33)—continues to the poles, where the period of solar rotation exceeds a month (as against twenty-five days at the equator). Since then these measurements have been repeated every year at Mount Wilson and in other observatories.

In 1908, Hale noticed that on his spectroheliograms taken in light of the red H Alpha line of hydrogen, the spots are surrounded by whirlpools—often very clearly defined—which he called 'Solar Vortices'. This phenomenon, when observed in the neighbourhood of a pair of spots, bears a remarkable resemblance to the 'magnetic ghost' of a horseshoe magnet; it gave Hale the idea that the spot might have intense magnetic fields. In 1896 the Dutch physicist P. Zeeman had observed that spectral emission lines are split when the source is placed in a strong magnetic field. The separation of the components of a line due to this effect is proportional to the intensity of the magnetic field, and the Zeeman effect thus provides an optical method of measuring the magnetic field strength responsible for the splitting.

In 1908 Hale undertook, with a high-dispersion spectrograph the study of the abnormally broad spectral lines of sunspots and noticed that they were resolved into very close components characteristic of the Zeeman effect. Thus he was able not only to demonstrate the existence of strong magnetic fields in sunspots, but also to measure their intensity—which often reaches some thousands of gauss. This magnetic field has been attributed to a vortical motion of electrified particles—ions and electrons—in the solar atmosphere; but a precise theory of the effect is still lacking.[1]

In the course of his investigations, Hale noticed that the Zeeman effect was observed on the Sun's surface in the regions of faculae preceding or following spots that appeared to be single; he concluded that under these faculae there existed spots which were incompletely developed and inaccessible to direct observation. Thus, one may in general consider spots as being always formed in pairs which he further observed to be of opposite magnetic polarities, showing by this that the vortical motions are also in opposite senses; this observation has been of the greatest importance in the theory of solar phenomena.

Since that time the determination of sunspot polarities has been carried out regularly at the Mount Wilson Observatory. In the course of these studies there has appeared a remarkable peculiarity

[1] It has become clear in particular that the 'Solar Vortices' are not an image of the vortical motion responsible for the field.

n relation to the cycle of solar activity, summarized by Spörer's
Law (V, 31). In fact it was immediately noticed that if at a given
time the *front* or preceding spot of a 'bipolar' group has a north
magnetic polarity, say, in the northern hemisphere of the Sun, then
it is the *rear* or following spot of a group that has this same polarity
n the southern hemisphere; in other words, the polarities of spot
groups are opposed in the two hemispheres. This relationship con-
inues throughout the cycle of solar activity as long as the spots
descend towards the equator. However, when solar activity reaches
a minimum and the first high-latitude spots of the next cycle
appear, the magnetic polarities are reversed in each hemisphere and

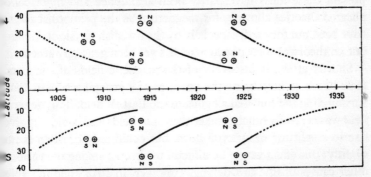

FIG. 20. MAGNETIC POLARITY OF SUNSPOTS, ACCORD-
ING TO HALE AND ADAMS (1926)

The variation in the mean latitude of spots during the cycle of
activity (Spörer's law) is also shown.

t is now the rear spot that has northern polarity in the northern
hemisphere of the Sun and the front spot in the southern hemisphere; these polarities continue throughout the cycle and are
inverted once more in the following cycle (Fig. 20). This inversion
has been regularly confirmed at each solar minimum since 1913,
so that—as Hale and Adams first pointed out in 1919 and then
emphasized more clearly in 1925 after the first repetition of the
effect in 1923—the true duration of the cycle of solar activity is not
eleven years but twenty-two years; the spots recur with identical
magnetic properties only after this period. This observation has
also been of great importance in theories of the origin of sunspots.

183

Such a theory, accounting for the new results, was soon proposed in 1926 by the Norwegian physicist V. Bjerknes. According to it spots are the manifestation of toroidal vortices situated at a small depth below the photosphere: spots appear when these rings emerge at the visible surface and give rise to vortices in opposite senses, accounting for the magnetism of bipolar groups; furthermore, by supposing that these toroids exist in pairs rotating in opposite senses in each hemisphere and are dragged round in a slow general circulation of twenty-two years' period, Bjerknes accounted for Spörer's Law and for the magnetic inversion of the groups in each hemisphere at the moment of solar minimum. At present these ideas have partly been abandoned and more complicated theories allowing for magnetism as the primordial factor have been put forward, especially by the Swedish physicist Alfvén; but no theory of solar phenomena has yet been generally accepted.

Shortly after his discovery of the magnetic fields of sunspots, Hale began to investigate the problem of a general magnetic field surrounding the Sun—analogous to the Earth's field. This general field was certainly much weaker than spot fields and could not give rise to a splitting of spectral lines, but could only broaden them slightly; this effect would be difficult to observe among the various other causes of line broadening. However, in 1918 Hale felt able to announce that such a field actually existed with an intensity of some 50 gauss at the poles (compared with Earth's magnetic field of about 0.5 gauss). This result was obtained with great difficulty and no further work along these lines appeared for a quarter of a century (IX, 48).

Along with these investigations of Hale's, the detailed spectroscopic examination of spots revealed particularities of their structure. In 1909 the British astronomer J. Evershed observed the spectra of spots close to the Sun's limb and noticed that their spectral lines were shifted by the Doppler effect in a characteristic manner which revealed the existence of opposite radial motions at the two edges of each spot; these observations were continued and confirmed at Mount Wilson by St. John, who was able to advance in 1913 a consistent scheme for the movements of gases around and above these spots. It appeared that the gases escape and recede from the spots in the low levels of the reversing layer and fall back on to them at high levels in the chromosphere. These results were developed and improved by the Italian astronomer G. Abetti between 1926 and 1930.

However, there is another effect associated with sunspots—the study of which owes a great deal to Hale's efforts—which of late years has come to occupy an important place in solar physics: *chromospheric flares*. The first known example of this phenomenon was observed by Carrington as early as 1859 in the course of his regular observations of sunspots: on the first of September of that year he saw two bright areas of extraordinary brilliance appear in a group of spots; they greatly exceeded the photosphere in brightness, were in rapid motion and disappeared only 5 minutes after they had appeared—50,000 km. away from their starting point. This amazing spectacle was observed independently by Hodgson, another British amateur. At the same instant there was a violent terrestrial magnetic disturbance followed 18 hours later by a magnetic storm of exceptional violence and duration which interrupted telegraphic communications and was accompanied by the appearance of magnificent aurora displays. For the first time the Sun had been 'taken in the act', as a British astronomer remarked at the time.

However, no other instance of the same kind was seen until towards the end of the century; the phenomenon therefore did not hold the attention of scientists and fell somewhat into oblivion. A similar outburst was observed in 1892 and Hale obtained a spectro-heliogram of it for the first time. In 1908 another 'flare' was recorded by Fox and Abetti at the Yerkes Observatory and in 1926 yet another was noticed by L. d'Azambuja at Meudon. As these observations had been made by pure chance until then, their small number could be due to the short duration of the effect rather than to its intrinsic rarity.

To check this Hale perfected a new instrument, the 'spectro-helioscope'—adapted to visual observations of monochromatic images of the Sun—which permitted a regular and continuous survey of chromospheric phenomena to be carried out conveniently; then, in 1932, an international organization of observers

equipped with spectrohelioscopes was founded for regular observation of the Sun. From then on, the number of 'solar flares' observed
has continued to increase and it has been realized that they are in
fact a very common solar phenomenon, since it is now estimated
that more than a dozen of them appear on the Sun's surface every
day—at least in periods of high activity.

The study of these manifestations of solar activity has developed
rapidly in the course of the last twenty years and has shown that
flares play an essential part in the Sun's influence on terrestrial
phenomena. It has been realized that the magnetic and electric
disturbances that immediately accompany their appearance are due
to the emission of intense ultra-violet radiation which produces an
abnormally strong ionization of the high levels of the Earth's
atmosphere.

Continuous observations and precise measurements of prominences and studies of their displacements carried out with the
spectroheliograph have also led to advances in our knowledge of
them. In this respect, the most remarkable results have been those
obtained by E. Pettit at Mount Wilson; in 1925 he announced that
the vertical motions of prominences are subject to two laws:
according to the first law, the velocity of ascent of an eruptive
prominence varies suddenly at certain instants, and according to
the second law the successive velocities are integral multiples of an
initial velocity. These two laws are very difficult to explain and have
been strongly criticized—especially the second, which has not been
confirmed by later work. Pettit further identified several distinct
types of prominences known as 'active', 'eruptive', 'spot'
'tornado' and finally 'quiescent' prominences. The most spectacular prominences are the eruptive (Plate V, a); at times they
appear literally to fly away at enormous speeds, occasionally
exceeding the critical velocity of escape from the Sun (720 km./sec.)
and then disappear in interplanetary space.

However, the equilibrium mechanism and the sources of energy
of these enormous gaseous masses remain a mystery for the most
part. Nevertheless their study in the last twenty years has benefited
from the introduction of a new instrument of research which will
now be discussed.

After the discovery of the spectroscopic method of studying prominences in broad daylight and the observation of the green coronal line, various astronomers had tried to find a method enabling them to study the solar corona outside eclipses. After a series of failures which continued for over half a century, the problem had been practically given up by everyone when it was suddenly solved in 1930 by the French astronomer B. Lyot (1897–1952) with his invention of the 'coronagraph'. Lyot's achievement was his recognition of the fact that the main obstacle in the way of seeing the corona in daylight was not, as his predecessors had thought, the light scattered by our atmosphere (the blue sky), but the much stronger light scattered by ordinary astronomical objectives. He therefore undertook the construction of an objective of very high optical quality, both as to the homogeneity of the glass and as to the perfection of polish of its surfaces, and, above all, completely protected from dust. Lyot installed his instrument at the Pic du Midi observatory, located at an altitude of 9,350 ft. in the Pyrenees and thus succeeded for the first time in 1930 not only in observing the green coronal line but even in obtaining a direct photograph of the brightest inner parts of the corona. Since that time the coronagraph has been perfected and similar instruments have been installed at various mountain observatories in France, Switzerland and the United States; no longer limited to the rare and brief intervals of total eclipse, the study of the corona has made rapid progress since then. It has been possible in particular to make a detailed study of its spectrum and to measure the wavelengths of the lines exactly.[1]

Thanks to these observations and to recent advances in spectroscopy, the Swedish spectroscopist B. Edlen succeeded in 1941 in solving the long-standing mystery of 'coronium' (VI, 33) and explained the origin of the coronal lines; he showed that they were due to 'forbidden' radiations of atoms of iron, nickel and calcium in a very highly ionized state, deprived of twelve to fourteen of

[1] Another notable application has been the production of cinematographic films showing the motions of the prominences greatly speeded up. This has helped our understanding of the stupendous forces at work in the solar atmosphere, although much remains to be learned in this direction.

their outer electrons. This high state of ionization indicates the existence in the corona of a very high temperature, of the order of a million degrees, and, although this agrees well with various other criteria, it is still difficult to explain.

The study of eclipses is nevertheless still important not only for the study of the outer regions of the corona but also because they permit the observation of a very important effect predicted by the General Theory of Relativity: the bending of light rays by the Sun's gravitational field. The illustrious physicist Albert Einstein (1879–1955) had predicted from his Special Theory of Relativity in 1905 that light should be deflected by gravitational fields; from his General Theory of Relativity in 1915 he deduced that this deviation should reach a value of $1''.75$ at the edge of the Sun if his new law of gravitation was correct, while the deviation predicted from Newton's law was only half as much.

Now, the only occasions when it is possible to photograph stars in the immediate vicinity of the Sun are total solar eclipses.

The first observation of the effect was carried out in 1919 by British expeditions led by A. S. Eddington (1882–1944). By comparing the positions of stars photographed around the Sun during the eclipse with the positions of the same stars photographed at night (away from the Sun) it was proved that light rays are indeed deflected by an amount very close to that predicted by Einstein—$1''.64$ according to these measures.

Similar observations carried out by a German expedition in 1922 confirmed this result, but led to a slightly greater deflection than predicted. The observations have been repeated during several more eclipses since that time. The most recent result, obtained in 1947 by G. van Biesbroeck leading an expedition of the Yerkes Observatory, is $2''.01$, which fully confirms Einstein's prediction if one bears in mind the inescapable errors inherent in such a delicate measurement.

Other observations, which will be discussed later, have provided a much more precise verification of the astronomical consequences of the Theory of Relativity.

9. The study of planets and satellites

The study of the Moon and planets has waited a long time for the benefit of astrophysical methods. Towards the end of the nineteenth century the distinctive feature of lunar studies was the application of photography to the compilation of great atlases of our satellite's surface. The most important were those published from 1890 onwards by the American astronomer E. S. Holden (1846–1914), using the great 36-in. refractor of the Lick Observatory in California, and from 1894 onwards by the French astronomers M. Loewy (1833–1907) and P. Puiseux (1855–1928), using a large photographic telescope of the 'elbow' type—the 24-in. 'equatorial coudé' of the Paris Observatory (Plate I).

This work permitted an objective detailed study of the lunar surface and formed the basis of various theories of the origin of its characteristic features. The main theories invoke either the raising of swellings or 'intumescences' by the action of internal gases, followed by their bursting, or the eruption of an internal magma through fissures in the crust, or, finally, bombardment by large meteorites. None of these theories has yet been generally accepted.

Few truly astrophysical investigations have been carried out on the Moon. One was due to the French astronomer B. Lyot, who between 1922 and 1927 measured at Meudon Observatory the degree of polarization of the light reflected from the Moon's surface and concluded that the Moon's surface was covered by a layer of dust analogous to fine volcanic ash.

Another involved the radiometric measurements carried out at the Mount Wilson Observatory from 1927 onwards by the American astronomers E. Pettit and S. B. Nicholson, from which they estimated the temperature of the Moon's surface to be about 100° C. after several days' exposure to the Sun.

Furthermore, in 1921, a systematic study by the French astronomer A. Danjon of the descriptions of eclipses accumulated during the nineteenth century indicated that the brightness and colour of the eclipsed Moon vary systematically according to the phase of the sunspot-cycle at the time of the eclipse; eclipses are generally dark after a minimum of activity and bright just before the next minimum. This variation has been confirmed later by photometri measurements and probably results from an as yet unexplaine influence of the Sun's activity on the upper atmosphere of th Earth.

After Schiaparelli's epoch-making investigations of the plane Mars, much attention was given to this planet. Among those wh devoted most effort to the study of Mars after Schiaparelli, th American astronomers P. Lowell (1855–1916) and W. H. Pickerin (1858–1932) and the French amateurs E. M. Antoniadi (1870 1944) and R. Jarry-Desloges (1868–1951) deserve special mentior

In 1894 P. Lowell set up at Flagstaff, in Arizona, a large observa tory devoted entirely to the study of Mars; he greatly increased th number of canals discovered by Schiaparelli and deduced from study of the whole range of phenomena observed on the planet tha this geometrical network of lines was an artificial structure designe to capture and utilize as well as possible the meagre aquati resources of this already very arid planet. In other words, h believed that there were present on Mars beings with a civilizatio more or less comparable with that of the human race.

Lowell's conclusions naturally aroused tremendous intere among the general public, but were vigorously disputed by sever astronomers, especially by Antoniadi, who made many observatior from 1909 onwards with the large 32-in. telescope at the Meudo Observatory and emphatically concluded that the lines observed b Lowell did not exist. According to Antoniadi, these lines merel arose from a simplifying optical illusion created by the eye fror irregular and perfectly natural features distributed over the planet surface. Nevertheless, his conclusions were themselves disputed b Lowell's successors—particularly by the American astronom E. C. Slipher, who has reaffirmed on several occasions that th visual observations carried out at the Lowell Observatory hav been completely confirmed by photographs.

In fact, from 1905 and 1907 onwards, Lowell and his collabor tors, Lampland and then Slipher, had succeeded in taking com paratively detailed photographs of planetary surfaces, in particul of Mars. However, it must be admitted that these photograph have still—even until recent times—been too vague to permit th

bservation of the very fine details which can occasionally be
erceived visually.

However, since 1941, Lyot and his colleagues at the Pic du Midi
)bservatory have succeeded in obtaining some much clearer
hotographs which, while they do not yet entirely supersede visual
bservation, do show fine enough detail to permit an objective
etailed study of the planets.

Nevertheless, photography has already produced important
esults in another field by providing images of planetary surfaces
iken in different colours of the spectrum and even in ultra-violet
r infra-red radiation invisible to the eye.

The first investigations in this field were carried out in 1909 by
he Russian astronomer G. A. Tikhov at Pulkovo and by the
rench astronomers A. de La Baume-Pluvinel and F. Baldet at the
'ic du Midi, then in 1911 the American physicist R. W. Wood
as the first to obtain ultra-violet photographs of the Moon and
lanets. However, these methods were chiefly developed from 1924
nwards by the American astronomer W. H. Wright and in 1926
y the optician F. E. Ross at the Mount Wilson Observatory.

These photographs revealed among other things dark spots on
'enus, which were invisible to the eye, but clearly photographed
i ultra-violet light; on the violet and ultra-violet pictures of Mars,
n the other hand, visually observable details disappeared under
he cover of an opaque atmospheric veil the nature of which is still
i doubt. Monochromatic images of the major planets Jupiter and
aturn similarly show important differences depending on the
olours of their various regions; though these differences are less
narked.

It was from this time onwards, about 1924, that physical methods
egan to be extensively applied to planetary studies.

Between 1922 and 1928 Lyot carried out, at the Meudon
)bservatory, systematic measurements of the polarization of the
ight from the planets; but in general the proportion of polarized
ight reflected from the planets depends on so many factors that
clear conclusion as to the nature of the reflecting layers could
iot be drawn from these measurements.

It is spectroscopy that has played the largest part in providing clear information on this topic. Detailed spectroscopic studies of the planets were undertaken in 1905 by V. M. Slipher at the Lowell Observatory and were continued with more powerful equipment from 1922 onwards by S. B. Nicholson at Mount Wilson. These observations disclosed intense characteristic absorption bands in the spectra of the major planets and of Venus, the strongest of which were found in the infra-red region.

However, it was not until 1931 that the American astrophysicists W. S. Adams and Th. Dunham succeeded in identifying the absorption bands in the infra-red spectrum of Venus as coming from a thick layer of carbon dioxide, and in the same year the German astronomer R. Wildt, then of Göttingen, was able to attribute the absorption bands in the spectra of the major planets to methane and ammonia. These identifications have led to a fundamental change in our ideas of the internal structure of the major planets as well as of their atmospheres.

As far as Mars is concerned no characteristic absorption could be conclusively identified in its spectrum, in spite of numerous efforts made at Mount Wilson from 1926 onwards in an attempt to identify the presence of oxygen and water vapour. After repeated attempts in 1933, 1937 and later years Adams and Dunham reached the conclusion that the amount of oxygen and water-vapour in the atmosphere of Mars probably does not exceed a few thousandths of the amounts present over the same area of the Earth. This conclusion seriously decreased the probability of the existence of advanced forms of life on Mars.

Another method of investigation which has made an important contribution to our physical knowledge of the planets in the last few decades has been the analysis of their spectra in the far infrared by means of thermocouples, as was first applied at the Lowell Observatory in 1922 by the American physicist W. W. Coblentz. In this method the radiation from a planet is concentrated on one of the junctions of a tiny, extra-sensitive thermocouple placed at the focus of a large telescope. By means of filters (glass, fluorite, water cell) which absorb different portions of the infra-red, it is possible to estimate the fraction of this radiation due to the intrinsic thermal radiation of the planet and to distinguish it from reflected unlight. It is then possible to estimate the temperature of the planet's radiating surface. Since 1924 the temperatures of the various planets have been measured directly in this way through the efforts of Coblentz, Lampland and Menzel at the Lowell Observatory and Pettit and Nicholson at the Mount Wilson Observatory.

The results of these measurements have been in general agreement with theoretical predictions based on the distances of the planets from the Sun. They range from several hundred degrees Fahrenheit above zero for the face of the planet Mercury that is always turned towards the Sun down to over 360° F. below zero (—200°C.) for the most distant planets. Intermediate temperatures are of the order of 120° F. (+50° C.) for the daylight face of Venus, range from —100° F. to +90° F. (—70° C. to +30° C.) according to place and season on Mars, are about —220° F. (—140° C.) on Jupiter and —260° F. (—160° C.) on Saturn.

On the basis of these results various astrophysicists—especially R. Wildt—have developed theories according to which the major planets Jupiter, Saturn, Uranus and Neptune consist mainly of cores of ice surrounded by enormous oceans of liquefied and compressed gas, covered finally by vast atmospheres of hydrogen and helium with floating clouds of the same substance, partially liquefied or solidified, which give rise to the spectral bands observed on these planets.

As far as Venus is concerned, no satisfactory hypothesis has yet been put forward to explain the clouds that cover its atmosphere. In the case of Mars it is agreed that its sparse atmosphere chiefly consists of nitrogen with some traces of carbon dioxide and possibly argon. Finally Mercury, owing to its small mass, has probably lost its atmosphere through the escape of the molecules into space[1] and the same applies to most of the satellites, as first derived from the dynamical theory of gases by the British astrophysicist J. Stoney

---

[1] This theoretical result, however, is still somewhat uncertain since from time to time temporary faint obscurations have been noticed on Mercury, especially by E. M. Antoniadi; furthermore, at the end of 1950, A. Dollfus announced that he had detected a very faint atmosphere from polarization measurements carried out at the Pic du Midi (IX, 48).

(1826–1911) and later established more accurately by the calcula
tions of the British theorist J. Jeans (1877–1946) published in 1916
These conclusions have been confirmed by spectroscopic observa
tions of most satellites that have been carried out in the last decad
by Kuiper at the McDonald Observatory (IX, 48).

In addition, the number of planetary satellites that have bee
identified has increased enormously since the end of the nineteent
century, particularly through the application of photography. *
fifth satellite of Jupiter—the last to be discovered by visual observa
tion—was detected in 1892 by the American E. E. Barnard (1857
1923); then a ninth satellite of Saturn—the first to be discovere
photographically—was announced in 1898 by W. H. Pickerin;
(1858–1938). Two other satellites of Jupiter—the sixth and sevent
—were discovered by C. D. Perrine at the Lick Observatory i
1904 and 1905; the eighth was discovered in 1908 by P. Melotte a
the Greenwich Observatory and the ninth by S. B. Nicholson o
Mount Wilson in 1914. After this there were no more discoverie
of satellites for over thirty years until, once again, it was Nicholsor
on Mount Wilson who in 1938 identified two new satellites o
Jupiter—the tenth and eleventh—and still others were discovered
during the last decade (see IX, 48).[1]

The number of minor planets was also greatly increased as ε
result of the systematic application of photography, introduced ir
1891 by the German astronomer Max Wolf (1863–1932); the
number of these small bodies known at present exceeds 1,600
Some of the minor planets discovered since 1891 are of particula
interest because they wander beyond the classical limits of the
asteroid belt, either by passing far from the Sun beyond the orbi
of Jupiter, or by approaching closer to it than Mars. Among the
latter, the most interesting is the planet *Eros* which was discovered
in 1898 by the German astronomer G. Witt; this minor planet ir
fact sometimes approaches within 20 or even 15 million miles o
the Earth and then provides an extremely favourable opportunity
for the measurement of the solar parallax (VII, 41).

[1] However, the announcement of additional tiny satellites to the major
planets no longer creates in astronomical circles the flurry of excitement
which used to follow such discoveries 100 or 150 years ago.

Finally, a new major planet—Pluto—was discovered through photography on 21 January 1930 by the American C. Tombaugh, at the Lowell Observatory. This discovery was the crowning achievement of a long series of systematic investigations that have been undertaken at the Lowell Observatory for the purpose of detecting the existence of a planet beyond Neptune; as early as 1915 Lowell had predicted the existence of such a planet from a study of unexplained residual perturbations in the motion of Uranus and Neptune. These perturbations had been too small to permit a repetition of the exploit of Neptune's discovery, but had been sufficient to give a rough indication of the part of the sky in which the unknown planet was to be found. Lowell's results had furthermore been confirmed by W. H. Pickering in 1919, but investigations carried out at that time had been unsuccessful and it was only by systematic photography of the entire Zodiacal belt that Tombaugh was able to detect the long sought for planet.[1]

10. Comet and meteor studies

Our physical knowledge of comets began to make rapid progress once it was possible to apply to their study the resources of spectrum analysis with the aid of photography. In this connection mention may be made of the work of the French astronomer F. Baldet who in 1907 was the first to apply successfully the objective prism to the study of comets; the slit spectrograph that had been used previously only produced spectra of the bright portions of a comet close to the nucleus; on the other hand, the use of the objective prism, while it sacrificed high dispersion, provided a series of monochromatic images of the entire comet separated according to each wavelength emitted, for both the head and tail. In this way it was discovered that—in addition to the bands of neutral mole-

---

[1] It should be mentioned that Pluto has turned out quite differently from what had been expected. Indeed, it is not a major planet similar to Uranus or Neptune, but a planet of small dimensions comparable to Mars (IX, 48). Furthermore, its orbit is highly elongated and inclined to the ecliptic and these unexpected characteristics raise a difficulty for theories of the origin of the solar system.

cules of carbon, cyanogen and hydrocarbons emitted by comet heads—the tails emit molecular bands of ionized carbon dioxide and ionized nitrogen.

However, in more recent times the slit spectrograph has been reintroduced in order to make possible more detailed studies of the light of comet heads and of their nuclei. Thus, since 1940—through the investigations of the Belgian astrophysicist P. Swings and of the German physicist G. Herzberg, then working in the U.S.A. and of some other spectroscopists—a large number of new emission features have been identified, notably from the radicals OH, NH_2, CH_2, etc. These discoveries have contributed to our understanding of the mechanism by which the gases in cometary tails are repelled by the Sun's light, and have also helped the recent theories of the composition of cometary nuclei.

After the development of the electromagnetic theory of light by the British physicist Maxwell, the Italian physicist Bartoli had shown in 1883 that light should exert a pressure on bodies which receive it. In 1892 the Russian physicist Lebedeff had shown that this repelling action of light must considerably exceed the force of gravitational attraction on sufficiently small particles and he proved the reality of the effect experimentally in 1900. Using these results, the Swedish physicist S. Arrhenius (1859–1927) in 1900, followed by the German astronomer K. Schwarzschild (1873–1916) in 1901, developed a theory of cometary tails which incorporated the earlier theory of Bredichin (VI, 35). According to this theory radiation pressure acting on particles of diameter comparable to the wavelength of light caused the repulsion of cometary matter. In fact, the progress in our knowledge of the interactions between matter and radiation that has resulted from the theory of light photons and from quantum mechanics has shown that ordinary radiation pressure is quite unable to repel the isolated molecules known from their spectra to be present in comets.

It has been realized that the relevant effect is actually what is known as 'resonance pressure', or selective radiation pressure, due to the impulse received by a molecule when it absorbs a photon corresponding to one of its characteristic absorption frequencies. This theory gives a satisfactory account of the formation of cometary tails and also of certain peculiarities of cometary spectra (IX, 48).

As far as cometary nuclei are concerned, observations have been carried out when comets have passed very close to the Earth—especially comet Pons-Winnecke observed by Baldet at Meudon in 1927—which have shown that these bodies are really very small, apparently less than a mile in diameter; it may be mentioned incidentally that this fact finally excludes any possibility of a world-wide catastrophe in the highly improbable event of a collision between the Earth and a cometary nucleus.

The study of meteors did not benefit so soon from the application of astrophysical methods; however, since 1930, photography has been systematically applied to the recording of the trajectories and spectra of meteors at the temporary Harvard field stations set up by Whipple in the United States. These observations have been continued and greatly extended since the second world war owing to the great interest attaching to meteor studies for our knowledge of the upper atmosphere and for the propagation of high-speed powered projectiles in this region (IX, 48).

41. Celestial mechanics and positional astronomy

As mentioned earlier (III, 21), certain unexplained difficulties continued to exist—notably in the theory of the motions of Mercury and the Moon—in spite of the high degree of perfection reached by celestial mechanics in the middle of the nineteenth century.

The excess in the secular motion of the perihelion of Mercury, discovered by Le Verrier, was confirmed in 1882 by the American astronomer S. Newcomb (1835–1909); using all the transits of Mercury across the Sun that had been observed between 1677 and 1881, he found that the observed motion of the perihelion of Mercury exceeded by 43″ per century the theoretical motion calculated from the best available values of planetary masses. In a study, published in 1895, on the *Fundamental Constants of Astronomy* Newcomb discussed the various hypotheses that had been put forward since Le Verrier's time to explain the discrepancy:

non-sphericity of the Sun, a belt of minor planets within the orbit of Mercury or between the orbits of Mercury and Venus, etc., and showed that none of these hypotheses provided a satisfactory explanation of the observations. The most plausible suggestion, which had been put forward by the American astronomer A. Hall, consisted in introducing a very slight correction to Newton's law, but no justification of this appeared at the time.

The mystery was not finally solved until the appearance in 1915 of Einstein's General Theory of Relativity, according to which the perihelia of planetary orbits should—as compared with Newton's theory—undergo a progressive advance the value of which can be precisely calculated purely from the theory and turns out to be just $43''$ per century for Mercury. This perfect agreement between the unexplained residual in the motion of the perihelion of Mercury and the value predicted by the Theory of Relativity was a striking success for the latter and one of its most convincing astronomical proofs.

This agreement has been checked with great care in the last few years at the U.S. Naval Observatory, by G. M. Clemence, who used a series of observations extending from 1765 to 1940 and found a value of $42''.6$ for the excess precession of the perihelion of Mercury unexplained by the Newtonian theory; this value is very close to the value of $43''.0$ predicted by the Theory of Relativity.

Furthermore, in 1945, H. R. Morgan, also of the Naval Observatory, Washington, found that observations of the sun show a secular advance in the perihelion of the Earth's orbit, of about $4''.6$, in good agreement with the value of $3''.8$ predicted by relativity.

The study of the Moon's motion has also led to an important discovery in recent times: the irregularity of the Earth's rotation. In fact, as early as 1870, Newcomb had shown that Hansen's tables still left a great deal to be desired in the accuracy with which they represented the observed positions of the Moon; Hansen's theory had greatly improved the calculation of short-period irregularities, but those of long period remained unaccounted for. The difficult problem of the lunar theory was therefore taken up once more by a number of mathematical astronomers, notably the Frenchmen C. Delaunay (1816–1872) and Radau (1835–1911), and

—apart from Newcomb himself—the Americans G. W. Hill (1838–1914) and especially E. W. Brown (1866–1938). The latter, faced by the persistent discrepancy between the observations and the most highly elaborated tables of the lunar motion, finally recognized in 1926 that this impossibility of representing the lunar motion correctly was due to random irregularities in the rotational motion of the Earth. He noticed that the observed positions of the Sun and planets presented the same small residuals with respect to the tables of planetary motion and that the discrepancies varied in the same sense and at the same time with those of the Moon, but with amplitudes reduced in proportion to the mean angular velocities of the respective planets in their orbits. The only possible explanation of this fact was that the standard of time, as determined by observations of the stars and representing the rotational motion of the Earth, did not flow uniformly as had always been thought and as is implicitly required for a correct application of the laws of celestial mechanics. More recently, the ever-increasing precision of astronomical clocks—particularly through the introduction of piezo-electric quartz clocks—has permitted the detection of a seasonal irregularity in the Earth's rotation; this irregularity was discovered in 1936 by N. Stoyko of the *Bureau International de l'Heure* (Paris Observatory) and later confirmed by others, in particular by H. Finch, at the Greenwich Observatory, in 1949.

These various irregularities, which have been ascribed to seasonal and random displacements of masses on the surface and in the interior of the Earth, have led to the abandonment of the use of sidereal time—as determined from stellar transit observations—as the fundamental unit of time (see IX, 47).

Finally, the solar distance has been precisely determined as a result of numerous investigations carried out after the end of the nineteenth century. In fact, no sooner had hopes based on the method of transits of Venus been finally frustrated than a new and much more promising application of the trigonometric method was found: the observation in opposition of minor planets, the stellar appearance of which enables much more precise measurements to be carried out than on the discs of Mars or Venus. This method was proposed by the German astronomer J. G. Galle and first applied by him to Asteroid No. 8 (Flora) in 1873; in 1877 the British astronomer D. Gill obtained a value of 8".77 from observations of Juno. However, the first characteristic successes of this method, which resulted in the introduction of a third decimal place, were obtained from cooperative measurements of three minor planets—7 Iris, 12 Victoria and 80 Sappho—carried out in 1888 and 1889 by half a dozen observatories in both hemispheres; in 1895 Gill deduced from the combined results a value of 8".802 ±0".005 for the solar parallax. This result was in turn combined with those of Newcomb (p. 159) to give a rounded-off value of 8".80 adopted by the International Conference of Fundamental Stars which met at Paris in 1896; the same value has remained in use since then for the computation of planetary ephemerides and there is no indication after more than fifty years that it will require revision in the near future.

Nevertheless, many attempts have been made since that time to check this value of the solar parallax. After the discovery of 433 Eros (p. 194), which offers the most favourable opportunities for the trigonometric determination of the solar parallax, two international observing programmes were organized, one at the 1900–1901 opposition from which A. R. Hinks (1873–1945) in England deduced the value 8".806±0".004, and the other at the 1930–31 opposition, from which the Astronomer Royal, H. Spencer Jones, deduced in 1942 the value 8".790±0".001, often considered in recent years as the best determination yet of the solar distance.

However, dynamical and physical methods based chiefly on the determination of the *parallactic inequality* of the Moon and on spectrographic measurements of the aberration constant have consistently led to higher values in the neighbourhood of 8".803, so that there remained between the various methods discrepancies that have given astronomers a great deal of concern (see IX, 47).

Plate XIII. THE CLOUDS OF MAGELLAN

Photographed from Mount Stromlo, Australia, with a small astrographic camera.

Already known to the Arabs in the tenth century and to the Portuguese navigators of the fifteenth century who used to call them the 'Clouds of the Cape', these two gems of the southern skies were first described with some semblance of accuracy by the chronicler of the expedition of Magellan in 1521. They were not submitted to detailed telescopic examination until the astronomical expedition of Sir John Herschel to the Cape of Good Hope in the years 1834 to 1838. From his minute investigations of them he concluded that the Clouds are 'systems *sui generis*, and without analogue in our hemisphere'.

In 1867, however, the American scientist C. Abbe correctly surmised that they were merely the nearest galaxies outside our own. This was finally established in 1912–14 when from the photographic studies of variable stars in them Miss H. Leavitt, at the Harvard College Observatory, established the period-luminosity relation for cepheid variables (cf. Fig. 22, p. 211); this was used by the Danish astronomer E. Hertzsprung and the American astronomer H. Shapley to show that the distance of the Magellanic Clouds is of the order of one hundred thousand light-years. Recent revisions of the extra-galactic distance scale and new determinations place it more accurately at 150,000 light-years. The apparent separation between the two Clouds, about 20 degrees on the celestial sphere, corresponds to 50,000 light-years in space.

On this wide-angle photograph only appear the brighter parts of the Clouds; special techniques disclose much greater extensions (cf. Plate XIV and Fig. 30).

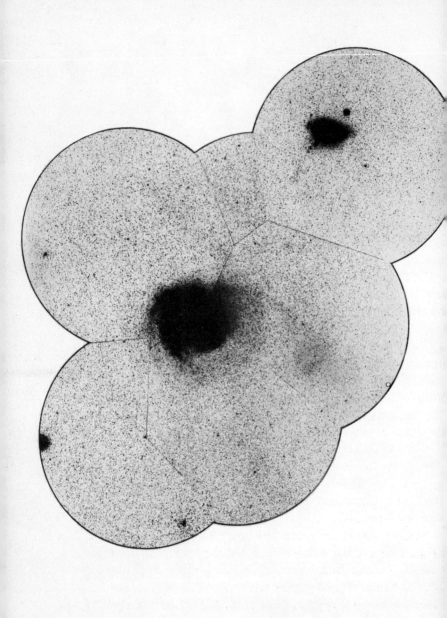

PLATE XIV. OUTER EXTENSIONS OF THE MAGEL-
LANIC CLOUDS

Mosaic of negative prints from long-exposure photographs
taken at Mount Stromlo, Australia, with a small astrographic
camera.

The bright inner parts of the Clouds, visible on Plate XIII, are
here completely black and all their detailed structure is lost. On
the other hand, repeated copying of long-exposure photographs
has brought out the fainter outer parts of the Clouds, disclosing
extensive spiral structure in the Large Cloud, an asymmetrical
prominence to the Small Cloud and the long, anomalous 'anti-
galactic' arm of the Large Cloud which, together with other
extensions, greatly increase the overall sizes of the Clouds.
Compare with the key map in Fig. 30. These outer extensions are
suggestive of gravitational and possibly magnetic interactions of
the two Clouds between them and with the Galaxy.

Following the discovery of spiral structure in 1953, the rotation
of the Clouds was established in 1954 through an analysis of
radial velocity measurements obtained in Sydney by the Australian
radio-astronomers F. J. Kerr and J. V. Hindman, by means of
the 21-cm. radiation of neutral hydrogen from the Clouds. This
also led Kerr and the author to estimate the masses of the Clouds
at about 5,000 million and 1,500 million solar masses for the
Large and Small Cloud respectively.

Being the nearest external galaxies the Clouds offer unequalled
opportunities for a detailed study of two great stellar systems at
an early stage of evolution.

* VIII *

The Rise of Astrophysics in the Twentieth Century and the Development of Contemporary Astronomy up to the Second World War

II. THE STELLAR SYSTEM AND THE UNIVERSE

42. Stellar studies

As was noted earlier (VI, 36) a vast study of the spectral classifi cation of stars was undertaken in 1885–6 at the Harvard Colleg Observatory with the aid of the objective prism. The first catalogu of the Henry Draper Memorial was published in 1890; it used ː new spectral classification developed by Miss A. C. Maury (1866– 1952). This classification has been progressively improved anɗ extended and has been universally adopted ever since; the stars arͤ arranged in order of decreasing temperature in a series of classeͤ designated by the letters O, B, A, F, G, K, M, R, N, S; the siː main classes B, A, F, G, K, M include practically all the stars (cͰ Plate VII). The work at the Harvard Observatory, begun by Misͤ Maury and continued by Miss A. J. Cannon (1863–1941), ha resulted in the spectral classification of over 225,000 stars in th *Henry Draper Catalogue* published from 1918 to 1924. Thiͤ catalogue, still further extended in later years (the *Henry Drape Extension*), gives the spectral types of practically all stars brightͤ than the 8th magnitude and a great many fainter ones (down to th 11th magnitude). It is one of the great monuments of moderͰ astronomy and has provided material for a large number of in vestigations of all kinds.

In 1905 the Danish astronomer E. Hertzsprung (later director of the Leiden Observatory, Holland) made an observation of fundamental interest; he noticed that among red stars of classes K and M some were nearby stars of low absolute luminosity—much less than that of the Sun—while others were distant stars of high absolute

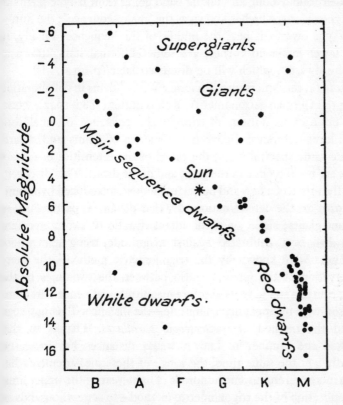

FIG. 21. THE HERTZSPRUNG–RUSSELL DIAGRAM gives the distribution of the stars as a function of their luminosity (absolute magnitude) and temperature (spectral type).

luminosity incomparably brighter than the Sun. He proposed that the first group should be called 'Dwarf' stars and the second 'Giant' stars. This distinction was confirmed and refined in 1913 by the American astronomer H. N. Russell who constructed a famous diagram known since then as the 'Hertzsprung–Russell Diagram'. On this diagram (Fig. 21), which represents the distribution of stars in absolute magnitude and spectral class, the giants are distributed along a horizontal band, above which are scattered certain other stars known as 'supergiants'. The majority of stars are distributed along an oblique band going from B-type giants to M-type dwarfs, which is known as the 'main sequence'; the Sun—a G-type dwarf—is near the middle of this sequence. Finally, in the lower left-hand corner, are some abnormal stars known as 'white dwarfs', which will be discussed later (p. 212).

In 1914, the American astronomer W. S. Adams in collaboration with the German astronomer A. Kohlschütter (1882–1942), working on Mount Wilson, discovered the existence of small but significant differences between the spectra of giants and dwarfs of the same spectral class; the ratios of the intensities of certain lines are not the same in the giant and in the dwarf. This discovery was the origin of a new and powerful method, introduced by Adams in 1916, for the determination of stellar distances, particularly of distant giants; since, once the intensity ratio of two convenient lines had been calibrated against magnitude, using stars whose distances were known by the trigonometric method,[1] the mere observation of the intensity ratio between the two lines in the spectrum of a star gave its absolute magnitude and hence—by comparison with its apparent magnitude—the distance. This has been called the method of *spectroscopic parallaxes*. Thanks to this method the number of known stellar distances has increased rapidly[2]; at the same time, the range of these measurements has been increased from some hundreds of light-years—the upper limit of application of the trigonometric method—to some thousands of

[1] The accuracy and hence the importance of this method had been greatly increased by the application of photography to parallax measurements, especially through the work of the American astronomer F. Schlesinger (1871–1943) from 1905 to 1911—soon followed by many others—and which resulted in a considerable advance in our knowledge of stellar distances within a radius of a few hundred light-years from the Sun.

[2] The number of stars with known distances has increased from 87 in 1892 and 305 in 1910 to over 7,000 in 1935 and nearly 20,000 in 1948.

ight-years, a result which is very important in galactic research section 43).

At the same time, the application of the laws of thermal radiation s given in 1900 by the German physicist Max Planck (1858–1947) nd the first determinations of stellar temperatures about 1910 by . Wilsing and J. Scheiner (1858–1913) at Potsdam and by Nordmann at Paris, enabled the diameters of stars to be determined. It was thus found that the expressions 'giant' and 'dwarf' pply not only to stellar luminosities but also to the dimensions of he stellar globes. This was confirmed in 1920 by direct measurements of the apparent diameters of certain supergiant stars by the American physicist A. A. Michelson (1852–1931), who in collaboration with the astronomer F. G. Pease (1881–1938) used a ery large interferometer mounted on the 100-in. telescope of the Mount Wilson Observatory. The largest observed diameter—that f the variable star Mira Ceti—was only 0″.05; these stellar discs re too small to be observed even in the largest instruments now in existence and can only be detected by indirect methods. Another method—which has been applied since 1938 by A. E. Whitford t the Mount Wilson Observatory—is to record the light fluctuaons due to diffraction when stars are occulted by the Moon; y comparing the observed fluctuations with those predicted om diffraction theory, the star's apparent diameter can be stimated.

However, the most fruitful method has been that based on clipsing variables. As was noted earlier (VI, 36), Pickering had een able as early as 1880 for the first time to find the diameter of lgol on the assumption that the periodic light variations of this ar were the result of eclipses due to the interposition of a dark ody. The correctness of this hypothesis was demonstrated in 1888 y Vogel when he saw that the spectral lines of Algol oscillate about mean position with the same period as that of its light variation; his he attributed to the variations in the star's radial velocity in e course of its orbital motion about the centre of gravity of the stem.

In the following year Miss Maury and Pickering—using spectra btained at Harvard—noticed the periodic doubling of the lines of the bright component of the double star Mizar (Zeta Ursae Majoris), thus discovering the first non-variable *spectroscopic binary*. The phenomenon of an eclipsing variable depends on the accident of the Earth being situated close to the orbital plane of the system. The doubling of lines was due to the fact that in this case each of the components was bright enough to show an observable spectrum. If, however, one of the components is much brighter than the other, only a single spectrum is seen—as with Algol—but in which the lines undergo a periodic oscillation.

The study of spectroscopic binaries, especially those which are also eclipsing variables, has led to some very important discoveries. In 1912, H. N. Russell and H. Shapley, at Princeton, developed the theory of the light variations of eclipsing binaries and computed tables from which the dimensions of the components of these systems may be deduced from their light variation; in this way it has been possible to derive the diameters of a large number of stars of all classes.

At the same time observational progress has permitted the detection of increasingly delicate effects. Thus, J. Stebbins in the U.S. succeeded in showing from very accurate observations of Algol—made in 1911 with one of the first photoelectric photometers—that the dark satellite actually emits an appreciable amount of light, so that, when it is eclipsed by the bright component, a very small diminution takes place in the amount of light emitted by the system. This was perfect confirmation of the eclipse theory.

In 1924, D. B. McLaughlin and R. A. Rossiter, also in the U.S.A., showed from a detailed study of the spectra of Algol and other eclipsing binaries that these stars rotate on their own axes. Shortly afterwards, O. Struve in America and G. A. Shajn in Russia succeeded in detecting the rotation of certain single stars on their own axes from the broadening of their spectral lines. It was found that rapid rotation was mostly confined to the 'early type' stars of classes O, B, A, i.e. very hot stars.

It should also be mentioned that the study of eclipsing variables and of spectroscopic binaries has provided many other important data—especially on the absorption of light by stellar atmospheres.

on their degree of internal condensation and on the emission of filaments or gaseous shells by rapidly rotating stars.

Other variable stars have played a not less important part in the development of ideas on the nature of the stars, especially the *Cepheids*—so called after their prototype Delta Cephei. In fact it was found from observations of their spectral lines that they showed periodic variations in radial velocity corresponding to their period of light variation and for this reason were thought for some time at the turn of the century to be spectroscopic binaries. In 1914, however, H. Shapley showed that this hypothesis was untenable because frequently it led to orbital dimensions for the system which were smaller than those of the stars themselves, requiring the stars to revolve inside each other.

Shapley suggested that the stars were actually pulsating, in other words that they have variable radii (so that the outer surface, alternately approaching and receding from us, produces the observed variation in radial velocity), and the theory of this effect was developed soon afterwards by the British astrophysicist A. S. Eddington (1882–1944). Application of this theory has given a new method of determining the sizes of these stars and has also provided an explanation of a very important relationship—discovered in 1912 by Miss H. S. Leavitt (1868–1921)—between the periods of Cepheids and their mean luminosities (cf. Fig. 22) which will be discussed later (VIII, 43).

During the same period, physical studies of the constitution of stars, whether variable or not, made considerable progress, chiefly through the work of the Indian astrophysicist M. N. Saha (1893–1956) who, in 1920, developed the first theory of atomic ionization in stellar atmospheres and calculated the abundances in the equilibrium of the various states of ionization as a function of atmospheric temperature and pressure; this theory was applied to the stars from 1925 onwards chiefly by Miss C. Payne (later Mrs. Gaposchkin) and D. H. Menzel at Harvard College, by A. Pannekoek in Holland and by A. Unsöld in Germany. These studies have shown that hydrogen and helium together constitute more than 99 per cent of stellar matter—a conclusion of fundamental importance for modern cosmology.

This predominance of hydrogen was confirmed in 1938, when R. Wildt identified a new constituent of stellar atmospheres—the negative ion of hydrogen[1]; it is absorption by this ion that produces the high opacity of stellar atmospheres of the solar type, as has been shown in particular by the theoretical investigations of the Indian theorist S. Chandrasekhar working at the Yerkes Observatory and by the observations of the French astrophysicist D. Chalonge and his collaborators.

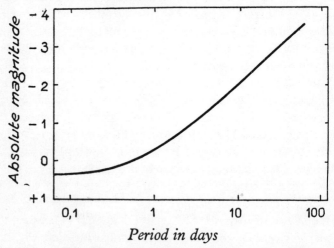

FIG. 22. PERIOD–LUMINOSITY RELATION FOR CEI HEIDS, ACCORDING TO SHAPLEY

Compare with the post-war revision (Fig. 34).

Simultaneously with this advance in the theory of stellar atmospheres, advances in physics enabled the theory of stellar interiors to be developed; these advances were due mainly to the German astronomers R. Emden (1862–1940) and K. Schwarzschild (1873–1916) about 1906, and especially to A. S. Eddington, who developed the theory of the *radiative equilibrium* of stars in an epoch-making series of investigations carried out between 1916 and 1924. According to this theory the equilibrium of a gaseous stellar mass is determined by the interaction of the expansive forces of gas pressure and

[1] Resulting from the capture of an electron by a neutral hydrogen atom

adiation pressure, opposed by the centripetal action of the weight
of its own matter. This theory led to very high temperatures for
the central regions of stars—expressed in millions or even tens of
millions of degrees (Fig. 23); the origin of these temperatures did
not receive a satisfactory explanation until 1938 when the physicists

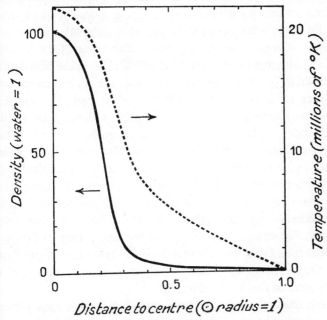

FIG. 23. THE SOLAR INTERIOR, ACCORDING TO
EDDINGTON

Curves showing the variation in density (left-hand scale) and temperature (right-hand scale) from the centre to the surface of the Sun.

H. Bethe in the U.S.A. and C. von Weizsäcker in Germany discovered a cycle of nuclear reactions by which hydrogen is slowly
transformed into helium in stellar interiors and releases energy
which finally emerges at the surface of the stars in the form of
visible radiation. This discovery of the source of the energy radiated
by the Sun and stars solved the problem of the origin of the Sun's
heat (VI, 33) and of its survival through the thousands of millions
of years required by modern estimates of the age of the Earth—

more accurately fixed at 3,500 million years by the British geo-physicist Holmes in 1946.

In 1924 Eddington discovered one of the most important consequences of the theory of the radiative equilibrium of stars—a relation between the mass and the luminosity of a star. Eddington first established the relation theoretically for giants only, considering them as entirely gaseous, but soon found that it was equally valid for dwarf stars of the main sequence although their central densities attained values much greater than those of the heaviest metals. Eddington discovered the reason for this in the high degree of ionization of the atoms resulting from the high temperatures prevailing in stellar interiors. This ionization strips the atoms of their outer electrons and thus considerably reduces their mutual interference, so that matter can reach enormous densities while keeping the general properties of a gas. The only stars to which Eddington's mass-luminosity relation does not apply are the 'white dwarfs', which are much more massive than might be expected from their luminosity; this is because their matter reaches an extraordinarily high density at which the ordinary gas laws cease to apply. For example, in the case of the Companion of Sirius, it has been found that the diameter is hardly twice that of the Earth while the mass is equal to that of the Sun, so that its mean density is over 100,000 times that of water.

These unusual conditions have provided another astronomical proof of the Theory of Relativity. According to the theory, the apparent frequency of a periodic phenomenon—such as atomic vibration—is changed when the source is situated in a strong gravitational field such as must exist at the surface of the Companion of Sirius. This slowing down manifests itself by a slight displacement of spectral lines towards the red and was observed in 1925 by Adams in the spectrum of the Companion of Sirius observed with a large dispersion spectrograph at the focus of the 100-in. telescope on Mount Wilson; as the observed effect was in good agreement with the theoretical prediction, both the theory and the existence of extremely dense matter in white dwarfs were confirmed. Immediately the physicist R. H. Fowler (1889–1944) in England, using the then very new methods of wave mechanics,

eveloped the theory of this 'degenerate' state of matter in white
warfs. The theory was later perfected by Chandrasekhar and
thers (IX, 49).

3. Galactic studies

Towards the end of the nineteenth century the structure of the
Milky Way was still obscure and no significant progress had been
made since the time of Herschel. The methodical study of the
tellar system was revived by the Dutch astronomer J. C. Kapteyn
1851-1922).

In 1904 Kapteyn noticed that stellar motions—corrected for the
ffects of the Sun's motion—were not distributed at random over
he celestial sphere as had been believed up to then, but appeared
o be grouped for the most part in two streams pointing in two
videly different directions of the sky. However, in spite of the
urther work carried out in following years by K. Schwarzschild in
Germany and then by Eddington in Britain which confirmed
Kapteyn's discovery, the reason for this preferential distribution
emained a mystery for a long time.

Kapteyn had also recognized the necessity for a systematic
esumption on a modern basis of Herschel's star counts or 'gauges'.
For this purpose he proposed in 1906 a detailed study of 206
Selected Areas' uniformly distributed over the celestial sphere
nd in which the numbers of stars of various apparent magnitudes
vere determined during the following decade by the combined
fforts of many observatories. On the basis of these results and
vith the further help of stellar statistics taken from the various
vailable star catalogues, Kapteyn proposed in 1922 a model of the
Galaxy—very similar to Herschel's—according to which the
lensity of stellar population decreased in all directions away from
he Sun, placed by him near the centre of a system some 40,000
ight-years in diameter.

This model, however, was in disagreement with another model
rrived at independently and somewhat earlier by H. Shapley.
Shapley's method was as follows: about 1900, S. I. Bailey at the
Harvard Observatory had discovered a large number of 'Cepheid'

variables in various globular clusters (Plate X). In 1912 another Harvard astronomer, Miss Leavitt, had also discovered some Cepheids in the two Magellanic Clouds and had found—as already mentioned (VIII, 42)—that there exists a well-defined relation between the period and apparent luminosity of these Magellanic Cepheids. Hertzsprung and Shapley both immediately realized that this relation also holds for the absolute luminosities, since the Magellanic Cepheids are all at the same distance from the Earth so that their absolute magnitudes differ from their apparent magnitudes by the same amount. Using the few data then available for the absolute magnitudes of galactic Cepheids, Hertzsprung was able in 1913 to calibrate the period-luminosity relation in absolute measure (Fig. 23). From then on a determination of a Cepheid's period was enough to give its absolute magnitude, and to deduce its distance from a comparison with its observed apparent magnitude. Hertzsprung applied this method to the Magellanic Clouds and found a distance of about 100,000 light-years. Thus for the first time distances had been measured that were incomparably larger than any previously met with in astronomy.

Shortly afterwards Shapley began to study the Cepheids in a large number of globular clusters with the aid of the 60-in. telescope on Mount Wilson—then the most powerful telescope in the world. In this way he was able within a few years to determine the distances of most known globular clusters. In 1918 he deduced from this study that the globular clusters form a system strongly concentrated towards the Milky Way, the centre of which was not close to the Sun—but some 50,000 light-years away in the general direction of the constellation of Sagittarius. Shapley then put forward the bold idea that the centre of the Galactic System coincided with that of the cluster system and that the extent of the latter which he then estimated at some 300,000 light-years, was also the extent of our stellar system. Shapley's discovery—driving the Sun from the centre of the Milky Way—has been justly compared with that of Copernicus, which it completed by finally liberating astronomy from the tenacious illusion of a central position of the Earth.

However, when Kapteyn published his galactic scheme a few years later the violent disagreement between the results obtained

214

by the two different methods cast some doubt on Shapley's scheme; these were removed in 1926 when B. Lindblad in Sweden was able to demonstrate the general rotation of the Galaxy around a distant centre which was also situated in the direction of Sagittarius; this discovery was at once confirmed by the Dutch astronomer J. H. Oort, who demonstrated the differential rotation of the Galactic System in the Sun's neighbourhood. In this rotation the Sun and nearby stars are carried towards the constellation of Cygnus with a speed until recently estimated at about 270 km./sec., corresponding to a rotational period of the order of 200 million years about a centre some 30,000 light-years away.

The disagreement over the distance of the Galactic centre as found by Shapley disappeared in 1930 when as the result of a general investigation of the 'galactic' or 'open' clusters, such as the Pleiades, carried out at the Lick Observatory, the Swiss astronomer R. J. Trümpler showed that interstellar space—far from being completely transparent as had been generally supposed —is actually filled with a highly rarefied material. This interstellar haze absorbs the light from distant stars and makes them seem much further away than they are in reality. The distances of the globular clusters were then corrected for the effect of interstellar absorption and gave 30,000 light-years for the Sun's distance from the Galactic centre, in agreement with the results deduced from Galactic rotation studies; at the same time the total diameter of the Galaxy was reduced to about 100,000 light-years or less.

Trümpler's discovery brought to the forefront of astronomical activity the study of interstellar matter. However, many indications had been obtained since the beginning of the century of the presence of rarefied matter in interstellar space. The first indication was obtained in 1904 when the German astronomer G. Hartmann found an absorption line (the K line of calcium) in the spectrum of the spectroscopic binary Delta Orionis which differed from the other lines by remaining in the same position during the periodic variation in the star's radial velocity. This surprising phenomenon of 'stationary lines' of calcium was soon observed in the spectra of other spectroscopic binaries, but it was for a long time mistakenly attributed to stationary calcium clouds surrounding the binary systems. In 1928, however, O. Struve, then at the Yerkes Observatory, showed that the apparent intensity of these stationary lines increases with the distance of the star, implying that the absorbing atoms are distributed throughout the intervening space between the stars and the Earth. Since then a number of interstellar absorption lines—due to many atoms and also some molecules—have been discovered in the spectra of distant stars, especially by Adams and Dunham from high-dispersion spectra obtained on Mount Wilson; in addition to the well-known lines of neutral and ionized calcium and of sodium, they identified those of potassium, titanium, and various molecular groupings such as cyanogen CN and the hydrides CH and NaH—showing incidentally the presence in interstellar space of large amounts of hydrogen. The latter has also been observed directly through its red line H alpha, the emission of which over vast areas of the Milky Way was discovered in 1938 by Struve and Elvey at the McDonald Observatory in Texas. Furthermore, theoretical calculations have been carried out which confirm quantitatively the high abundance of hydrogen relative to the other elements. This recognition of the predominance of hydrogen has had a considerable effect on the development of recent theories of the nature and possible origin of the Universe (section 44).

A further sign of the presence of obscuring matter in interstellar space had been observed at the turn of the century by the German astronomer M. Wolf (1863–1932) and the American E. E. Barnard (1857–1923); they were the first to draw attention to the dark regions which appear all along the Milky Way and seem sometimes entirely devoid of stars on photographs of star fields.[1] They showed that these regions could not be true voids or 'holes' in the Milky Way, but must actually be due to the presence of obscuring masses which hide the distant stars; Wolf even devised in 1923 a method by which the distances and thicknesses of these dark clouds could be determined (Plate IX).

---

[1] These dark markings had already been discussed by A. Secchi and their nature correctly surmised by him in a little-known memoir published in 1877.

Again, in 1912 V. M. Slipher at the Lowell Observatory had found that the spectrum of the nebulae surrounding the Pleiades was not a bright-line spectrum like that of the gaseous nebulae, such as the Orion Nebula,[1] but a continuous spectrum reflecting that of the stars embedded in the nebulae. This discovery of 'reflection nebulae' was another indication of the existence of rarefied dust clouds in space able to scatter the light of nearby stars.

The properties of this impalpable interstellar 'haze'—and the sizes of the particles of which it consists—have been established since 1930 by a series of experimental and theoretical investigations due to various astronomers, especially J. Stebbins, who demonstrated, in 1932, the reddening of the light of distant stars seen through a thick layer of interstellar matter, and the Swedish astronomer C. Schalén, who was one of the first to calculate the average size of the particles from the observed law of selective absorption. It appears that these absorbing particles are of the order of a tenth of a micron (a few millionths of an inch) in diameter. Their exact nature is still not too well known, but it is generally believed that they are composed mainly of the same elements as are found in comets and meteors.

During all this period when rapid progress was being made in the detailed study of the stellar and interstellar content of the galactic system, very little was found about its general structure. From its general rotation Lindblad and others estimated the total mass of the system at about 100,000 million times the mass of the Sun; but nothing was known of its shape and structure except in the immediate vicinity of the Sun. Beyond a few thousands of light-years the accumulated absorption of the interstellar dust clouds is so high that very little information on the distant parts of the Galaxy could be obtained from optical observations. It was only supposed, from the general analogy with external galaxies (section 44),

---

[1] The origin of the bright lines of gaseous nebulae was explained in 1927 by the American astrophysicist I. S. Bowen (now director of the Mount Wilson and Palomar observatories), who proved that they were due to 'forbidden' radiations of ionized oxygen and nitrogen; he thus finally established that the so-called 'nebulium' was non-existent.

that our Galaxy was probably a spiral system. The solution of this problem has been an outstanding achievement of the post-war period (IX, 50).

44. Extragalactic studies and the expansion of the universe

In spite of the tremendous advances of the last half-century in our knowledge of the solar and stellar systems, the most important and characteristic revelations of contemporary astronomy have undoubtedly been the final recognition of external galaxies and the discovery of the expansion of the Universe.

As was earlier mentioned, little progress in the study of the nebulae was possible until the application of photography; since then, however, the number of known objects has increased rapidly as more and more powerful telescopes have been set into operation.

Among the main astronomers who have contributed to these photographic investigations—apart from the British amateur I. Roberts (VI, 37)—mention must be made of G. E. Keeler (1857–1900), who at the end of the nineteenth century used the 36-in. reflector of the Lick Observatory; then, at the beginning of the present century, the American optician G. W. Ritchey—who used the 24-in. telescope at the Yerkes Observatory and, after 1909, the 60-in. telescope of the Mount Wilson Observatory—and F. G. Pease—who used the same telescope and then, after 1918, the 100-in. telescope of the same observatory.

It was by the use of this telescope—which for thirty years was the largest in the world—that the American astronomer E. Hubble (1889–1953) was able in 1924 finally to establish the nature of these objects. For, as has been noted (VI, 37), the status of these 'white' nebulae (with continuous spectra) remained quite uncertain until the end of the nineteenth century. In 1899, however, the German astronomer J. Scheiner (1858–1913) managed by means of a very long exposure to obtain a faint photographic image of the spectrum of the Andromeda Nebula and observed that it was crossed by dark lines similar to those in the Sun's spectrum; he concluded that the nebula was actually an immensely distant cluster of stars, but doubt was again cast on this by Slipher's discovery in

1912 of 'reflection nebulae' which show a stellar-like spectrum section 43).

In 1917 Ritchey revived the question by discovering a nova in a spiral nebula. Immediately after this, an examination of plates of the Andromeda Nebula showed that faint novae appeared in it very frequently and a comparison of the apparent observed magnitudes of these novae with the known absolute magnitude of novae in our Galaxy indicated that the nebula must be at a very great distance— of the order of a million light-years, a conclusion most clearly reached in 1918 by H. D. Curtis (1872–1942) then working at the Lick Observatory.

The question was, however, finally settled only when Hubble— using the great Mount Wilson telescope—succeeded in 1923–4 in resolving the outer parts of the Andromeda Nebula and of some other large nebulae into distinct stars among which he was soon able to identify some Cepheid variables. He was now in a position to make precise determinations of the distance of the nebula, using the period-luminosity relation (section 42), and found a value of 800,000 light-years—in good agreement with the value deduced from novae. This discovery established beyond doubt the extragalactic character of the majority of the nebulae and opened an enormous field of research. In 1925, Hubble showed that extragalactic nebulae may be classified according to their appearance into three main groups: spiral nebulae, such as the Andromeda Nebula (Plate XV), the nebula in Triangulum and that in Canes Venatici (Plate XVI); elliptical nebulae such as the satellites of the Andromeda Nebula; and irregular nebulae such as the Magellanic Clouds, which were regarded as satellites of our own Galaxy.

The new field was vigorously explored by Hubble, who in the short space of ten years from 1925 to 1935 was able to sound the depths of the extragalactic universe out to the limit of penetration of the Mount Wilson telescope. He used the methods developed by Shapley to find the distances of globular clusters, starting with the Cepheid variables; these enabled him to find the distances of the nearest nebulae which—together with our Galaxy—constitute the so-called 'local group' of nebulae in which about a score of members are known at present.

Starting from here he was able to find the absolute magnitudes of the brightest supergiant stars of these systems; these are considerably brighter than Cepheids and could therefore be used to gauge the distances of further nebulae out to about 10 million light-years—at which distance the Mount Wilson telescope still revealed the brightest supergiants of extragalactic systems. At a distance somewhat less than this limit—some 8 million light-years away—there is a large *cluster* of nebulae in the constellation of Virgo; Hubble used this cluster to find the total absolute magnitude of a typical sample of nebulae. In this way he showed that most galaxies have an absolute luminosity somewhere between 10 and 100 million times that of the Sun, providing a new criterion for the distance of nebulae in remote clusters even when individual stars are no longer visible. In this way Hubble could quickly explore the immense extragalactic universe that he had discovered out to distances of the order of 500 million light-years. He estimated that this immense volume contains nearly 100 million galaxies comparable with our own.

In fact the strict similarity between extragalactic nebulae and our own Galaxy was still disputed around 1930, for, while Shapley obtained a value of 300,000 light-years for the diameter of our Galaxy, Hubble found dimensions of the order of only 30,000 light-years for the largest spirals such as the Andromeda Nebula. After 1930, however, this difference was greatly reduced if not removed altogether, partly through the discovery of interstellar matter, which has resulted in a considerable reduction of the dimensions ascribed to our Galaxy, and partly through the application of refined photometric analysis to the nebulae, which has shown that they are actually much larger than would be deduced from a simple inspection of photographs. Nevertheless, our Galaxy still seemed to be one of the largest known spirals; this only concession that modern astronomy seemed prepared to make to human vanity raised some suspicions among astronomers and in fact has been proved illusory by more recent work (IX, 51).

Meanwhile the spectroscopic study of nebular rotation has led to estimates of their masses which are of the same order as that of the Galaxy. For example, the total masses of the Triangulum

Nebula and of the Andromeda Nebula—first measured in 1939 and 1942 by the American astronomers H. W. Babcock, A. B. Wyse, N. U. Mayall and L. H. Aller at the Lick Observatory—have been found to be of the order of from several thousand million up to 100,000 million times that of the Sun.

A further result of the study of spiral nebulae has been the recognition of a new class of variable stars previously confused with Novae, and which are the most prodigious stellar explosions known to man; we refer to the 'supernovae'. Indeed, as soon as the distances of some nebulae were known, it was realized that, if the faint novae observed in the Andromeda Nebula by Ritchey were normal novae comparable to those observed in our Galaxy, then the nova of 1885 (VI, 37)—which reached a maximum brightness some 10,000 times greater—must be of a different kind. Several similar examples had been observed in other nebulae so that the existence of a special class of novae incomparably brighter than those previously known had to be acknowledged.

The systematic search for these supernovae was undertaken in 1936 on Palomar Mountain by F. Zwicky using a special large-field photographic telescope of a new type designed some years earlier by the Estonian optician B. Schmidt (1879-1935) of the Hamburg Observatory. With this instrument Zwicky was able in a few years to discover several supernovae, which were studied in detail by W. Baade and M. L. Humason at the Mount Wilson Observatory. These studies showed that the spectra of supernovae are entirely different from those of any other celestial object and the origin of the radiations observed is still something of a mystery; but it is generally believed that they represent the effect of extremely high temperatures and velocities. The absolute luminosity reached by these bodies is prodigious, since, at the maximum phase, supernovae are 10 to 100 million times brighter than the Sun; in other words, at that particular time they alone emit almost as much light as the thousands of millions of stars populating the galaxies in which they appear.

However, these fantastic stellar explosions are very rare; in 1940 Zwicky deduced from his observations that there are hardly more than two supernovae per millennium in the average galaxy;

nevertheless some nebulae are already known in which two or even three supernovae have exploded in less than fifty years.

It has been concluded that in our own galaxy at least three supernovae have appeared in the last thousand years. One of them is none other than the extraordinary star of 1572 which so fascinated Tycho Brahe (II, 9); another has been identified with the brilliant nova seen by Kepler in 1604; the appearance of the third is related in ancient Chinese and Japanese chronicles of the year 1054, and its remains are still visible in the sky in the form of a strange filamentary gas cloud—the 'Crab Nebula'—which has always fascinated astronomers with its exceptional appearance. The origin of these strange apparitions is still obscure; some astronomers regard them as a result of the violent collapse of stars such as white dwarfs, going through stages of instability in the course of their evolution.

We must finally discuss the most extraordinary and unexpected phenomenon revealed by the study of extragalactic nebulae: the *expansion of the Universe*. It has already been explained (VI, 36) how since the end of the nineteenth century the application of the Doppler effect had enabled the radial motions of stars, along the line of sight, to be measured. These studies had led—among other things—to the discovery of the rotation of the Galaxy and had accustomed astronomers to finding velocities of the order of some tens of kilometres per second for celestial bodies. When the first radial velocities of spiral nebulae were determined, they immediately turned out to have unexpectedly large values, measured in hundreds and then in thousands of kilometres per second.

The first determination was made in 1912, at the Lowell Observatory, by V. M. Slipher, who was able to make long enough exposures to measure the radial velocity of the Andromeda Nebula; then, in 1914, he published the first list giving the velocities of thirteen nebulae. He noticed that the majority of these velocities were positive, corresponding to very rapid motions of recession. The explanation of this curious phenomenon vainly occupied the ingenuity of many astronomers for a dozen years. It was not until 1929 that Hubble, with his first estimates of nebular distances, was able to clarify the problem by showing that these velocities of recession increase proportionally to the distance of the observed nebula (Fig. 24). In this way he discovered the fantastic pheno-menon of the recession of the galaxies, the basic manifestation of the expansion of the Universe.[1]

This discovery was completely confirmed after 1930 by the observations of M. L. Humason on Mount Wilson, who by using special high-speed spectrographs was able to measure the radial

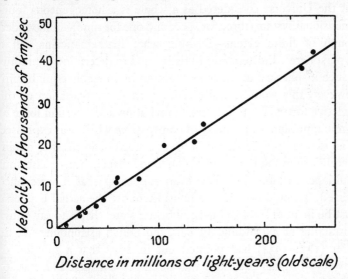

FIG. 24. EXPANSION OF THE UNIVERSE, ACCORDING TO HUBBLE AND HUMASON (1936)

Relation between the distance and recessional velocity of extragalactic nebulae.

Compare the post-war revision (Fig. 31).

velocities of nebulae out to a distance of 240 million light-years reached in 1936, and it appeared that Hubble's relation remained valid to the very limits of observation. At this distance of 240 million light-years, the observed velocity of recession reaches 42,000 km./sec.—nearly one-seventh of the velocity of light. These

[1] A moment's reflection will be enough to realize that this recession of the galaxies does not imply any kind of central position for our own Galaxy, since an observer situated on any other galaxy would see precisely the same phenomenon.

observations found an immediate explanation in the theory that had already been put forward in 1927 by the Belgian mathematician G. Lemaître of Louvain, even before the phenomenon had been found observationally; this theory was one of the cosmological theories deduced from an application of General Relativity to the study of the general structure of the Universe.

Einstein's General Theory of Relativity had led to the conclusion that the Universe considered as a whole is a homogeneous four-dimensional system (three for space and one for time)—unbounded though of finite extent—forming what mathematicians call a 'hypersphere'. Einstein had initially tried to determine the radius of such a spherical universe assumed to be in stable equilibrium. However, this would require strict mutual compensation of the attractive forces due to universal gravitation and a certain force of cosmic repulsion—a property of empty space which was expressed by an extra term introduced in his equations in an effort to obtain an equilibrium solution. It was soon found that such an equilibrium would be unstable and that, even supposing that it were once realized, it would not survive long; therefore the actual Universe must be in an unstable, non-equilibrium state, that is to say either contracting or expanding. In fact, the Dutch astronomer W. de Sitter (1872–1934) had pointed out in 1917 that a solution of Einstein's original equations was an empty Universe in a state of expansion.

However, it was Lemaître in 1927 who first studied a non-empty model of the Universe with variable radius, capable of representing the actual Universe. It was not until 1930, however, that this theory was brought to public attention through the intervention of Eddington, who demonstrated the relationship between the theory and the phenomenon of the recession of distant galaxies just discovered by Hubble.

Using later estimates of the mean density of matter in the Universe—believed to correspond to the presence of one atom of hydrogen in a volume between one cubic metre and one cubic decimeter—it was possible to calculate the present radius of the Universe from Lemaître's theory; this led to values of the order of 5,000 or 10,000 million light-years, and a total mass of several tens of thousands of million times that of the Galaxy. From this followed that the volume of space explored by Hubble with the aid of the 100-in. telescope on Mount Wilson represented less than one-thousandth of the total volume of the Universe. It was clear—at least to many of those actively engaged in this field—that theoretical conclusions derived from such a limited observational material had to be regarded with considerable caution.

It was to remedy this situation as far as possible that the construction of a new telescope—much more powerful than that on Mount Wilson—was undertaken in 1928 on the initiative of G. E. Hale, who devoted the last ten years of his life to planning (for the third time in his career) a new large observatory equipped with the biggest telescope in the world. This supergiant telescope with its 200-in. mirror was completed only after twenty years of toil and at a cost of 6 million dollars; as is well-known, the Hale telescope, installed on Palomar Mountain, in Southern California, was dedicated in 1949 after the most exacting trials in the history of telescope-making. The first results of its application to the study of external galaxies and their velocities of recession will be reviewed in the final chapter (IX, 51).

45. Modern theories of cosmology and cosmogony

Since the time when the Copernican revolution caused the rejection of the crude cosmologies of primitive peoples, the problem of explaining the origin and evolution of celestial bodies and of the whole Universe has been incorporated into the realm of scientific theory. However, for a long time and until quite recently, the successive cosmogonic theories have been put forward solely to explain the origin of the Solar system and the formation of the planets.

The nebular hypothesis of Kant and Laplace (III, 18) was generally accepted throughout the nineteenth century and it was only slowly that its difficulties were realized. Among the alternative theories advanced at the turn of the century, the 'Planetesimal Hypothesis' proposed in 1901 by the American geologist T. C. Chamberlin (1843–1928) and the astronomer F. R. Moulton

(1872–   ) deserves special mention; it revived some earlier ideas of Buffon, A. W. Bickerton and others, on the solar origin of the matter out of which the planets were formed. The theory envisaged a close approach of a star to the Sun during which tidal forces may have caused the ejection of a small fraction of the Sun's matter. This matter was then supposed to condense into small planetary bodies or 'planetesimals' revolving round the Sun all in the same direction and whose subsequent coalescence with the larger fragments was regarded as the mechanism by which the planets were formed.

A decade later the English theorist J. Jeans (1877–1946) developed further the theory of the formation of a tidal filament of solar matter through the close interaction of the Sun and a perturbing star; his theory of the origin of the planets, first published in 1916, retained considerable attention during the next two decades. Because of the very small probability of an encounter between two stars in the Galaxy Jeans' theory led to the belief widely held a quarter of a century ago that planetary systems must be exceedingly rare. This conclusion was contradicted, however, by the demonstration in the 1930's by E. Holmberg of Sweden, K. A. Strand in the U.S. and others of very small perturbations in the motions of the visible components of some double stars which indicated the existence of invisible satellite bodies having planetary rather than stellar masses. In view of the extreme difficulty of these observations, their success in a few cases suggests that planetary systems are probably quite common and certainly much more so than Jeans' theory would permit.

Actually, it was also difficult to understand how a thin filament of hot solar matter could condense into planets and in 1939 the American astrophysicist L. Spitzer demonstrated that at the temperature of the solar gases such a filament was in fact highly unstable and would disperse explosively in a matter of minutes after its extraction from the Sun.

Numerous other theories have been put forward during the last twenty years by many astronomers, physicists or geologists, such as R. A. Lyttleton in England, A. Dauvillier in France, C. von Weizsäcker in Germany, O. J. Schmidt in Russia, and lately by H. C. Urey and G. P. Kuiper in the United States. Many are marked by an effort to combine the more satisfactory features of both the nebular and the planetesimal hypotheses. The theory advanced by von Weizsäcker in 1943 has, perhaps, attracted the most attention and it may be taken as an example of recent trends. According to this theory the planets were formed in a flattened envelope of gas and dust rotating round the Sun (the question of the origin of this envelope is not specifically discussed in the theory); in this envelope nuclei of condensation would be formed from the mutual interaction of temporary vortices. The most interesting and remarkable achievement of this theory is that it provided, through the geometric distribution of the vortices in the primeval cloud, the first explanation of the famous Titius-Bode law of planetary distances (III, 19).

Nevertheless, it must be admitted that despite later additions to the theory the precise mode of formation of the planets remains to a large extent a mystery and the many theories still under discussion can hardly be expected to survive.

However, the attention of cosmogonists has in the last twenty years turned to a much larger problem: that of the formation and evolution of atoms, stars, galaxies and even the entire Universe. Their ambitions have been thus enlarged by the discovery of the expansion of the Universe and by the recognition of the speed of cosmic evolution evidenced both by the expansion itself and by the agreement between various estimates of the age of the Earth and of the Galaxy.

It has thus been realized that some thousands of millions of years ago the Universe must have passed through a 'pre-stellar' stage during which matter must have been subjected to enormous temperatures and pressures. In 1941 S. Chandrasekhar, taking into account the known nuclear reactions between various nuclei and atomic particles, showed that under these conditions it is possible to explain—at least in general terms—the relative cosmic abundances of the various atomic species revealed by recent advances in physics, geophysics and astrophysics. These calculations have been refined and developed since then by various other workers and constitute one of the most remarkable successes of modern cosmology; they constitute for many an *a posteriori* confirmation of the past existence of a hyperdense pre-stellar phase of the Universe.

Such a state was first postulated as early as 1932 by G. Lemaître, whose hypothesis of the 'primeval atom' constitutes the most far-

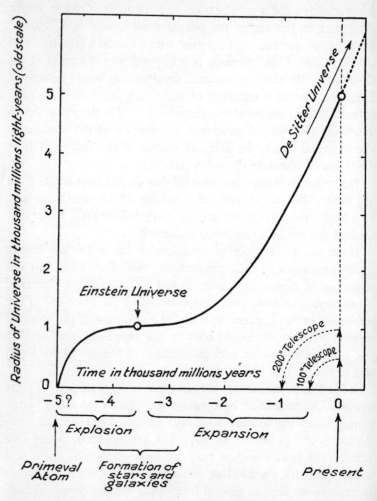

FIG 25. PRINCIPAL PHASES IN THE EVOLUTION OF THE UNIVERSE according to Lemaître's cosmology. The arrows (*lower right*) and their projections on the horizontal axis represent the limits of penetration—in space and time—of the great telescopes on Mount Wilson and Palomar Mountain on the pre-war distance scale.

reaching cosmogonic theory and the most comprehensive cosmology which had ever been proposed until that time. Using as a basis modern astronomical discoveries and the fundamental principles of physics, this theory supposes that some 5,000 or 10,000 million years ago all the matter in the Universe was concentrated at a certain 'initial' instant into a gigantic nucleus or primeval 'atom' of hyperdense material. Such an agglomeration of elementary atomic particles could only be extremely unstable; the primeval atom would thus have exploded instantaneously with prodigious violence—as a giant super-radioactive nucleus—leading through a series of successive disintegrations to a progressive dispersal of material and ending in the formation of atoms of many natural elements—in particular of present-day radio-elements which are the last unstable descendants of heavier and still more unstable nuclei that have long since disappeared. The still mysterious 'cosmic rays' which bombard us from all directions of space would then be simply the attenuated and diluted remnant of the radio-active radiation of the primeval atom; since the beginning of the world this radiation would have been travelling 'round and round' inside the closed spherical Universe of relativistic theory.

After this initial explosive phase, the expansion of the material would have been rapidly slowed down by strong attractive forces arising from the high density of material and the Universe would then have passed—3,000 or 4,000 million years ago—through a phase of quasi-equilibrium between universal gravitation and cosmic repulsion, which is the characteristic state of the Einstein Universe (Fig. 25). It is during this slowing-down phase that the galaxy, stars and planets would have been formed, since the mean density of matter in the Universe at this time—perhaps a thousand times greater than now—would favour a suitable interaction between clouds of gas and cosmic material. However, as the expanding motion continued and the mean density of matter steadily decreased, cosmic repulsion would have finally predominated over universal attraction and the world would have entered into its present phase of expansion which would continue for ever, tending through indefinite dilution to the final state of the empty Universe of de Sitter (Fig. 25).

Such is the striking picture painted by Lemaître of the origin and general evolution of the Universe; in later years he has attempted to incorporate the various particular cosmogonic theories—relating to different types of celestial object—into its framework. Naturally, the highly hypothetical and speculative character of the conditions envisaged for the beginning and end of this evolution must be recognized and it is highly probable that future discoveries will force us to alter the scheme profoundly, if not to reject it altogether; but for the moment it certainly represents the most far-reaching cosmological synthesis which has ever yet been imagined.

Nevertheless, it is far from being universally accepted and more recently other cosmologies have been proposed, chiefly in England. Reference may be made to the bold hypothesis of 'continuous creation' put forward in 1948 by T. Gold and H. Bondi, and linked with relativity theory by F. Hoyle, of Cambridge. According to it the expansion of the Universe occurs not at constant mass —as in earlier theories—but at constant density, requiring the continual appearance of matter in space at a rate which, however, is much too small to be detected by direct observation, thus preserving the principle of conservation of matter of ordinary experience. Whatever may happen to these last hypotheses—between which the future must decide—one cannot but admire the extraordinary outcropping of discoveries and theories which, in less than half a century, have revealed to us a Universe whose beauty, richness and immensity leave the naïve dreams of our ancestors far behind.

Nevertheless all these cosmogonic and cosmologic hypotheses are most likely to be soon made obsolete by the startling new discoveries which have resulted from the introduction since the end of the Second World War of new and unexpected methods of exploration of the Universe and from the drastic revision of some of the pre-war results which have followed the first few years of operation of the 200-in. reflector. Our last chapter will be devoted to a brief survey of these latest advances.

Plate XV. THE GREAT SPIRAL NEBULA MESSIER 31 IN ANDROMEDA

Photograph taken by N. U. Mayall with the 36-in. reflector of the Lick Observatory, California.

This great nebula, which was discovered by the German astronomer S. Marius in 1612, is one of the nearest and biggest spiral galaxies outside our own. Its spiral structure was revealed for the first time in 1888 on photographs taken by the British amateur I. Roberts with a 20-in. reflector. Its distance, now estimated at 1,800,000 light-years, was first determined by the American astronomer E. Hubble in 1924 from observations of cepheids detected in its outer arms on plates taken with the 100-in. telescope on Mount Wilson. Novae, globular clusters, emission nebulosities and other familiar objects of our own stellar system have been observed by Hubble, Baade and other Mount Wilson and Palomar astronomers in this great galaxy. Its rotation, first detected by the American astronomer F. G. Pease at the Mount Wilson Observatory in 1914, was studied in detail at the Lick Observatory since 1939 by Babcock and Mayall, who deduced a mass of the order of 100 thousand million times that of the Sun, comparable with that of our Galaxy. The spiral nebula is accompanied by four elliptical satellites, of which the two brightest are visible on the plate. Together with our Galaxy and the Magellanic Clouds, it is a member of the 'Local Group' of nebulae, of which altogether about twenty members are known at present.

Plate XVI. THE GREAT SPIRAL NEBULA
MESSIER 51 IN CANES

Photograph taken by J. Texereau with the 48-in. reflector of the Haute Provence Observatory, France.

This magnificent cosmic vortex is one of the nearest external galaxies; its spiral structure was discovered visually in 1845 by W. Parsons using his large telescope 72-in. in aperture, then the largest in existence, but it has taken photography to reveal its fine complex structure. Some supergiant stars may be distinguished along its outer arms. It is accompanied by an irregular satellite and connected with it by an extension of one arm, probably as the result of some form of tidal interaction. The notion of interacting or even colliding galaxies has come to the fore in recent years, mainly through the work of F. Zwicky and R. Minkowski at the Mount Wilson and Palomar observatories.

This spiral is also a member of a small group of nebulae estimated to be some eight million light-years away. It recedes from us at a speed of about 300 miles per second, 100 of which are due to the effect of galactic rotation which carries us in the opposite direction, while the remaining 200 mi./sec. represent the true recessional velocity of the nebula relative to our Galaxy and due to the expansion of the Universe.

* IX *

Astronomy Today: the Development of Contemporary Astronomy since the End of the Second World War

46. Instrumental advances

During the last few years a considerable development in astronomical instruments, accessories and techniques has taken place which is bound to revolutionize not only astronomical methods, increasing their range and efficiency, but possibly our understanding and basic theories of cosmic phenomena.

In the field of classical optics the trend towards larger and larger telescopes has culminated in the 200-in. Hale reflector which began regular operation on Palomar Mountain late in 1949. Some of the outstanding results already obtained with it will be reviewed in subsequent sections. In its wake several other large reflectors have been projected or are approaching completion in a number of observatories: a 120-in. reflector for the Lick Observatory at Mount Hamilton, California, should be ready some time in 1956, while a 98-in. telescope is in project for the Isaac Newton Memorial Observatory on the new site of the Royal Greenwich Observatory, at Herstmonceux Castle in Sussex. Two 74-in. reflectors of standard design have been in operation at the Radcliffe Observatory, Pretoria, South Africa, since 1948 and at the Commonwealth Observatory on Mount Stromlo, near Canberra, Australia, since 1955. Similar instruments are soon to be installed at the Helwan Observatory, in Egypt, and the Haute-Provence Observatory, in France. As part of a scheme for an international observatory in the southern hemisphere, a project has been recently announced for the installation of a 120-in. reflector in South Africa which, together with the large reflectors at Pretoria and Canberra mentioned above, should go some way towards reducing the great disparity between the two hemispheres. Other plans including large reflectors have also been discussed in India and Japan.

The development of the Schmidt camera in the 1930's (cf. VIII, 44) has placed in the hands of astronomers a very powerful instrument for the exploration of large areas of the sky and has led to the establishment of a new photographic sky map in two colours (blue and red). This project, sponsored by the (American) National Geographic Society and carried out by the Mount Wilson and Palomar Observatories with the 48-in. Schmidt telescope on Palomar Mountain, should be completed in 1956. The N.G.S.-Palomar Sky Survey will constitute by far the most complete and homogeneous atlas of the sky ever attempted and successfully achieved in the short space of seven years; reaching down to the 20th (photographic) magnitude and covering three-quarters of the sky it should show over 500 million stars and supply enough material to keep astronomers busy for two generations. A pressing need to give full value to the work is its extension to the southern-most regions of the sky inaccessible from Palomar (south of de-clination $-30°$). Two instruments in the southern hemisphere might be suitable for this, the 32-in. 'A.D.H.' Schmidt telescope, erected in 1950 at the Boyden Station of the Harvard College Observatory, at Bloemfontein, South Africa, as a joint venture of the Armagh and Dunsink Observatories in Ireland and the American institution, and another of the same aperture in project for the Australian Commonwealth Observatory. A 26-in. Schmidt has been in operation since 1942 at the favourable latitude of the National Astrophysical Observatory of Mexico at Tonantzintla, where most of both hemispheres can be conveniently studied.

Instruments of smaller size, derived from the Schmidt telescope, such as the Maksutov telescope developed in the Soviet Union, and the Baker-Schmidt (or 'super-Schmidt') camera perfected in the United States, have led to striking results in the study of galactic nebulosities and meteors. The Schmidt camera principle has found many other applications in the field of spectrography where fast, short-focus optical systems are required for the efficient study of very faint stars or nebulae. Since its first application by O. Struve to the study of faint galactic nebulosities (VIII, 43) in the Yerkes and McDonald nebular spectrographs, the Schmidt camera has proved extremely useful both for the direct photography and spectrography of galactic and extra-galactic nebulae; a full battery of such cameras of various apertures and focal ratios is an essential part of the auxiliary equipment of the 200-in. telescope. Another type of wide-angle camera of short focus developed in recent years is the Henyey-Greenstein catadioptric system in which a reduced image of the celestial sphere formed by a spherical mirror is photographed by a small, fast camera; it was first used at the Yerkes observatory in 1951-2 for the detection of very large, faint galactic emission areas (cf. section 50).

In the field of auxiliary equipment used in conjunction with optical telescopes considerable advances have been made as a result of the application of the photoelectric cell and, more recently, of the photomultiplier. Experiments in astronomical photoelectric photometry were carried out as early as the first two decades of the century by Stebbins in the U.S. and by Guthnick in Germany (cf. VIII, 42) and were steadily followed up in later years. It was not until after the last war, however, that the impact of photoelectricity on astronomical techniques began to be fully appreciated. Among important technical improvements contributing to this progress were the perfection of the thermionic amplifier, first applied to stellar photometry by Whitford in 1932, and the development of the electron-multiplier by Zworykin, soon incorporated in the photoelectric cell and released for non-military application at the end of the war in the R.C.A. photomultipliers.

Since then photoelectric photometry has largely displaced photographic photometry in most fields where high accuracy is essential, such as the establishment of magnitude standards and their transfer from the North Polar Sequence to other areas and in particular to the southern sky (a problem of considerable difficulty which former methods had failed to solve satisfactorily), or the derivation of highly accurate luminosity and colour curves for eclipsing variables and cepheids (cf. section 49), or again the comparison of extended objects (nebulae, clusters) with stars. Phenomena of a delicacy placing them beyond the capabilities of previous photometric methods have become observable and amenable to rigorous analysis. Let us mention here only the discovery of polarization in the light of distant stars by Hall and Hiltner in 1947–8 (section 50), the detection of fine structure in the Hertzsprung-Russell diagram by O. Eggen at the Lick Observatory in 1949–50 (cf. section 49), the multicolour photometry of obscured stars by Stebbins and Whitford, at Mount Wilson, leading to more accurate determination, in 1949, of the absorption curve of the interstellar medium, and the refined spectral and luminosity classification of bright stars using accurate narrow-band photometry in several colours, by Johnson and Morgan and by Strömgren, at the Yerkes Observatory (section 49) since 1952.

Other striking applications of the photocell and multiplier in the field of auxiliary equipment have been the development by H. W. Babcock in 1948 of automatic guiding devices, now standard equipment at the Mount Wilson and Palomar Observatories, relieving the astronomer of the drudgery of eye and hand control of the telescope during long spectrographic exposures; and later his perfection, in 1952, in collaboration with his son H. D. Babcock, of the Solar Magnetograph', an amazing instrument which through the skilful use of polarization effects in spectral lines broadened by the Zeeman phenomenon displays continuously on a cathode-ray tube screen the changing pattern of weak magnetic fields on the Sun's surface. Automatic direct intensity microphotometers and isophotometers have been designed and tested in several places; these are instruments tracing directly from a photographic plate the distribution of light intensity in a spectrum (and not merely as before of photographic blackening requiring subsequent reduction to intensity by lengthy procedures) or mapping as contour lines (isophotes) the distribution of luminosity in an extended object such as solar flares, nebulae, etc. Such instruments will greatly increase the value of photographic observations by permitting a fuller exploitation of the information stored in the plates and films.

Another important and recent application of the photocell and servo-mechanisms, this time to astrometric problems, has been the adaptation of a conventional measuring machine to automatic operation and recording of results by the I.B.M. Corporation for the great catalogue work of the Yale University Observatory. This automatic measuring machine, completed in 1954, determines star positions in two coordinates on large photographic plates with an accuracy and a speed far exceeding that of a human operator and automatically records the results on punched cards for storage and future use. The slow business of star cataloguing and the subsequent derivation of proper motions should thus be greatly speeded up in the future and its accuracy improved. Star-counting machines have been planned or designed which work on similar principles, making it possible to count star images on photographic plates between preselected magnitude limits, while ordinary star plate photometers have also been improved both in accuracy and convenience of operation.

A new departure in technique of considerable significance has been the application to astronomical problems, in particular to orbit computing and the construction of tables of planetary motions, of high speed computing methods, using either punched card machines or electronic digital computers. A striking example was the complete recomputation, in 1950, by direct numerical integration of the motions of the five outer planets—Jupiter to Pluto—for 407 years, from 1653 to 2060, by G. M. Clemence of the U.S. Naval Observatory and D. Brouwer, of Yale University, in collaboration with W. J. Eckert of the International Business Machines Corporation. The work, which was carried out with the help of the I.B.M. Selective Sequence Electronic Calculator in New York, required 12 million arithmetical operations. It resulted in a considerable improvement of the representation of the more than 20,000 observations of the five planets accumulated by astronomers since the middle of the eighteenth century as compared with the previous tables computed over half a century ago, by G. W. Hill and S. Newcomb, through a lifetime of laborious calculations. It will also result in much better predictions of the future positions of the planets during the next century as published in the four great astronomical ephemerides: the *Nautical Almanac*,

The American Ephemeris, the *Connaissance des Temps* and the *Berliner Jahrbuch*. It is estimated that 'an operator with a desk machine, working 40 hours a week, might have done the job in about eighty years, if he had made no mistakes', while the 1,000 times faster electronic calculator repeated each calculation twice as a check against mistakes, and a third time for control in cases of disagreement. Since then even speedier machines have been developed (such as the I.B.M. Model 701, which is 25 times faster and 4 times smaller than the S.S.E.C.), which will make it possible to tackle computations of a length or complexity previously forbidding.

Still another application of electronics which may in the long run have an even more profound influence on the progress of astronomy, is the development of the 'electron telescope' first experimented with in 1936 by A. Lallemand, then at the Strasbourg Observatory, and further developed by him since the end of the war at the Paris Observatory. This is a piece of electronic image-intensifying apparatus whereby the optical image formed by a conventional telescope is projected, enlarged on a semi-transparent photocathode, the photoelectrons emitted being accelerated and focused on a photographic plate by the methods of electron optics, somewhat as in the electron microscope. The object of the operation is to increase the energy available for blackening the photographic emulsion which is of the very fine-grained type used in nuclear physics, the energy increase being obtained through acceleration of the electrons in a field of up to 30,000 volts. Experiments performed in 1952–3 at the Paris Observatory produced the first electronic photographs of stars and of Saturn, showing an overall effective speed increase of about 100 times as compared with direct photographs taken through the same telescope. Further experimentation will, however, be required before the method can be applied to routine astronomical observation and it is likely to require always rather elaborate facilities not usually found in observatories. Nevertheless, it holds great promise in fields where insufficient sensitivity of the photographic emulsion has hitherto been an obstacle—in fact, in most fields of stellar astronomy where lack of light has been a chronic ill against which astronomers have been battling ever since the introduction of photographic recording of the telescopic image.

In this battle another success was scored in 1953-4 with the perfecting by W. Baum, at the Palomar Observatory, of a photon-counting photometer. Although photon-counting techniques had been tried before, notably by Yates in Cambridge in 1948, their application to the photometry of bright stars is not very interesting since conventional recording of the amplified photoelectric current gives satisfactory and perhaps more convenient results; when applied to the photometry of very faint stars in conjunction with the 200-in. telescope, however, the benefit of the photon-counting method becomes much more significant. Where direct current recording fails at about the 20th or 21st magnitude, the integration of individual electrical pulses generated by the extraction of individual electrons from the photocathode of a multiplier makes it possible not only to detect but to measure with any desired accuracy—given sufficient time—stars of the 23rd magnitude, i.e. down to the threshold of photographic detection with the longest practicable exposure at the focus of the Hale telescope. In fact it is stated that the photon-counting photometer would potentially permit the measurements of 25th magnitude stars, if such stars could be located from photographs. The luminosity of the night sky prevents, however, the very long exposures which would be necessary for the photographic detection of such stars.

It is not possible to review here all applications of photoelectric phenomena and electronic techniques to astronomy developed in recent years. Some mention should, however, be made of the lead sulphide photoconductive cell which has opened the exploration of the infra-red spectrum of the Sun down to 3 microns, and of the planets beyond 2 microns; some attempts have already been made to apply it to stellar photometry but its low sensitivity has so far prevented its general application, except to the brightest stars. Recent advances in amplification techniques may, however, modify the situation in the near future. The direct photoelectric recording of the energy distribution in stellar spectra, at least for bright stars, has been successfully tried out in several observatories as an advantageous substitute for standard photographic methods for the spectrophotometric determination of stellar (colour) temperatures and spectral types, and new applications appear almost every year, slowly displacing the photographic emulsion from its formerly undisputed position as 'the retina of the astronomer'. Nevertheless, the unique aptitude of the photographic plate to record permanently and accurately the position and brightness of immense numbers of stars for convenient future study remains unchallenged and there is no sign of its replacement by electronic devices in the foreseeable future. On the contrary, the development of such auxiliary apparatus as the electron telescope is bound to enhance its value.

Astronomy has also benefited from instrumental developments in allied fields; the exploration of the upper atmosphere by rockets has brought back a rich harvest of new information on the far ultraviolet spectrum of the Sun, normally blocked off by the absorption in the ozone layer (cf. section 48); experiments have been made with artificial meteors fired from shaped charges, and increasing awareness of the potentialities for astronomical studies of the establishment of an artificial satellite has led to much useful preliminary discussion between various interested groups which may bear their fruits when actual launching becomes practicable.[1] Reference is made in this connection to the extensive literature on astronautics or space travel published during the last few years.

Mention should also be made of the development by H. Lyons and his collaborators, at the American National Bureau of Standards, of the so-called 'atomic clock' which may, conceivably, transfer in future the burden of the time service from astronomers to physicists—although this is not likely to happen in our day. Nevertheless the establishment of a primary, reproducible stable laboratory standard of time would be of value to test the uniformity of the newly defined astronomical time (ephemeris time) (see section 47). In a related field, at the indefinite boundary between astronomy and physics, the new accuracy reached since the war in electro-optical and radio-electrical methods of measuring the velocity of light has finally settled the problem of the value of this

[1] Programmes for the launching of artificial satellites during the International Geophysical Year 1957-58 are under way in the U.S.A. and the U.S.S.R.

fundamental constant ($c=299,792$ km./sec. *in vacuo*), while the repetition of the Michelson–Morley experiment—foundation of the relativity theory—with an accuracy increased by the use of standing radio-waves in a resonant geometrical cavity, has been successfully carried out by G. Essen at the National Standards Laboratory in Teddington (1955).

Dwarfing, however, all these developments, the fantastic progress of the new science of radio-astronomy, since the end of the war, revealed an entirely unforeseen aspect of the Universe which we are still very far from understanding, but which has already resulted in revolutionary advances in almost all branches of astronomy and astrophysics. It constitutes such a new departure in the field of both astronomical techniques and astro-physical theory that it deserves separate and rather detailed treatment which will be reserved, for convenience, until the end of this chapter.

47. Astrometry and celestial mechanics

It would be wrong to think that the astonishing progress in celestial physics during the last fifty years has reduced the importance of the classical fields, such as the accurate measurement of the positions of heavenly bodies—sometimes called astrometry —or that the great mathematicians and astronomers of the nineteenth century have so perfectly solved the problems of celestial mechanics that nothing remains to be done. On the contrary, classical astronomy has greatly benefited from the new technical advances of recent years and the solution of problems which had baffled generations of astronomers or defied their methods of computing has become possible with an accuracy far surpassing all they could have hoped for. The increased accuracy has in turn brought to light new departures from theory leading to an ever deeper knowledge of the motions of the Earth, planets and stars.

It has been recalled (VII, 41) how, about 1925, E. W. Brown had been led to ascribe the perpetual vagaries of the Moon's motion to irregularities of the rotation of the Earth, so that the time used in recording observations, the Greenwich mean solar time—or Universal Time—is not a uniformly, smoothly flowing time as required by the equations of celestial mechanics. This was quickly confirmed in 1926 by Sir Harold Spencer Jones through a study of the motions of the Sun and planets which display similar irregularities in proportion to their respective angular velocities on their orbits (the so-called 'mean motion'). In 1939 he produced what is substantially a definitive treatment of the problem and paved the way for the post-war decision to discard the mean solar time as our fundamental time unit.

An international conference which met in Paris in 1950 proposed that in future the tables of lunar, solar and planetary motions be expressed in a new unit of time, called Ephemeris Time, defined by the length of the sidereal year 1900. This Ephemeris (or quasi-uniform) Time is related to the current Universal Time through a formula taking into account both the secular slowing down of the rotation of the Earth by tidal action and the erratic changes as detected by the apparent irregularities in the motion of the Moon. The recommendation was confirmed in 1952 at the meeting of the International Astronomical Union in Rome and will come into force on 1 January 1960.

It should be understood that this will bring no change in ordinary time-keeping where Universal Time, i.e. Greenwich mean solar time, will remain in use. Its accuracy, of the order of one part in 10 million, is quite good enough for most practical applications. But when the utmost accuracy is required, say of the order of one part in 1,000 million, as in radio-electricity for the control of standards of frequency, or when dealing with events spreading over a long period of time, say several centuries or millennia, as in celestial mechanics, Ephemeris Time will give a much better approximation to the ideally uniform time scale.

While the secular accelerations of the Sun and Moon determined from old eclipses and occultations dating back to the earliest times (cf. III, 21) give a determination of the tidal slowing down of the Earth's rotation with sufficient accuracy to allow an extrapolation many years in advance, the irregularities cannot be predicted with any accuracy. In fact as was demonstrated by D. Brouwer and J. van Woerkom, of Yale University, in 1952, these irregularities are apparently perfectly random, i.e. do not seem to follow any other law than the laws of chance; consequently, they must be determined afresh each year through comparison of the observed and computed positions of the Moon obtained from Brown's theory, which is believed to be so perfect as to leave no room for any error other than the apparent one due to faulty time-keeping when Universal Time is used. A graph of the discordance between Mean Solar Time and Ephemeris Time for the last two hundred years is shown in Fig. 26.

The difference between Ephemeris Time—which for all practical purposes is a measure of the 'true' or ideally perfect and uniform time—and Greenwich Mean Solar Time may be expressed

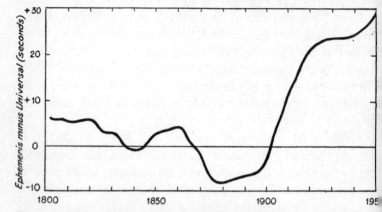

FIG. 26. IRREGULARITY OF THE ROTATION OF THE EARTH

Difference between Ephemeris (uniform) Time and Universal (Mean Solar) Time since 1800, after D. Brouwer (1952).

in another way. Since the rotation of the Earth is not perfectly uniform, the mean sun does not return to the Greenwich meridian after 24 'uniform' hours but only after 24 (irregular) hours of mean solar time. After 24 'uniform' (or Ephemeris) hours it is transiting at some other meridian, slightly different from the standard Greenwich meridian. In this way another zero meridian may be defined at which the mean sun will transit indefinitely and exactly at noon and which, for convenience, may be so selected as to coincide more or less with the Greenwich meridian over the last two or three hundred years. At the moment the Ephemeris zero meridian is about 8 minutes East of Greenwich, but there is no way of predicting exactly where it will be in fifty or a hundred years.[1]

The adoption of Ephemeris Time is only one of the many devices tending to permit the prediction of planetary motions with ever-increasing accuracy. Another has been the exact recomputation of the motions of the outer planets through numerical step-by-step integration by means of the I.B.M. Selective Sequence Electronic Calculator as described in section 46. Coupled with the corrections for the irregularities in the rotation of the Earth it permits the prediction of the positions of the planets with negligible error for perhaps the next hundred years.

The magnitude of this work, published in 1951, may be appreciated when it is realized that it involved a set of simultaneous non-linear differential equations of the thirtieth order which was solved numerically with an accuracy of fourteen decimals. Approximately 25,000 observations of the four planets, Jupiter, Saturn, Uranus and Neptune, extending from about 1780 to 1940, were used in the discussion and the computed positions are given at 40-day intervals from 1653 to 2060. The numerical work involved was described as follows by the Superintendent of the U.S. Naval Observatory:

'The direct numerical approach to the problem has long been known but has been impractical in the past because of the magnitude of the numerical work. This volume of three hundred pages contains approximately one and a half million figures, yet these constitute less than one per cent of those produced and temporarily stored in the calculator in the course of the integration. Over five million multiplications and divisions and seven million additions and subtractions of large numbers were performed by the machine. It should also be pointed out that the nature of the problem is such that a single error could render the entire calculation useless.'

More recently the power of electronic computing was brought to bear on the lunar problem, the headache of so many mathematicians over the last 300 years (cf. III, 21; VII, 41). Under the

[1] An account of 'Ephemeris Time' was given by D. H. Sadler in the 'Occasional Notes' of the R. Ast. Soc., No. 17, 1954.

direction of W. J. Eckert, of the Watson Scientific Computing Laboratory at Columbia University, the Moon's positions were computed directly from Brown's theory for a trial lunation of 1948. The 1,650 terms of Brown's equations were stored in the memory of the machine and evaluated (and rigorously checked) in a mere 7 minutes for each required date. When the positions so computed directly from the basic theory were compared with those derived through Brown's tables, an unsuspected error was detected in the latter which was traced to a term having been included twice in their construction. The electronic calculator will, in future, free astronomy from such human mistakes.

It was, in fact, decided that the positions of the Moon computed for the U.S. and British Nautical Almanacs should henceforth be obtained entirely by electronic computing; a beginning was made with the twenty years 1952–1971 which involved 15,000 positions requiring 25 million multiplications. A comparison of these perfectly accurate theoretical positions with the positions observed each year will give a direct measure of the irregularity of the terrestrial clock and the correction required to convert Mean Solar Time to Ephemeris Time. The work was carried out at the Watson Laboratory in 1954.

For full advantage to be taken of the increased accuracy in the theory, the accuracy of the observational techniques must be correspondingly increased. The position of the Moon is obtained by reference to the stars and usually through the timing of occultations. From the instant at which a star—or better several stars—is hidden by the Moon's limb the position of the centre of the disc of the Moon with respect to the celestial coordinates may be derived and then compared with its predicted position. The irregularities of the limb, due to the variable skyline of mountains and valleys brought into view by the constantly changing libration, introduce an uncertainty on the true radius of the Moon at any particular point where an occultation takes place and thus set a limit to the accuracy with which the position of the Moon may be deduced from such an observation.

To overcome this difficulty detailed maps of the lunar profile at all possible librations were produced at the Paris Observatory by

Th. Weimer using plates taken many years ago with the great coudé refractor (cf. VII, 39). His atlas of 71 approximate contours of the eastern limb of the Moon was published in 1952. A more detailed mapping based on plates taken since 1932 with the 26-in. refractor of the Yale Southern Station, then at Johannesburg, has been in progress at the U.S. Naval Observatory, Washington, since 1949. An automatic scanning machine designed by C. B. Watts and A. N. Adams, draws directly on a greatly enlarged scale the profile of the bright limb of the Moon. When the 600 or 700 odd photographs to be used in this project have been scanned and reduced, it will be possible to know the reduction to the centre of the Moon for any occultation taking place at any point of the limb and any libration with an accuracy of the order of a few hundredths of a second of arc.

At the same time experiments in the timing of occultations by photoelectric methods have been carried out, in particular by H. E. Butler at the Dunsink Observatory, Dublin, D. S. Evans and others at the Cape and Radcliffe Observatories, and by the U.S. Army Map Service for geodetical applications. Although fraught with special difficulties on account of seeing fluctuations and still limited to fairly bright stars observed at the dark edge of the Moon, the photoelectric method gives, when applicable, an accuracy ($\pm 0^{S}01$) far in excess of that possible by the old visual method with or without chronograph recording ($\pm 0^{S}1$).

Another method of measuring with greater accuracy the position of the Moon with respect to a star field has been developed since 1952 by W. Markowitz of the U.S. Naval Observatory, Washington. In his instrument the image of the Moon is received in the centre of the field of a photo-visual camera through a dark absorbing glass plate reducing the light of the Moon while the stars are recorded through a light yellow filter on the photographic plate. During the short time-exposure required to record a number of reference stars with satisfactory density, the motion of the Moon with respect to the stars is accurately compensated by progressively tilting the plane parallel glass plate at a suitable rate governed by a motor so as to keep the Moon's image still during the exposure. The glass plate is exactly parallel to the photographic plate at mid-exposure so that the position of the Moon is accurately obtained for this time which is recorded automatically by an electric contact.

In this way the position of the Moon can be compared with many reference stars at any time without waiting for occultations, and limb profile difficulties are avoided since some sharp details close to the centre of the disc may be directly referred to the stars. The positional accuracy is very high, about $\pm 0''.1$ per plate.

The second half of this century should thus witness new and considerable progress in man's incessant efforts to keep track of our satellite with ever-increasing accuracy.

In the relentless quest for greater accuracy in tracking the Moon and planets all factors must be taken into account. The time used in our reckoning, the methods of making the observations, the theories with which they are compared have all been subject to great improvements, but there is still another factor which has lately come under critical review: the system of celestial coordinates to which the Moon is referred, or more exactly the systems of coordinates used in the standard fundamental catalogues of stellar positions. Here again we meet a subject as old as astronomy and which, after 2,000 years, is no less alive today than it was at the time of Hipparchus. Not only is improved accuracy needed for star positions used as a reference background for motions in the solar system, but it is also required for the investigation of large-scale motions in the stellar system. The quest for increased accuracy was marked during the pre-war years by the publication in 1910 of Boss's *Preliminary General Catalogue* (P.G.C.) followed in 1937 by the *General Catalogue* (G.C.) which includes the positions and proper motions of 33,342 stars derived from a general rediscussion of all earlier fundamental catalogues.

Another important catalogue of star positions is the FK_3 or 3rd Fundamental Katalog of the *Berliner Jahrbuch*, the German National Ephemeris, adopted, since 1940, as the international standard. It includes only 1,535 stars but is of greater accuracy than the G.C.

As more independent new determinations of greater accuracy became available, small discordances between these catalogues and systematic errors affecting them were brought to light, indicating the need for a new re-evaluation of the fundamental system of celestial coordinates. The publication in 1952, by H. R. Morgan of the U.S. Naval Observatory, of a new catalogue of 5,268 standard stars based on seventy different recent catalogues reduced to the so-called N30 system marked a considerable advance both in accuracy and homogeneity.

One of the main difficulties in such work is to ensure that the system of stellar coordinates is homogeneous over the whole sky, i.e. that no small regional distortions of the coordinates system exist. Because of the seasonal irregularities of the rotation of the Earth and since stars situated in widely different parts of the sky are observed at different epochs of the year, this is a most difficult problem. In fact it was established by H. M. Smith and R. H. Tucker, at Greenwich in 1953, that a substantial part of the seasonal irregularities first attributed to changes in the rotation of the Earth are due to slight inconsistencies in the right ascensions formerly used for the clock-stars; with the improved coordinates now at hand the seasonal effect is appreciably reduced. A scheme to overcome this difficulty and ensure the homogeneity of the stellar coordinates over the whole sky first proposed by B. V. Numerov of Pulkovo in 1932 and D. Brouwer, of Yale, in 1935, is now being applied in cooperation by several observatories. It involves the observation of a number of minor planets which, in the course of their motion, sweep a broad band of the celestial sphere, carrying with them, as it were, the coordinates system of one region into another. The orbits can be computed now with such accuracy and speed by electronic calculators that any discrepancy between observed and computed places (the latter adjusted to represent accurately the observations over a certain arc of the orbit) must be attributed to errors in the star places to which the planet is referred. In this way a thoroughly homogeneous system of coordinates will be set up over the whole sphere. The initial Yale programme carried out between the years 1935 and 1948 involved 6,000 photographs of sixteen minor planets; but further work is planned or in progress.

Another difficulty which has been realized ever since the discovery of galactic rotation (VIII, 43) is the slow rotation of the system of the stars with respect to the ideal (inertial) reference system postulated by celestial mechanics. To overcome it a plan was conceived by W. H. Wright at the Lick Observatory to determine star positions and motions with respect to the background of faint and distant extragalactic nebulae, which, for all practical purposes, may be regarded as providing a system of reference perfectly fixed and, especially, free of any motion of rotation. This plan has been vigorously pursued since the war by C. D. Shane and C. A. Wirtanen with a specially designed astrograph of 20 in. aperture. Between 1947 and 1954 the whole sky north of $-23°$ was photographed in 1,246 2-hour exposures on 17×17 in. plates (each covering 6° square) which record 18th magnitude nebulae; in order to provide for easy comparison with the much brighter stars measured with meridian instruments a coarse grating is placed in front of the objective and produces diffraction images of these stars. On such plates positions can be measured with an accuracy of about $0''.1$ for stars and $0''.15$ for nebulae so that when the series is repeated, about 1985, as planned, proper motions of high accuracy (perhaps $\pm 0''.004$ per year) should be derived, directly referred to the essentially fixed background of distant galaxies. As Bradley two centuries ago, astronomers of today are working for the benefit of future generations. The 20-in. plates have, however, another important and immediate application to the study of the distribution of faint nebulae which will be discussed later (section 51).

A similar project started in 1939 is in progress in the U.S.S.R. (Pulkovo, Moscow, Kiev, Taschkent) where some preliminary absolute stellar motions directly referred to nearby external galaxies photographed at various times since the beginning of the century with the *Carte du Ciel* astrographs, have already been published. A vast programme of revision and improvement of fundamental catalogues of star positions is also in progress in Germany and the U.S.S.R. involving the extension of the FK_3 system to large numbers of fainter stars listed in the successive catalogues of the Astronomische Gesellschaft AGK1, AGK2 (1930), etc. On the other hand, the mass production of photographic positions is carried out at the Yale Observatory and in the southern hemisphere at the Cape Observatory. So that within the next few decades positions of high absolute accuracy, perhaps 0".1, will become available for well over a quarter of a million stars brighter than the 9th magnitude. This will afford, in turn, the basis for the reduction of the immense material provided by the *International Astrographic Catalogue* (*Carte du Ciel*). The introduction of automatic measuring machines (section 46) and electronic or punched-card computing will greatly speed up the execution of such enormous programmes.

Together with the problem of improving the system of angular coordinates on the celestial sphere that of determining with greater accuracy the fundamental unit of cosmic distances, the astronomical unit (cf. III, 17; VI, 33; VII, 41), has made notable progress since the war. In 1950 the German astronomer E. Rabe, now in the United States, published a new determination of the solar parallax which is incomparably more accurate than all earlier ones, being based on the mass of the Earth (or rather the Sun relative to the Earth) as deduced from the perturbations exerted by our planet on the motion of Eros between 1926 and 1945. His value, viz. 8".7984 ±0".0004 is actually very close to the mean of all earlier determinations and marks a considerable advance in the long history of human effort to obtain an ever more precise value for the solar distance which it gives as 92,900,000 miles, with a probable error of only 4,500 miles (about one Earth radius).

Stellar distances have also continued to accumulate despite a notable slackening of effort in the field of trigonometric parallax work. The latest general catalogue of stellar parallaxes published in 1952 by Louise F. Jenkins of Yale lists 5822 stars, an increase of 50 per cent over the 1935 Catalogue. Unless, however, new methods capable of producing more quickly parallaxes of greater accuracy are soon found it may be that this fundamental field will not be able to satisfy the requirements of present-day astronomy. Nevertheless, a number of observatories are still very active in it and some improvement in accuracy has been achieved, in particular through the work of P. van de Kamp and his collaborators, at the Sproul Observatory, Pennsylvania. The difficulty is that despite the relatively high accuracy of modern trigonometric parallaxes, say $\pm 0''.01$, the parallaxes of most stars are so small (the largest that of Proxima Centauri is $0''.75$ and only 160 exceeding $0''.1$ are known) that even for stars a few tens of parsecs away, the relative uncertainty constitutes a considerable fraction of the distance and, accordingly, absolute magnitudes are poorly known. This is a grave difficulty in studies which would require accurate knowledge of absolute luminosities of stars (cf. section 50) and is specially serious in the case of some very important types such as the cepheids and the cluster variables, the Novae or the O and B supergiants, none of which is close enough to have a parallax measurable with any accuracy. For such stars recourse must be had to other less accurate, indirect methods of determination of distances in which serious errors are easily present and may remain undetected for a long time, thus vitiating fundamentally the results of our probe of the depths of the universe (cf. section 51).

This brief and necessarily sketchy account will be sufficient to show that the field of classical positional astronomy, although the oldest, is more than ever active and has lost nothing of its fundamental importance for the progress of the other newer branches.

48. Solar system physics

The vast field of the physics of the solar system has greatly expanded since the war, in particular through the introduction of the new methods of radio-astronomy which will be reviewed in section 51. Here only the post-war developments of the more classical astrophysical studies will be briefly discussed.

The study of the Sun has benefited from the war-time V-2 rocket and its application to high-altitude experimentation, which is being pursued mainly at the White Sands Proving Grounds, New Mexico. There the far ultra-violet solar spectrum was photographed for the first time on 10 October 1946 during the flight of an instrument-carrying rocket which reached an altitude in excess of 50 miles (80 km.), well above the absorbing screen of the ozone layer. In the new spectral region, down to about 2,100 A., where the limit is set by absorption by oxygen, thousands of new lines were recorded including the two strongest lines of the whole solar spectrum (the resonance doublet of Mg II at 2,796 and 2,802 A.) which exceed even the H and K lines of Ca II. The greater strength of these lines is due to the greater abundance of magnesium in the Sun as compared with calcium. Many more lines are due to iron, both neutral Fe I and ionized Fe II.

Subsequent flights reaching to higher altitudes have brought back evidence of radiations of still shorter wavelengths. A rocket fired on 29 September 1949 carrying photon counter tubes sensitive to the far ultra-violet and soft X-rays reached 150 km.; it detected ultra-violet radiation in the band 1,750–2,150 A. above 10 km., in the band 1,425–1,700 A. above 100 km., in the band 1,150–1,350 A. above 70 km. and soft X-rays down to 7 A. above 85 km. The intensity of such radiations is quite small but their existence is of importance for the theory of the solar chromosphere and corona. More recently 'Aerobee' rockets flying above 80 km. have also procured photon counter evidence and even direct photographs of the very important Lyman L-alpha line of hydrogen in emission at 1,216 A. This line originates from a transition of the hydrogen atom to its ground state, while the visible Balmer line H-alpha corresponds to a transition to the first excited level above the ground state.

While this extension of the solar spectrum to far ultra-violet wavelengths was obtained through high-altitude rocket flights, ground-level physicists have achieved no less important progress in mapping the far infra-red spectrum of the Sun. This has resulted mostly from the introduction of the lead sulphide photoconductive cell which is sensitive up to 3 microns and the lead selenide cell which goes to 4 microns; still further in the infra-red and up to 10 microns the thermopile may be used with some recently devised means of amplifying its weak current. A large-scale atlas of the solar spectrum from the near ultra-violet to the near infra-red, in the form of intensity tracings based on photographs taken at Mount Wilson, had been published during the war by the Dutch astronomers at Utrecht, under Minnaert; an extension into the infra-red reaching to 2·5 microns from lead sulphide cell tracings was published in 1950 by the McMath-Hulbert Observatory, while tracings obtained since 1950 at the high-altitude station of the Jungfraujoch in Switzerland by the Belgian astrophysicist Migeotte reach to 10 microns. The high altitude by reducing the strength of the telluric lines, especially of water-vapour, makes it easier to detect solar lines where absorption by our atmosphere is a serious obstacle near sea-level. An interesting by-product of such studies was the detection of small traces of methane, CH_4, and carbon monoxide, CO, in the terrestrial atmosphere even far from industrial areas.

The continuing work of classification of lines among the several thousand still unattributed to known elements in the normal Fraunhofer spectrum has led to the detection of the rare element Technetium 43 identified by Mrs. C. E. Moore-Sitterly of the U.S. Bureau of Standards in 1951; shortly afterwards the same element was identified in stars of the rare S spectral type by P. W. Merrill at Mount Wilson. The presence of other rare elements like Indium and Osmium has also been announced by Babcock, Moore and Coffeen, while the forbidden lines of neutral oxygen [O I] at 6,300 and 6,364 A., which are so prominent in the terrestrial airglow at night and in the aurora, were identified with very faint lines in the normal solar spectrum independently by I. S. Bowen in the U.S.A. and by J. Cabannes and J. Dufay in France during 1948.

The continuous spectrum of the Sun, especially in the infra-red, was investigated both in France by D. Chalonge and his collaborators at the Astrophysical Institute, Paris, and in the U.S. by A. K. Pierce and others at the McMath-Hulbert Observatory, Michigan. These studies have led to better determinations of the absorption curve of the hydrogen negative ion (cf. VIII, 42) and the suspicion that another source of continuous absorption may be present.

The improved knowledge of the ultra-violet and infra-red extensions of the solar energy curve has inspired several attempts to ameliorate the accepted value of the solar constant, fixed at 1·90 cal./cm.^{2}/min. by C. G. Abbot of the Astrophysical Observatory of the Smithsonian Institution (a value again confirmed in 1947). As a result of considerable discussion in 1948 and 1949 involving many astronomers, it seems that the round value 2·0 cal./cm.^{2}/min. may be provisionally adopted as the most probable estimate of the solar constant at the top of the terrestrial atmosphere (and, or course, at the mean distance of the Sun, i.e. 1·00 astronomical unit). It is, however, acknowledged that this fundamental quantity is still in doubt to an extent of perhaps 2 or 3 per cent and that after more than a century since its first determinations (VI, 33) and half a century of concentrated work by the Smithsonian Institution observers, further more careful investigation will be required before a final value may be safely accepted.

Much discussion has been also devoted to the question of possible variations of the solar constant, but the difficulty of the measurements, of their standardization and correction for atmospheric absorption has so far prevented definite conclusions from being reached. Careful photoelectric photometry of the Moon, planets and satellites may provide indirectly the solution of this problem so important for all terrestrial phenomena, including life, which depend on solar radiation as their primordial source of power.

It should be mentioned here that since the war renewed interest has been shown in several countries (France, India, the United States, Australia, etc.) in the direct utilization of solar energy captured by huge mirror systems. In a power-hungry world this untapped source is bound to attract more and more attention and may ultimately provide an inexhaustible energy supply in many tropical and subtropical areas. The engineering difficulties are, however, considerable on account of the high degree of dilution of the radiation as it reaches the Earth.[1]

Considerable attention has been devoted since the war to the problem of the general magnetic field of the Sun (VII, 38). In 1945 a German astronomer, G. Thiessen, of Hamburg, announced that he had been able to repeat Hale's observation and had obtained evidence for a general field of some 50 gauss. At the Mount Wilson Observatory, on the other hand, where Hale's work in this field has been continued by H. D. Babcock, observations carried out from 1939 to 1947 had given no clear result and Thiessen himself was not able in 1947 to reobserve the delicate effects by which the field was revealed. In 1950 he announced that

[1] The first 'World Symposium on Applied Solar Energy' was held in 1955 at the Stanford Research Institute, in Phoenix, Arizona.

he had observed the field again but with an intensity reduced to only 1·5 gauss, while another German astronomer H. von Kluber, working at the Cambridge Observatory, found a field of practically zero strength. Further observations by von Kluber have confirmed this nil result. Hence, after some suggestion that the field may be variable the balance of the evidence from these exceedingly delicate observations is that the general magnetic field of the Sun, if any, must be very much weaker than Hale had thought and probably less than 1 gauss (polar field).

Meanwhile, however, the solar magnetometer developed by H. D. and H. W. Babcock at the Hale Solar Observatory in Pasadena (section 46) has provided fresh and conclusive evidence of the presence on the surface of the Sun of rapidly changing *localized* fields of several gauss. Such fields may have misled earlier investigators by creating a spurious general field pattern. The solar magnetograph in regular use since 1952 is rapidly accumulating much new information on the physical processes connected with sunspots and other solar phenomena. It has already been proved that magnetic fields persist several days after the disappearance of sunspots and often are present and persist for some time in areas where no sunspot is visible; in such cases, however, perturbed structures may frequently be detected on spectroheliograms. Interesting connections with the sources of solar radio noise may also be expected, but the general laws of these weak solar fields will not be in evidence before a complete solar cycle, or better two (cf. VII, 38), have been followed with the new instrument.

In 1954 the Babcocks reported the presence of a dipolar 'general' field of 1 or 2 gauss which is, however, limited to high solar latitudes. This field is variable. In lower latitudes the fields are bipolar and associated with spots or flocculi and follow Hale's polarity laws. Weak unipolar regions lasting several weeks or months have been discovered which are followed by terrestrial magnetic storms about 3 days after crossing the central meridian.

Another new instrument which was developed in recent years by Lyot and his collaborators at Meudon Observatory is the so-called 'monochromatic heliograph', which makes it possible to photograph the Sun in monochromatic light of the H-alpha radia-

PLATE XVII. THE MOUNT STROMLO OBSERVATORY NEAR CANBERRA, AUSTRALIA

Now a branch of the Australian National University after a decade of post-war expansion, it was originally established in 1925 as the Commonwealth Solar Observatory. The main domes house a 74-inch reflector [*left centre*], one of the two largest in the Southern Hemisphere, a 50-inch reflector [*right centre*], being the modernized 'Great Melbourne Telescope' built in 1868, and a 30-inch reflector [*right*]. The southern stations of the American universities of Yale and Columbia, equipped with the 26-inch Yale long-focus refractor [*large shiny dome at left*], and of the Swedish University of Uppsala, equipped with a 20-inch Schmidt camera [*small dark dome in centre*], are also located on Mount Stromlo (lat. 35°, alt. 2,500 ft.). Most of the pine trees which covered the slopes of Mount Stromlo were burned in a forest fire in 1952.

(*Courtesy Australian News and Information Bureau*)

PLATE XVIII. THE 26-INCH LONG-FOCUS PHOTO-GRAPHIC REFRACTOR OF THE YALE-COLUMBIA SOUTHERN STATION, MOUNT STROMLO

This instrument (focal length 35 feet), originally located at Johannesburg, South Africa, from 1926 to 1952, has been used mainly for the accurate determination of stellar parallaxes by photography according to the principles laid down by F. Schlesinger nearly half a century ago. From over 66,000 photographs taken with this instrument, the parallaxes of several thousand stars were derived at the Yale University Observatory.

(Courtesy Australian News and Information Bureau)

tion of hydrogen. It uses, instead of a prism or grating mono-chromator like the spectroheliograph, a polarizing interference filter of the type invented by Lyot before the war and already in regular use at the Pic du Midi and other high-altitude observatories for the photography of the corona in the monochromatic light of one of its emission lines. The advantage of the monochromatic heliograph over the standard spectroheliograph is that it gives a complete image of the Sun's disc in a short exposure, while the slit mechanism of the spectroheliograph builds up the image through a slow scanning in several minutes. In conjunction with a cinemato-graphic camera the monochromatic heliograph will permit a con-tinuous motion picture study of chromospheric phenomena with increasing continuity and resolution. Several solar observatories around the world are now being equipped with this new instru-ment.

Photospheric phenomena have been the subject of a great many investigations, many of a routine character. Among some rather new results may be mentioned measurements by C. Macris at Meudon of high-resolution photographs of the granulation ('rice grains') taken at the Pic du Midi by Lyot and his collaborators. Diameters were found to range from 0".7 to 2".1 and no appreciable lateral motions of the granules, suggested by some earlier observers, were detected. Such apparent motions were probably due to blur-ring by air currents in the tube of the telescope violently heated up by the intense radiation. A new type of investigation was a spectroscopic study of the granules by R. S. Richardson of Mount Wilson and M. Schwarzschild of Princeton. They found an average turbulent velocity of the order of one-third of a kilometre per second and some indication that very turbulent and bright sub-granules of the order of 100 or 200 miles in diameter should be present. Atmospheric turbulence prevents the recording at ground level, with existing equipment, of such elements subtending only 0".2 to 0".4, but they might be photographed from balloons carrying specially designed telescopes to high altitudes.

During 1947 solar activity reached an extremely high maximum, the highest since 1779 (cf. Fig. 18) and outstanding solar pheno-mena were observed. The largest single sunspot ever photographed was recorded in March and April 1947 and the largest group in February 1946, while the highest altitude ever observed for a prominence was reached by an eruptive phenomenon which, on 4 June 1946, rose to over 1 million miles above the Sun's surface.

The outer layers of the Sun, chromosphere and corona, have also been the subject of many new investigations, and work in this field has not yet developed the routine character of many photospheric studies.

Chromospheric flares have been the subject of prolonged research and detailed investigations by M. A. Ellison at Edinburgh, M. Waldmeier in Zurich, F. Link and his collaborators in Czechoslovakia, and many others. Their connection with magnetic and other disturbances has been further demonstrated and analysed. A singular effect first noticed in February 1942 and again in July 1946 is that of some very intense flares on the observed intensity of cosmic radiation. The most outstanding instance occurred on 19 November 1949 when an exceptionally intense flare was accompanied by an increase of nearly 200 per cent in the overall intensity of cosmic radiation received at sea-level and by an increase of 500 per cent in the intensity of the neutron component. Such observations are as significant for our understanding of solar phenomena as for tracing the origin of cosmic rays though for the moment their explanation is still uncertain.

The international organization for the continuous patrol of flares and chromospheric phenomena (VII, 38) attained a new peak of efficiency in post-war years when for the first time since its inception in 1934 it achieved, on 6 and 7 September 1949, its ideal of uninterrupted observation of the Sun for a period of 48 hours.

Strange prominence phenomena, for example, sudden occasional disappearances, were observed at the Meudon, Mount Wilson and McMath-Hulbert Observatories. The causes and mechanism of this sudden vanishing of large prominences are still very mysterious. Sometimes they reform gradually in the same places and may afterwards remain quiet for long periods.

The fine structure of the chromosphere (*solar spicules*) as seen at the edge of the Sun's disc, first observed visually many years ago by Secchi, was photographed at the Climax high-altitude station of the Harvard College Observatory.

New instruments for the observation of the corona in full day-light were developed by B. Lyot at Meudon. One is the polarizing interference filter perfected during the war; another a highly sensi-tive photoelectric polarimeter which, in 1948, detected the green line of the corona even under the indifferent conditions prevailing at Meudon, while daylight observation of the corona had pre-viously been restricted to high-altitude stations where the sky is pure and unwanted particle scattering very low. Regular observa-tions with the new instrument at Meudon, between 1950 and 1952, showed good agreement with simultaneous coronagraph observa-tions at the Pic du Midi.

Besides the Pic du Midi, continuous observation of the corona is carried out in Switzerland by W. Waldmeier at Arosa, and in the U.S.A. by W. O. Roberts at Climax, Colorado. Since 1950 a new and larger coronal station of the Harvard College Observatory has been erected on Sacramento Peak, New Mexico, at an altitude of 10,000 ft. Other coronal high-altitude observatories have been in existence or are being organized in the Bavarian Alps, in the Caucasus, in Japan and in other suitable places. The importance of a close study of the solar corona has become apparent in recent years, especially as a result of the radio investigations which will be discussed in section 52.

Beyond the indefinite limits of the outer corona, the zodiacal light, long considered more as a celestial curiosity than a subject of scientific investigation, has since the war received a good deal of attention and great progress has been made towards its physical interpretation. An important advance was the introduction of photoelectric techniques to measure the distribution of the faint glow over the celestial sphere; after some early determinations by C. T. Elvey and F. E. Roach at the McDonald Observatory in 1934-5, long series of fairly continuous photoelectric measurements of the zodiacal light were obtained between 1945 and 1949 by Huruhata in Japan, and more recently in 1952-3 by the German astronomers A. Behr and H. Siedentopf, working under the favour-able sky of the high-altitude station of the Jungfraujoch, Switzerland.

Polarization measurements in France and Japan and spectro-photometric determinations in the U.S.S.R. have also provided a good basis for the post-war theories of the zodiacal light developed mainly by F. L. Whipple in the U.S.A. (1940), Van de Hulst in Holland (1947) and more recently by H. Elsaesser in Germany (1954). Whipple suggested that the light-scattering particles making up the zodiacal light are the residues of disintegrated comets, while Van de Hulst introduced the important conception of a connection with the solar corona or rather one component of it, the so-called F-corona (the non-polarized component). It appears that the zodiacal cloud includes both small particles ranging from perhaps 1 micron to 1 millimetre and free electrons which diffract and scatter light. It forms a circular ring around the Sun within which is located the Earth's orbit (this is shown by the faint 'zodiacal band' joining the evening and morning cones of the zodiacal light). A delicate mechanism involving radiation pressure from the Sun, capture by the major planets, in particular Jupiter, disintegration and evaporation of comets approaching the Sun, collision between solid bodies, such as meteorites and minor planets, seems to be at work in this inner region of the solar system to produce and maintain the zodiacal light. More work will, however, be required to solve all its problems, including such little-understood phenomena as the 'gegenschein' or anti-solar glow and the so-called 'false zodiacal light' announced by the Russian astronomer V. G. Fessenkov in 1950 and attributed by some of his compatriots to a gaseous appendage or 'tail' to the Earth. This phenomenon and its interpretation are, however, vigorously criticized by most Western and many Soviet astronomers.

In the related field of meteor and cometary astronomy tremendous progress has been achieved since the war, from both the experimental and theoretical points of view. Of outstanding importance have been the achievements of radio methods discussed in section 52, but the more classical photographic methods have also added considerably to our knowledge, mostly thanks to the efforts of F. L. Whipple and his collaborators at the Harvard Meteor Field Stations in the U.S.A., and of P. M. Millman and his co-workers in Canada. Interest in meteor studies was renewed after the war on account of their bearing on the problems of high-speed flight in the upper atmosphere; the Harvard Field Stations were equipped in 1951 with extreme wide-angle extra-fast cameras of the so-called 'Super-Schmidt' type designed by J. G. Baker. With these instruments a large number of doubly observed meteors have been made available for investigations on radiants, orbits and space velocities, upper air densities, temperatures, etc., which are of astronomical as well as geophysical and aeronautical interest. Similar stations have been operated in the U.S.S.R. by the Stalinabad Observatory, and others have been active in Japan, Czechoslovakia and Canada.

An important event in post-war meteor astronomy was the return on 10 October 1946 of the rich shower associated with comet Giacobini-Zinner, first observed in 1933. Many photographic observations were obtained, in particular by P. M. Millman in Canada, who recorded over 200 measurable trails on this occasion, which also saw the first large-scale application of the radio methods.

In Canada a unique collection of over 100 meteor spectra has been accumulated during the last twenty years by Millman; common metals such as iron, sodium, potassium, magnesium, manganese, chromium, aluminium both neutral and ionized, the presence of which had already been indicated by the chemical analysis of recovered larger meteorites, have been identified.

The hunt for meteorites of all dimensions from the tiny residues recovered in the atmospheric dust and visible only through a microscope, to the large blocks which at times bury themselves deep in the ground at the bottom of giant craters, has been pursued with renewed interest in recent years. As a new branch of science the subject has been dignified with the name *meteoritics*, and is being most actively studied in the U.S.A. and in the U.S.S.R. An outstanding fall of meteorites was observed on 12 February 1947 in a Far-Eastern province of the U.S.S.R. and investigated by V. G. Fessenkov. More than 100 craters ranging from a few feet to nearly 100 ft. in diameter were found, and over 37 tons of meteoritic debris recovered, one unit which proved to consist mainly of iron weighing close on 2 tons. Another fall, this time in the U.S.A., observed on 18 February 1948, was remarkable for the recovery of a stony meteorite weighing over a ton, the largest authenticated stony meteorite so far investigated.

Several large meteor craters resulting from unrecorded falls of giant meteorites in a distant past have been discovered since the war. In Western Australia the Wolf Creek Crater, discovered in 1948, is half a mile in diameter and judging by its 'fresh' appearance must be of comparatively recent origin. Another, found in 1950, in Northern Canada, in the Ungava district of the Quebec Province, has a diameter of nearly 2 miles and is by far the largest known, far exceeding the celebrated Meteor Crater of Arizona. The Ungava Crater levelled by the advancing and retreating of glaciers must be of rather ancient formation, dating from perhaps 10,000 years ago or more. Both of these craters which are in desert and almost inaccessible country were discovered on aerial photographs.

It should also be mentioned that meteoritic dust was identified in samples of the ocean bed and subsoil collected during a Swedish oceanographic expedition. The chemical and physical analysis of meteorites has provided further independent information on the solar system, their lead content giving clues as to its age and their helium content indications of the past intensity of cosmic radiation.

Thus meteoritics appears as an interesting meeting ground for several sciences and techniques and its implications are much more important than the relative insignificance of its subject, on the astronomical scale, might at first sight suggest.

No less important has been the progress achieved in the physical theory of comets in post-war years. In this field the one major contribution was made in 1950 by F. L. Whipple, whose theory accounts for a large number of known but previously unconnected facts; according to it the nuclei of comets consist of a conglomerate of frozen gases and meteoritic matter at a very low temperature when the comet is far away from the Sun. The analysis of cometary spectra (VII, 40) suggests that the chief frozen constituents of the conglomerate are water ice, carbon dioxide (dry ice), ammonia, methane and cyanogen. The evaporation of the substances near perihelion under the influence of the Sun's heat gives ise to the gases in the comet's gaseous head and tail. Furthermore, f the rotation of the nucleus is taken into account, it is possible to xplain quite simply the previously mysterious acceleration bserved in the motion of the Encke's comet in the nineteenth entury (V, 30) or the deceleration of other comets and also to ccount for other peculiarities such as disintegration which ccurred in the case of Biela's comet (VI, 35).

On the other hand, the origin of comets has been the subject of nvestigations by many astronomers. A hypothesis put forward by Oort in 1950 postulates the breaking up of a planet, part of it orming the ring of minor planets and the other the comets. According to it the solar system should be visualized as surrounded by a vast envelope or cloud of very distant cometary nuclei, with aphelia ranging up to 100,000 astronomical units, most of which emain invisible. The few exceptions are brought about by stellar perturbations which throw the nuclei on very elongated, nearly parabolic orbits bringing them into the solar neighbourhood where hey develop the usual cometary appendages according to the Whipple mechanism; some are captured by the major planets, particularly Jupiter and Saturn and become periodic comets until epeated passages close to the Sun exhaust them or break them into smaller fragments some of which may eventually reach the Earth and other planets as meteorites. Other theories are based on con-densation out of interstellar matter. There is still no general agree-ment on this difficult subject.

Meanwhile the observational physics of comets and the inter-pretation of their spectra have recorded important advances. Since he initial identifications of the early years of the war (VII, 40) considerable work has been devoted in several countries to the difficult problem of identifying further cometary radiations, the most important contributions in this field being made in Belguim by P. Swings and his collaborators at the Astrophysical Institute of Liège, and in France by Mme Herman at Meudon. Much additional work, assisted by elaborate laboratory experiments on he unfamiliar line and band spectra of common elements excited under unusual conditions, will be required before all the common adiations observed in cometary spectra can be finally explained.

In 1947 and 1948 two very bright comets were observed, visible mostly in the southern hemisphere, the brightest that had been seen for many years. A General Catalogue of 1,619 comets observed between 2315 B.C. and A.D. 1948 was published by F. Baldet, o Meudon Observatory, in 1950. It was supplemented in 1952 by a General Catalogue of Cometary Orbits compiled by F. Baldet and G. de Obaldia which includes 763 comets observed between −466 and 1952.

Considerable attention has also been devoted to minor planet not only for their astrometric applications, but also from a physica point of view because of their possible bearing on such problem as the origin of the solar system and collisions between celestia bodies.

Extensive programmes of observation have been in progres during the last few years at the Goethe Link Observatory of th University of Indiana and at the McDonald Observatory in Texas 10-in. wide-angle astrographs have been used to obtain thousand of photographs of hundreds of old and new minor planets, resultin in the 'recovery' of many lost minor planets, i.e. planets which ha once been found but which, for many years, could not be locate for want of an accurate orbit. This tedious but necessary work i also being carried out in several other observatories: Nice (France Turku (Finland), Johannesburg (South Africa), Heidelberg (Ger many), Uccle (Belgium), etc., and must go on indefinitely. Astro nomers have often wondered whether the very considerable effor time and money spent on keeping track of the constantly growin 'herd' of minor planets, now numbering over 1,600, are justifie by a corresponding importance in scientific results. Proposals hav been made to limit observation and computation to a few importar objects and to neglect the many 'useless' planets. The trouble that if all the 'useless' planets are not followed it is difficult or im possible to decide if an object is new or not and some new objec do prove to be important ones by reason of their peculiar orbits

An outstanding example discovered in 1949 by W. Baade wit the 48-in. Schmidt telescope at Mount Palomar is (1566) Icaru which at perihelion is less than 0·2 astronomical unit (20 millio miles) from the Sun and hence well within the orbit of Mercur

As it approaches this orbit closely it may help to improve our knowledge of the mass of Mercury which, in the absence of a satellite, is still imperfectly determined. Icarus also comes close to the Earth's orbit, within 4 million miles. Hundreds of minor planets are recorded on plates taken for the Lick and Palomar sky surveys, but only outstanding objects are followed for orbit determination.

The long-neglected subject of the physical study of the minor planets has been vigorously attacked since the war in particular by G. P. Kuiper and his collaborators at the Yerkes and McDonald Observatories. Light-curves in several colours were determined by photoelectric photometry for a number of bright asteroids and some information on their periods of rotation, irregular shapes, surface structure, etc., will be obtained from a searching analysis of such curves.

Studies of the major planets have also made steady progress since the war; only a few major advances may be noted.

In 1950, A. Dollfus at the Pic du Midi Observatory obtained polarization measurements of Mercury which seem to indicate, in contrast with theoretical expectations based on the kinetic theory of gases, that a very tenuous atmosphere may have been retained by this planet. The atmospheric pressure at ground level was estimated at about 1 mm. of mercury. The nature of the gas making up this tenuous atmosphere is unknown, but it must clearly be a dense heavy gas.

The infra-red spectra of Venus taken by Kuiper at the McDonald Observatory have established that the intensity of the absorption bands of carbon-dioxide gas changes from day to day, presumably on account of the changing level and variable opacity of the layer of clouds which obscures the surface. The nature of the clouds in the atmosphere of Venus is still a perplexing problem; in 1954 D. H. Menzel and F. L. Whipple suggested that they are simply aqueous clouds (droplets or ice crystals) as on the Earth, and that failure to detect water-vapour in spectroscopic tests is due to the low temperature in the upper atmosphere, above the cloud layer. The persistence of free carbon dioxide in the atmosphere could be explained if the surface of Venus were covered by an uninterrupted ocean. This hypothesis does not agree with the presence of a more or less permanent pattern of surface markings as recorded by many visual observers, due allowance being made for the changing configurations of the cloud cover.

Kuiper's search for a lunar atmosphere through spectroscopic tests at the McDonald Observatory and Lyot and Dollfus's effort through polarimetric tests at the Pic du Midi Observatory have failed to detect any trace of a gaseous envelope around our satellite. An upper limit of about one hundred millionth of the density of the terrestrial atmosphere is indicated for any residual lunar atmosphere.

Outstanding progress in the study of Mars has been achieved during and since the war, mostly through the work of French, American and Russian astronomers. The atmospheric pressure was determined through photometric and polarimetric methods; it amounts to 65 mm. of mercury at ground level, rather less than one-tenth its terrestrial value. The same pressure obtains in the stratosphere of the Earth about 11 miles up. The presence of a small amount of carbon dioxide in the atmosphere of Mars was established in 1947–8 by G. P. Kuiper through a spectrophotometric investigation of the infra-red spectrum of Mars with a lead sulphide cell. The amount present is about twice that in the terrestrial atmosphere.

The final identification of water ice as the material of the snowy polar caps was also obtained by Kuiper through infra-red spectrophotometry. But repeated spectroscopic tests by Adams and Dunham at Mount Wilson failed to detect water-vapour in the planet's atmosphere. No other gas has been detected either so that nitrogen, which evades spectroscopic detection in the observable part of the spectrum, appears as the most likely constituent of the Martian atmosphere.

Extensive polarimetric observations of Mars by A. Dollfus at the Pic du Midi have added considerable new information on the properties of its surface. He suggested in 1950 that the main constituent of the red-coloured deserts which cover most of the planet is limonite (hydrated ferrous oxide); in 1948, however, Kuiper had selected a brownish felsite (a silicate of aluminium and potassium) is the most promising identification, so that the exact mineralogical nature of the Martian surface is still in doubt.

The 'violet layer' which conceals the surface markings in violet light has been the subject of various investigations; it is not yet clear whether it is made up of fine crystals of ordinary ice (Schatzman, 1951; Kuiper, 1952), of dry ice (Hess, 1950) or of some other constituent. In 1954, E. C. Slipher pointed out that the periods of extensive clearing up of the layer which he had first observed in 1937 seem to occur always within a few days of opposition, i.e. when the Sun, the Earth and Mars are on a straight line. This mysterious phenomenon will continue to receive attention.

A new determination of the rotation period of Mars by J. Ashbrook, at Yale University, in 1953, gave a revised value of 24 h. 37 m. $22\overset{s}{.}6679 \pm 0\overset{s}{.}0026$ whose accuracy is far in excess of earlier determinations. This accuracy justifies the hope that in the not too distant future irregularities in the rotation period of Mars similar to those found in the rotation of the Earth (IX, 47) may become detectable and thus throw additional light on the origin of such irregularities.

In 1953 an International 'Mars Committee' was organized by the Lowell Observatory for a concerted attack during the favourable oppositions of 1954 and 1956.

As in the case of Venus, some of the absorption bands produced by gases in the atmosphere of Jupiter have been found to vary in intensity. Studies by S. L. Hess at the Lowell Observatory and by G. P. Kuiper at the McDonald Observatory indicate that while the absorption by methane CH_4 is nearly constant, that produced by ammonia NH_3 displays conspicuous variations, depending probably on the level of the clouds and perhaps on temperature changes modifying the liquid–vapour equilibrium.

A very delicate observation which resulted in important new information on the composition of the Jovian atmosphere was obtained on 20 November 1952 by W. A. Baum and A. D. Code at the Mount Wilson Observatory. The occultation of a star was observed and recorded photoelectrically during the time (about 10 seconds) it took to disappear gradually behind Jupiter's atmosphere. From the rate of fading of the star the mean molecular weight of the upper atmosphere of Jupiter was found to be about 3·3, indicating that hydrogen and helium must be its main constituents. This is an important result since these gases cannot be detected spectroscopically, although from the abundance of methane and ammonia it was clear that the bulk of Jupiter's atmosphere must be hydrogen.

A twelfth satellite, JXII, was discovered in 1951 by S. B Nicholson with the 100-in. telescope at Mount Wilson. As all those discovered by photography since 1900 (VII, 39) it is very faint and moves in a large eccentric orbit.

Infra-red spectra of Saturn's rings by Kuiper disclosed, in 1948, that they are probably covered with ice crystals at a very low temperature, about 70° K. This readily accounts for the high albedo of the rings.

In 1944 Kuiper had discovered the presence of absorption bands of methane in spectra of Saturn's largest satellite Titan, which is thus the first known and probably the only satellite endowed with an atmosphere; although largely unexpected this finding is not in contradiction with theory. It also agrees with the known constitution of Saturn's atmosphere.

Between 1946 and 1950 infra-red spectra of Uranus and Neptune obtained by Kuiper at the McDonald Observatory disclosed a new absorption band or line near 8,270 A. which could not be attributed to either NH_3 or CH_4. It was identified in 1951 by G. Herzberg as due to molecular hydrogen; he succeeded in reproducing this line in the laboratory by observing the spectrum of a source through a tube containing hydrogen at a pressure of 100 atmospheres and a temperature of 78° K., the path length being increased to 80 metres through multiple reflections on mirrors placed at the ends of the tube. It was estimated from these experiments that the partial pressure of hydrogen above the cloud layer in the atmosphere of Uranus is about 2 atmospheres.

A fifth satellite to Uranus, Miranda, and a second satellite to Neptune, Nereid, were discovered by Kuiper, the first in 1948, the second in 1949, both with the 82-in. reflector of the McDonald Observatory. Miranda is closer to the planet than the four classical satellites and hence similar in this respect to Jupiter's fifth satellite.

A search by Kuiper for atmospheric absorption bands on Pluto gave no indication of an atmosphere. But in 1950, when observing with the 200-in. reflector, he succeeded in detecting a measurable disc, the diameter of which appears to be less than 0″.23, corresponding to about half the Earth's diameter. This has raised an as yet unsolved problem regarding the mass of Pluto. With such a diameter and a density of the same order as that of the other planets its mass could hardly exceed one-tenth of the mass of the Earth, while, in fact, from the perturbations it produces in the motions of Neptune and Uranus its mass has been estimated at about nine-tenths of the mass of the Earth.

No further planet has been discovered beyond Pluto, but one or more have been predicted from the occurrence of 'families' of comets having aphelia clustered around certain values beyond the orbit of Pluto. In 1950 K. Schuette, in Germany, called attention to a group having a mean aphelion distance of 85 astronomical units, suggesting the possible presence of a transplutonian planet at a mean distance of about 77 astronomical units.

9. Stellar physics

The vast domain of the physics of the stars has also been marked by considerable developments since the war.

In the classical field of variable stars the most significant discovery has been the recognition of the 'flare stars', i.e. late-type dwarf stars which at irregular intervals flare up in a matter of seconds to a brightness two, three or more times their normal and then subside more or less exponentially. The first two were detected in 1939 and 1943 on parallax plates by Van Maanen at the Mount Wilson Observatory but remained as isolated oddities until after the war when several were discovered in rapid succession through photometric and spectroscopic observations at various observatories. The best known is the faint component of the double star L726–8 discovered by Luyten at the University of Minnesota; since its discovery as a flare star in 1948 it has flared on more than half a dozen occasions, the most remarkable instance was observed by V. Oskanjan at the Belgrade Observatory on 25 September 1952,

when the star brightened by more than five magnitudes (a hundred
fold increase) in less than 20 seconds! Several observers have kep
a patient visual watch for hours in the hope of witnessing furthe
flares of the star, now designated UV Ceti, and from the numbe
of flares so far observed it appears that the phenomenon, althougl
irregular, takes place once or twice a day on the average.

Irregular, flare-like variations have since been noted in an in
creasing number of stars, mostly faint red dwarfs, and appear to
be a quite general phenomenon of this category. Spectra taken
during flares show bright emission lines of hydrogen and ionize
calcium which are not normally present. According to G. E. Kron
of the Lick Observatory, the phenomenon is probably rathe
similar to the chromospheric flares observed on the Sun (VII, 38)
but owing to the small intrinsic luminosity of such stars change
considerably their total light output, while it hardly affects th
much greater total luminosity of the Sun.

Small distortions of the light-curves of eclipsing binaries observe
by G. E. Kron outside eclipses may be due to similar phenomen
or perhaps to large 'spots' more or less similar to the sunspots.

Some unusual variable stars have been discovered; a cluster-typ
cepheid variable (SX Phoenicis) of the 7th magnitude having th
shortest known period, only 80 minutes, was discovered in 195
by O. J. Eggen, of the Lick Observatory, while observing souther
stars at the Commonwealth Observatory on Mount Stroml
Australia. The shortest period previously known, that of C
Aquarii, was 106 minutes.

By contrast, the eclipsing variable having probably the longes
period on record was discovered in 1950 by D. O'Connell, then a
the Riverview College Observatory, near Sydney, New Sout
Wales. This 10th magnitude star in the constellation of Centauru
may have a period of 100 or perhaps 200 years, as only one dee
minimum was observed since the beginning of Harvard photo
graphic records dating back to 1884; it started more than a decad
ago and is still in progress, the total duration of the eclipse ma
well exceed two decades. The longest period of an eclipsing binar
previously known, that of the supergiant star S Doradus in th
Large Magellanic Cloud, is only forty years.

Of interest also was the brightening, after many years of quiescence, of the once famous nova-like star Eta Carinae (IV, 24), which was detected only in 1952 by the author although photographic records at the Riverview College Observatory established that the brightening of the star, by more than one magnitude, had taken place as far back as 1941 (Fig. 27). For more than ten years it had remained unnoticed, a striking illustration of the incompleteness of our patrol of the southern sky.

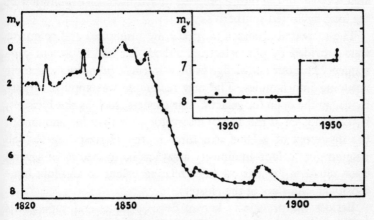

FIG. 27. LIGHT CURVE OF ETA CARINAE, 1822–1952

A plot of visual magnitude against time showing the great flare-up of the first half of the nineteenth century and, in the inset, the minor brightening of recent years.

The advent of the photomultiplier or electron multiplier photocell, first introduced in stellar photometry by G. E. Kron at the Lick Observatory shortly after the war, and widely used in a great many observatories ever since, has resulted in revolutionary progress in this classical field. Small undetected errors in the international standards of stellar luminosity and colour, set up during the first quarter of the century by photographic methods were brought to light and corrected; new fundamental standards have been evolved through the work of many investigators, especially J. Stebbins and A. E. Whitford at the Mount Wilson Observatory, G. E. Kron and O. J. Eggen at Lick Observatory, and H. L. Johnson and W. W. Morgan at the McDonald and

Yerkes Observatories. Others have attacked the difficult problem of transferring to the southern sky the northern standards, so as to ensure homogeneity of astronomical photometry over the whole sky, a problem which earlier visual and photographic methods had failed to solve satisfactorily. Meanwhile comprehensive photometric surveys of southern stars have been conducted, mostly at the Cape Observatory, by J. Stoy and his collaborators. Such long-term and rather tedious programmes, involving thousands of stars, are essential for the future progress of astronomical exploration in the long neglected southern sky.

The increased accuracy in measuring brightness and colour of stars provided by photoelectric methods has had important consequences for our knowledge of their intrinsic properties and their grouping into families. The new technique was applied in particular to the open (or galactic) star clusters, such as the Pleiades, by O. J. Eggen at the Lick Observatory. In 1950 he announced the discovery of a 'fine structure' in the Hertzsprung–Russell diagram (or 'colour–luminosity array' as he termed it) of several open clusters, i.e. narrow lines relating colour to absolute luminosity among stars of the clusters.[1]

Besides the previously known dwarfs, giants and supergiants (VIII, 42), the existence of sub-giants and sub-dwarfs had already been recognized in the 1930's by G. Strömberg at Mount Wilson and G. P. Kuiper at Yerkes. Eggen introduced further subfamilies such as blue-dwarfs, bright-dwarfs, etc., which he identified in several clusters and among nearby stars. These distinctions have, however, been criticized by various investigators who from observations of similar or greater accuracy failed to confirm all the details of the announced fine structure; the problem is not yet finally solved. This work, however, has had the great merit of focusing attention on the advantages of highly accurate photometry of star clusters and many important discoveries have followed bearing on the problem of stellar evolution.

---

[1] Since all stars in a cluster are practically at the same distance from the Earth, the difference $m - M$, apparent magnitutude m minus absolute magnitude M, is the same for all the cluster stars and is called the 'distance modulus'.

PLATE XIX. THE 74-INCH REFLECTOR OF THE MOUNT STROMLO OBSERVATORY

This instrument (focal length 30 feet), installed in 1955, is the latest in a series built during the last two decades by Grubb, Parsons & Co. of Newcastle-on-Tyne for observatories all round the world. It was on display in London during the Festival of Britain Exhibition of 1951. The Mount Stromlo reflector and another of the series at the Radcliffe Observatory, Pretoria, South Africa, are the largest in the Southern Hemisphere.

(Courtesy Australian News and Information Bureau)

PLATE XX. THE 36-FOOT RADIO-TELESCOPE OF THE
RADIOPHYSICS LABORATORY NEAR SYDNEY, AUSTRALIA

This instrument has been used in recent years for the study of the 21-cm. line emis
of interstellar neutral hydrogen in the Galaxy and in the Magellanic Clouds.

For instance, a comparison of colour-luminosity diagrams of several open clusters made by H. L. Johnson, at the Lowell Observatory, in 1954 has disclosed clear indications of a progressive evolution of the stars populating the upper part of the main sequence in these clusters. The evolution is in the sense from early-type dwarfs to late-type sub-giants and giants for stars brighter than the Sun; fainter stars do not seem to evolve perceptibly during the corresponding time. This is in at least qualitative agreement with recent views on stellar evolution.

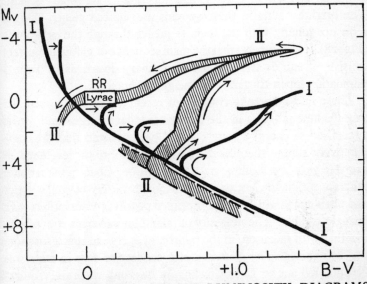

FIG. 28. SCHEMATIC COLOUR–LUMINOSITY DIAGRAMS OF OPEN CLUSTERS (I) AND GLOBULAR CLUSTERS (II), after H. L. JOHNSON and A. R. SANDAGE (1954), illustrating the main lines of evolution of stars of the two main population types.

Similar and perhaps more significant findings have resulted from a systematic study of the brighter stars in globular clusters. Such studies had already been made by photographic methods by Shapley nearly forty years ago, and were repeated by several other investigators in more recent years. The full significance of the results could not, however, be appreciated until the recognition in 1943 by W. Baade at Mount Wilson of the two main types of stellar population: Type I is typical of the solar neighbourhood and the spiral arms of galaxies, and Type II typical of globular clusters, elliptical galaxies and the nuclei of spirals (see sections 50, 51).

Systematic determinations of colour–luminosity diagrams of several globular clusters carried out since 1950 at the Mount Wilson and Palomar Observatories by A. R. Sandage, W. A. Baum and others have emphasized the fundamental difference between the H–R diagrams of the two main population types. In globular clusters the main sequence dwarfs brighter than the Sun are rare or absent and the blue giants and supergiants are totally absent. The brightest stars in these systems are the red giants, along a sequence joining with the main sequence through the sub-giants (Fig. 28). It also appears that the main sequence of globular clusters consists of sub-dwarfs and not of ordinary dwarfs as in Type I population (open clusters, solar neighbourhood).

These and other observations of recent years have paved the way for new progress in the theory of stellar interiors and of the generation of energy in stars. It has been realized that the comparatively simple theories of radiative equilibrium developed in pre-war years by Eddington, Jeans, Milne, Chandrasekhar and others were insufficient to account for the variety of stellar types and phenomena which the more refined post-war observations have brought to light. The necessity of taking into account convection, together with radiation, in the transfer of energy in stellar interiors was recognized. The existence of a convective core in stars was first pointed out by T. G. Cowling, in England, while the requirement for a convective zone of hydrogen at or below the level of the photosphere was indicated by L. Biermann, in Germany; considerable work was devoted to these convective regions during the last decade. The importance of rotation, turbulence and shockwaves, of pulsations, magnetism, chemical composition, and possibly accretion of interstellar matter, has been the subject of many searching analyses, but only slowly is agreement being reached between the multitude of different points of view and many difficulties are still confronting theorists in their efforts to bring order into the multiplicity of newly found properties of stars.

Among these new and often unexpected phenomena one of the

most significant, discovered in 1947 by H. W. Babcock at the Mount Wilson Observatory, is the presence of strong general magnetic fields, often exceeding 1,000 gauss, around certain fast rotating stars of spectral types O and B. The origin of these stellar magnetic fields was first ascribed to the stars' rapid rotation—a theory tentatively put forward by the British physicist P. M. S. Blackett; but laboratory experiments failed to detect any magnetization effect of rapidly rotating bodies. Further, the discovery by Babcock of 'magnetic variables', i.e. stars having periodically variable magnetic fields, soon proved that some other mechanism peculiar to those stars or to their atmospheres had to be found. Although we still ignore the origin of these fields it is clear that the discovery of such large-scale magnetic fields in stars is bound to influence strongly future theories of stellar atmospheres and interiors. Magneto-hydrodynamic phenomena had, in fact, already been investigated not only theoretically in the Sun and other stars, but also experimentally in liquids under laboratory conditions by H. Alfven and his collaborators in Sweden.

The number of known white dwarfs has steadily increased, in particular through the efforts of W. J. Luyten of the University of Minnesota who in the course of his extensive proper-motion surveys (IX, 50) discovered about one hundred of them. A statistical interpretation of the data indicates that some 3 per cent of all stars in our vicinity are white dwarfs (95 per cent are main sequence dwarfs and perhaps 2 per cent sub-dwarfs and sub-giants with an infinitesimal proportion of giants and supergiants). The early theories of the white dwarfs have been considerably developed and refined since the war through the work of E. Schatzman, in France, and F. Hoyle and L. Mestel in England. It appears that white dwarfs have no nuclear sources of atomic energy since they have exhausted their internal hydrogen; only a thin superficial pellicle radiates, accounting for the small energy output compared with the mass. It is generally believed that white dwarfs are the end product of the evolution of superluminous O and B stars after they have exhausted their supply of hydrogen and thrown off excess mass, perhaps through nova and supernova explosions.

Although the early test made by Adams in 1925 (VIII, 42)

had indicated in the spectrum of the Companion of Sirius a displacement of spectral lines in agreement with the predicted Einstein effect, a further test was carried out in recent years by D. M. Popper at Mount Wilson Observatory. The star selected was 40 Eridani B which is fainter but more clearly separated from its primary than Sirius B. From a long series of carefully measured spectrograms he concluded in 1954 that the shift of the spectral lines towards the red unaccounted for by space and orbital motions amounts to 21 ± 2 km./sec., in good agreement with the predicted gravity shift of 17 ± 3 km./sec.

Another delicate series of observations was carried out during the same period by D. S. Evans and his collaborators, at the Cape and Radcliffe Observatories in South Africa. The diameter of the supergiant star Antares was measured on several occasions from 1950 to 1953 when the star was occulted by the Moon; this method, first introduced by A. E. Whitford shortly before the war, rests on a measurement by photoelectric methods of the fading of the light of the star as it is progressively occulted by the limb of the Moon. For a point source a diffraction intensity pattern is observed, while for a star having an appreciable apparent diameter a somewhat slower and smooth extinction curve is recorded. From several observations a mean diameter of 0".04 was computed for Antares in very good agreement with the diameter measured thirty years ago at Mount Wilson with the Michelson interferometer (VIII, 42).

In the field of spectral classification the important studies of W. W. Morgan at the Yerkes Observatory, of D. Chalonge and his collaborators at the Astrophysical Institute in Paris and of B. Strömgren at the McDonald Observatory, should be mentioned. While Morgan refined the spectral classification, in particular by the introduction of luminosity classes, based on the simple visual examination of spectra, and published in 1943 a detailed spectral atlas of bright stars, Chalonge established the importance of the spectrophotometric investigation of the continuous spectrum for the quantitative determination of spectral types and luminosities, and in particular of the sudden decrease of intensity taking place in early type stars at the limit of the Balmer series of hydrogen in the near ultra-violet (the so-called 'Balmer jump'). A rather similar approach tried by Strömgren involves measurements by photoelectric photometry through interference filters isolating narrow spectral bands in and near the hydrogen line H-beta and in the Balmer continuum, the measured strength of which gives a good determination of the spectral type.

A related method introduced by W. Becker of Bonn, Germany, involves measurements of quasi-monochromatic magnitudes in three colours: yellow, blue and ultra-violet; a suitable combination of these makes it possible to determine rather accurately the spectral type and interstellar reddening separately, while the use of the ordinary blue-yellow colour index does not normally allow this separation. Becker's method has, in recent years, been widely applied to open clusters, mostly by photoelectric technique. This method has proved especially useful in galactic studies for the accurate determination of distances of open clusters.

50. Galactic studies

It is perhaps in the exploration of the Galaxy that the most out-standing advances have been made since the war, both as regards the analysis of interstellar space and the mapping of galactic structure.

The physics of the interstellar medium has been investigated at great length, in particular by Dutch astronomers (Oort, van de Hulst, ter Haar), who prefer to call the non-gaseous component 'smoke' rather than 'dust' because a 'dust' is produced by the breaking down of large chunks of solid matter while it appears from their studies that the minute solid grains which make up the dark, absorbing clouds are formed by condensation or coalescence of gaseous molecules and subsequent accretion. Van de Hulst, in particular, has shown that the temperature of the grains is of the order of 10° to 20° K. and that the atoms of the gas upon hitting a grain immediately freeze down, i.e. are captured and thus slowly build up the size of the grain. The atoms of hydrogen, helium and nitrogen must, however, later evaporate again out of the grains, except when included in chemical combination (as in the various ices). According to these views the average grain of interstellar matter may be regarded as a minute, impure icy particle rather than metallic or stony as was generally believed before the war when a fallacious analogy between interstellar matter and interplanetary meteorites was still in vogue. Nevertheless, it must be admitted that the last word has not yet been said on this subject and

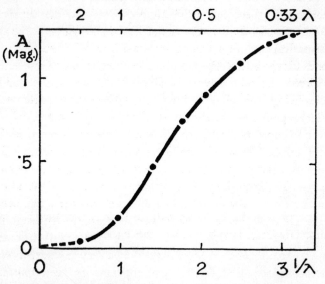

FIG. 29. ABSORPTION CURVE OF INTERSTELLAR MATTER, AFTER J. STEBBINS AND A. E. WHITFORD (1948)

The mean absorption in magnitudes per kiloparsec around the Sun is plotted as a function of $1/\lambda$ (λ in microns), assuming that neutral absorption is negligible. The greater absorption of the shorter wavelengths causes the interstellar reddening of starlight.

a direct test of the chemical composition of interstellar grains is still wanting.[1]

On the other hand, more information has been obtained on the average size of the particles through an extensive investigation by Stebbins and Whitford of the colours of distant early-type stars.

[1] A new point of view, first suggested in 1953 by P. Swings of Liége, Belgium, and developed in 1954 by R. Cayrel and E. Schatzman, in Paris, considers the possible presence of graphite particles in interstellar space.

Pre-war studies had shown that in the visible spectrum the absorption varies roughly in inverse proportion to the wavelength of light, hence the reddening of the light of distant stars. By extending the observations to the ultra-violet and infra-red Whitford established in 1949 that the actual law of interstellar reddening is more complicated and can be represented by an S-shaped curve (Fig. 29) in agreement with theoretical predictions of Oort and Van de Hulst (1946). A comparison between the observed absorption curve and the theoretical curves for various sizes and densities of the particles indicates for the interstellar grains a mean diameter of a few tenths of a micron. Actually there is a range of diameters, the smaller particles being more abundant than the large, as the formation of very large grains by accretion is effectively prevented by the opposite phenomenon of destruction in head-on collisions, so that a fairly stable statistical equilibrium has been reached. The equilibrium between gas and dust depends, however, on the density of the gas, and according to the theoretical studies of the Dutch astronomers a gas density of a few dozen atoms per cubic centimetre is most favourable to the formation of grains. Although the problem of the gas to dust ratio is still far from solved, it is now generally agreed that dust contributes only a very small fraction of interstellar matter, and that the two are more or less coexistent, the proportions depending on the local density of the gas and probably on other factors as well.

The structure of the interstellar medium has also figured prominently in post-war discussions. B. J. Bok of Harvard has called attention to the frequent occurrence of minute absorbing clouds or 'globules' roughly circular in shape, which are best seen when projected against the luminous background of bright nebulosities; these globules are quite small as compared with ordinary dark clouds, the largest having diameters of the order of 200,000 astronomical units—or 3 light-years—while the smallest observed have diameters of no more than a few thousand astronomical units and this is probably an observational limitation only. Some astronomers have held the view that these globules represent early stages in the condensation of a star out of interstellar matter, but it is not yet known whether interstellar gas is also concentrated in globules, and a concentration of grains alone would not provide enough material for a star.

More and more evidence of turbulent motions in interstellar gas and dust clouds has been obtained and investigated theoretically since the war; through a study of the irregularities of the absorption exerted by interstellar matter on distant objects, such as external galaxies, the Russian astronomer V. A. Ambartsumian has computed the mean absorption and average diameter of interstellar clouds and by comparison with the observed absorption the average number of such clouds intersected by each kiloparsec of the line of sight; in the galactic plane this number is of the order of ten. The density of such clouds varies over a considerable range from a few times the average up to several thousand times in the dense globules. This refers only to the grains which contribute a mean density of about 10^{-27} g./cm.^{3} to the mean density of matter in the galactic plane estimated by Kapteyn, and later Oort, at approximately $6 \cdot 10^{-24}$ g./cm.^{3}, or about one atom of hydrogen per cubic centimetre. More information on the variations of density of the gaseous component which consists mainly of hydrogen have resulted in recent years from the study of the radio emission of interstellar hydrogen (see section 52).

An outstanding discovery made in 1949 by W. A. Hiltner and J. S. Hall, then at the Yerkes Observatory, was that of the polarization of light of distant stars seen through clouds of interstellar matter. Many years ago polarization had been sought among bright stars, by photography, but none found and the subject was virtually abandoned. Although starlight must be almost perfectly non-polarized as it leaves the photosphere of a star, it may become polarized if on its way through space it suffers absorption effects which depend on the direction of the vibration. This is possible, as was soon pointed out by Van de Hulst and others, if the interstellar grains responsible for this absorption are not spherical and randomly distributed: elongated grains which show on the average a tendency to be oriented along a direction not coincident with the line of sight can produce slightly different absorption effects on vibrations of different orientations around the line of sight and thus introduce a small polarization. The amount or proportion of polarized light will, on the average, increase with the length of the light-path through the medium as was demonstrated by Hiltner and Hall through a correlation between polarization and colour excess. On the average polarization and colour excess are maximum in the galactic plane and the proportion of polarized light amounts to 2 per cent when the colour excess is 0·2 mag., corresponding to a total (photographic) absorption of about 1 mag.

Nevertheless, the correlation between colour excess, i.e. absorption, and polarization is often poor and the direction of the electric vector of the vibration, usually more or less parallel to the galactic plane, shows strong deviations in some regions. The general impression is that the polarization takes place in some discrete clouds where conditions favour a privileged orientation of the grains; if the stars are seen through one such large cloud they show a strong similarity in their planes of polarization and good correlation with colour excess; if several clouds are on the line of sight or if the clouds are small and independent the agreement of the polarization planes and the correlation with the colour excess are poor. This is not difficult to understand in view of the known turbulence of the interstellar medium.

It is more difficult to explain adequately why the grains should be elongated mostly in a given direction. Some theoretical astronomers such as T. Gold in Great Britain, suggested that the elongated grains are thrown into rotation through collisions with other grains and that the direction of the axes of rotation is imposed by the prevalent direction of flow of interstellar matter in a given region. Most other theoreticians, however, regard the polarization as direct evidence for the existence of weak magnetic fields in interstellar space, a suggestion first put forward in 1943 by Alfven, of Sweden, and later adopted by Fermi to provide an acceleration mechanism for cosmic-ray particles. According to the theory first proposed by L. Davis and J. L. Greenstein in 1951 the elongated ice grains can be oriented by a weak magnetic field even if they do not include ferromagnetic impurities, through the phenomenon known as paramagnetic relaxation involving an interaction between the field and the spin of the grains somewhat similar to the interaction between the gravitational field of the

Earth and a spinning top. To explain the observed polarization a field strength of 10^{-4} to 10^{-5} gauss would be required, while independent estimates of the magnetic field in the local spiral arm of the galaxy made by Chandrasekhar and Fermi in 1953 indicate a value of $6 \cdot 10^{-6}$ gauss. It is hardly necessary to add that in the present state of our knowledge of the physics of interstellar space only very rough estimates are possible.[1]

The spiral structure of the Galaxy at large distances is now being mapped by radio-astronomy (see section 52), but the first definite indication of spiral arms in the vicinity of the Sun was obtained by optical methods as the result of a most remarkable series of investigations by many astronomers. It has been known for some years that emission nebulosities in other galaxies are almost exclusively located in spiral arms, and this was particularly well shown through systematic studies of the Andromeda nebula by Baade at Mount Wilson, during and shortly after the war (see section 51). Further, the development during the last decade of selective interference filters isolating the H-alpha line of hydrogen has made it possible to detect much more easily very weak emission regions surrounding very hot, early-type supergiant stars which excite the fluorescence of the gas; the theory of this phenomenon was developed in 1940 by B. Strömgren, of Copenhagen, who computed the radius of the sphere surrounding a hot star where hydrogen is ionized (the so-called 'H II region' by contrast with the non-ionized or H I interstellar medium). Finally, more accurate estimates of the distances of early-type stars and hence of the associated nebulosities have become possible through the refinement of spectral classification methods introduced by W. W. Morgan and his associates at the Yerkes Observatory.

A systematic search for galactic H II regions, i.e. emission nebulosities, undertaken by W. W. Morgan, H. Sharpless and D. Osterbrock, resulted in 1952 in a map of the location of the nearest H II regions which, for the first time, clearly revealed their

---

[1] According to Cayrel and Schatzman (1954) thin graphite crystals in the interstellar smoke may be oriented by weak magnetic fields of the order of 10^{-5} gauss and the observed polarization explained even if only a small percentage of the grains are oriented.

string-like arrangement in what were obviously short sections of the nearest spiral arms of our system (Fig. 30). Subsequent work by several groups of astronomers in both hemispheres quickly confirmed and extended these results which were further supported

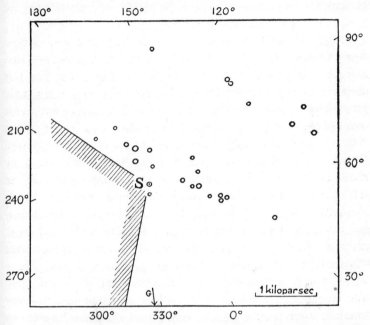

FIG. 30. SECTIONS OF SPIRAL ARMS OF GALAXY NEAR THE SUN (S) OUTLINED BY EMISSION NEBULOSITIES (H II REGIONS), AFTER W. W. MORGAN *ET AL.* (1951).

The direction of the centre G of the Galaxy is marked by the arrow; galactic longitudes are shown at the edge. The hatched sector (southern sky) was unobserved. Compare with Fig. 34.

by the independent evidence of the H I distribution obtained through radio-astronomy.

The solution of this problem of the spiral structure of our Galaxy which had baffled astronomers for nearly a century and which, only two decades ago, was considered as hopelessly complicated, is one of the outstanding successes of post-war astronomy. Although much remains to be done to clarify all details of galactic structure the most difficult step, the first, has been successfully taken and rapid progress is now being made.

A great deal of attention has also been devoted to the groups of OB stars associated or not with emission nebulae. In 1947 the Russian astronomer V. A. Ambartsumian predicted on theoretical grounds that such groups or 'associations' would prove to be of recent formation and in a state of expansion. In the first place, superluminous stars are very rare and must have a very short lifetime on the cosmic scale (say, no more than a few tens of millions of years); further, such groups have small total masses and are, in consequence, dynamically unstable against the disruptive forces of differential galactic rotation. The present existence of such 'associations' points, therefore, to a recent origin, dating back only a few million years, and a rapid dispersion. This prediction was brilliantly verified in 1952 by the Dutch astronomer W. Blaauw, of Leiden, when he proved through an analysis of proper motions that the rate of expansion of the stellar association around the star Zeta Persei is such that all its members must have been concentrated in a small volume of space only a million years ago when they were presumably formed nearly simultaneously. Blaauw and Morgan have since proved many other associations to be expanding and computed ages ranging from about 1 million years to upwards of 50 million years. One of the most remarkable examples is the association of which the great Orion nebula is the centre; Blaauw and Morgan noted in 1954 that two stars, AE Aurigae and Mu Colombae, at present located at great distances from the nebula are moving directly away from it at the considerable speed of 127 km./sec. and the backward tracing of their motion shows that some 2,600,000 years ago they must have been in its immediate vicinity.

Although the origin of these groups and the reason for their expansion are not yet known they seem to give some important evidence on star formation mechanisms. E. Öpik, of Armagh Observatory, has advanced the idea that the condensation of the stars and their outward motion result from a supernova explosion producing an expanding shell of gas and sweeping the surrounding interstellar medium.

These studies on expanding associations and motions in the Galaxy are intimately linked and are often possible only because astronomers of the last two centuries, ever since Bradley produced the first accurate star positions (III, 14), have patiently accumulated the basic observations which now enable us to derive proper motions of good accuracy for thousands of bright stars. This emphasizes the permanent and fundamental importance of positional astronomy and great efforts have been made during the last two or three decades to increase the accuracy of the measurements (see section 47) and to obtain more information on the motions of more distant stars which will enable astronomers of the future to push ever deeper this exploration of our home Galaxy. An outstanding contribution to these long-term projects is the systematic survey of W. J. Luyten completed in 1954 after twenty-five years of assiduous work. Luyten compared by means of a 'blink-microscope' pairs of plates taken at a suitable time interval and after examining close to 100 million stars found about 100,000 to have measurable proper motions.

Exploration of the Galaxy at great distances has also made much progress since the war in the direction of the galactic nucleus which is obscured in visible light by heavy, nearby dark clouds. The wavelength dependence of absorption by interstellar matter is, however, such that obscuration effects are greatly reduced in the infra-red. This property was taken advantage of by Stebbins and Whitford who, in 1947, succeeded in detecting the central bulge of our Galaxy through systematic scanning of a region in Sagittarius with an infra-red-sensitive photoelectric cell. The roughly elliptical isophotes of the radiation were clearly concentric with the previously known direction of the galactic centre. This result was quickly confirmed and more details added by the Russian astronomers Kaliniak, Krassovsky and Nikonov who, in 1949, obtained infra-red photographs of this region by means of an image converter or 'electron telescope'. Both the American and Russian observers worked at a wavelength of about 1 micron, but in 1952 a group of French astronomers under J. Dufay, at the Haute-Provence Observatory, succeeded in securing direct photographs at a wavelength of only 0·8 micron and were thus able to resolve the distant star cloud into individual stars.

The distance of the galactic nucleus has also been determined with increased accuracy partly thanks to a better knowledge of interstellar absorption but mostly through the work of W. Baade on cluster variables in the nucleus or in globular clusters imbedded in it; estimates of 9 kpc. by Baade in 1946 and 7·5 kpc. by Parenago in 1948 have since been superseded by a value of 8·2 kpc. obtained by Baade in 1953 and which is probably a very close approximation to the ultimate determination of this fundamental distance.

51. Extra-galactic studies

The 200-in. telescope on Palomar Mountain and its companion the 48-in. Schmidt camera were mainly intended to advance deeper into the extra-galactic field and to bring within our reach the solution of problems which had been raised by the first explorations conducted in the last three decades with the 100-in. telescope (VIII, 44) but whose solution exceeded the power of this instrument. During the first five years since they were first trained on the sky in 1948–9 the large telescopes on Mount Palomar have brought a wealth of new and often unexpected results which fully justifies the high hopes that Hale and his colleagues had placed in them.

In the course of the Sky Survey with the 48-in. Schmidt (IX, 46) several new nearby dwarf galaxies were discovered by A. G. Wilson and others, thus confirming pre-war suspicions that even the nearest parts of extra-galactic space are still far from having been exhaustively explored. From earlier surveys with the 18-in. Palomar Schmidt, F. Zwicky had already concluded that dwarf galaxies are far more abundant than was generally assumed, but the relative abundance of systems of various total absolute magnitudes, i.e. the 'luminosity function' of galaxies, is not yet known with any degree of accuracy. Nor is it known whether there is, in fact, a lower limit to the size and content of a stellar system: it may well be that very small systems of low luminosity remain undiscovered simply because they are too small and too faint to be recorded even at comparatively small distances. The difficulty here is quite similar to that which besets the detection of intrinsically faint stars.

F. Zwicky has been for many years the main exponent if not the

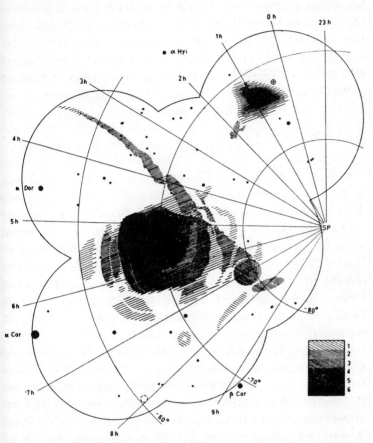

FIG. 31. KEY MAP TO THE SPIRAL STRUCTURE OF THE MAGELLANIC CLOUDS showing the newly detected extensions. Compare with Plate XIV.

sole of the existence of dispersed groups of stars, and clouds of gas and dust of sub-galactic size between galaxies, i.e. of inter-galactic matter in what was, before the war, regarded as nearly perfect vacuum. The debate is still not closed, but in recent years direct photographic evidence has accumulated to support the view that matter does exist in perceptible amounts, at least between neighbouring galaxies and in particular in pairs, groups and clusters of galaxies. In 1934 P. C. Keenan, then at the Yerkes Observatory, discovered a strange pair of galaxies apparently connected by a faint nebulous band forming a sort of bridge between them. This example remained isolated and little noticed until Zwicky recently discovered a large number of such systems on photographs taken with the 48-in. telescope. Such filaments offer a great variety of forms depending on the type (spiral or elliptical) of the galaxies involved and their lesser or greater proximity and, generally speaking, appear to be due to some sort of tidal phenomena connected with their gravitational interaction, but no detailed theory has yet been proposed.

A remarkable instance of such a filament was discovered in 1954 by the author working on Mount Stromlo, Australia; it appears as an outer spiral arm of the Large Magellanic Cloud stretching over a total length of some twenty degrees of the southern sky in a general direction away from the Milky Way and probably represents an effect of tidal interaction between our massive Galaxy and the much lighter Cloud. Some evidence was also obtained of a much weaker direct link between the Galaxy and the Large Cloud, while H. Shapley had already in 1940 discovered an asymmetrical extension of the Small Cloud in the direction of the Large Cloud. This prominence is much stronger when observed at radio wavelengths (section 52).

All these recent observations prove that the pre-war conceptions of galactic forms and dynamics were over-simplified and inadequate and that a much more involved situation actually prevails in which the simple laws of classical dynamics will have to be replaced by the more complicated phenomena of hydrodynamics and possibly magneto-hydrodynamics. This was acknowledged in 1949 when the first international congress of astronomers and hydrodynamicists met in Paris to study the large-scale problems of cosmical hydrodynamics. Similar reunions since held have greatly benefited both sciences.

Another important characteristic of the extra-galactic universe which has more and more clearly emerged since the war is the strong and universal tendency of galaxies towards clustering. The conception of a 'general field', i.e. of a random distribution of isolated galaxies or small groups, diversified only by a few isolated clusters, suggested by the early samplings surveys of the 1930's, has been gradually replaced by the notion that the majority, if not all galaxies belong to clusters of various sizes, i.e. that gravitation plays a dominant part in the distribution of galaxies, as it does of stars in individual galaxies. This conclusion was first reached from partial surveys of the distribution of galaxies conducted during the last two decades by H. Shapley and his collaborators, at Harvard, by F. Zwicky, at Palomar. It has been firmly established by an exhaustive investigation carried out during the last few years at the Lick Observatory by C. D. Shane and his collaborators who are engaged in a complete mapping of the distribution of galaxies brighter than the 18th magnitude photographed with the 20-in. astrograph in the course of the accumulation of plates needed for the great proper-motion project which will ultimately refer stellar motions to the fixed background of distant galaxies (cf. section 47).

Preliminary evidence that the nearer and brighter galaxies including our own are also organized in a vast super-system or 'Super-galaxy' was presented by the author in 1953 and confirmatory evidence was shortly afterwards obtained by radio-astronomy studies (section 52). It appears that the Galaxy, together with many thousands of others, belongs to a gigantic flattened cloud of galaxies, perhaps 50 million light-years across, whose centre is roughly marked by the well-known Virgo cluster of galaxies at a distance of about 20 million light-years (Fig. 32). It should be understood that such clusters or super-clusters are highly irregular and are perhaps more appropriately described as 'clouds' or 'cloud complexes'. Although the flattening of such clouds suggests a general rotation, much irregularity must prevail in the motions of individual member galaxies.

Such studies have been hampered by the lack of data on motions among bright galaxies, a list of about 100 radial velocities published by Humason in 1936 having been the only available for nearly two decades. M. L. Humason, at Mount Wilson and Palomar, and N. U. Mayall, at Lick, have, however, by patient and continuous work, accumulated measurements of radial velocities for over 800 bright galaxies which were finally published in 1956. Meanwhile accurate photoelectric magnitudes of these galaxies were measured by Stebbins and Whitford and by Pettit at Mount Wilson, while similar work was conducted by E. Holmberg in Sweden and J. Bigay in France. Magnitudes, colours and radial velocities are the fundamental elements needed for extragalactic exploration and as long as reliable values are not available theoretical constructions are at best precarious and their verification almost impossible.

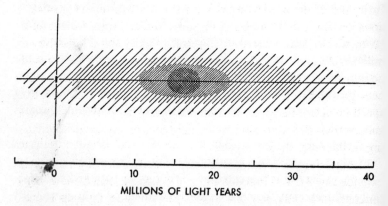

MILLIONS OF LIGHT YEARS

FIG. 32. SCHEMATIC CROSS SECTION of the local supergalaxy shows its strong flattening. The centre is towards Virgo. The central plane of our galaxy, shown at the left and in much exaggerated scale, is nearly at right angles to the central plane of the supergalaxy.

A much-debated phenomenon announced by Stebbins and Whitford in 1948 may be mentioned here. They had reasoned that the red-shift in the spectra of distant galaxies (VIII, 44) must produce an overall reddening of their light as compared with nearby ones. Since the measurement of colours by photoelectric methods is less time-consuming than the very long exposures needed to record the spectra of these distant galaxies, there was a possibility of mass-producing red-shift measurements through this photometric method. The result of their observations and its avoured interpretation was quite unexpected, for the reddening of distant elliptical galaxies which predominate in the clusters used or the establishment of the velocity–distance relation (VIII, .4) was found to be much in excess of what could be computed or the observed red-shift and the adopted spectral energy curve of the nearby elliptical M 32 (a dwarf companion of the Andromeda nebula) used as standard by Stebbins and Whitford.

This started off a great many speculations on possible intrinsic changes in the stellar population of elliptical systems in the course of time. Distant systems are observed as they were several hundred million years ago when the light we now receive from them left those systems; M. Schwarzschild, of Princeton, E. Schatzman, of Paris, and others tried to account for the effect through considerations on the rapid evolution of some stellar types which were postulated to have existed in elliptical galaxies some hundreds of millions of years ago and to have vanished since so that they would no longer exist in nearby systems. All these speculations have now been proved baseless, since new determinations by Whitford of the spectral energy distribution in several nearby and distant elliptical galaxies have failed to confirm the existence of any excess reddening in the more distant systems.[1]

Meanwhile the distance–velocity relation has been greatly extended by M. L. Humason using the 200-in. telescope in conjunction with extremely fast low-dispersion spectrographs reducing considerably the exposure time needed to record readable spectra of very faint and distant galaxies. Red-shifts in clusters beyond the reach of the 100-in. telescope were quickly obtained and in 1951 Humason published data on a number of clusters, the

[1] This means that either the standard energy curve used since 1948 for M 32 was erroneous or perhaps that M 32 is atypical. It is amusing to note that in a short paper published in 1948 in the *Comptes-Rendus* of the Paris Academy of Sciences the author had pointed out immediately after the initial announcement of Stebbins and Whitford that if elliptical galaxies have the solar-type energy curves suggested by their spectra (G0–G5), the colours of distant ellipticals are in agreement with expectations with no appreciable excess reddening. This publication was generally overlooked, but it must be conceded that plain physics is not nearly as glamorous as fancy cosmology . . .

most distant being a cluster in Hydra where red-shifts corresponding to velocities of 61,000 km./sec. were measured. This is one-fifth
of the velocity of light where second-order effects, vainly looked
for in pre-war years by Hubble and others using the Mount Wilson
data, might become perceptible and help decide between various

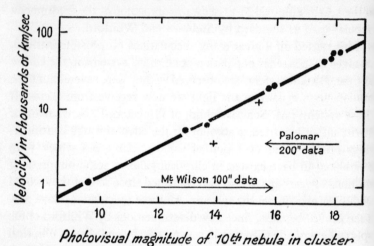

FIG. 33. THE VELOCITY–MAGNITUDE RELATION.
AFTER HUBBLE AND HUMASON (1953)

The velocity (on a logarithmic scale) of distant clusters is plotted
against the apparent photovisual magnitude of the 10th brightest nebula
in each cluster. The last four dots represent new data obtained with the
200-inch telescope. The largest velocity measured, 61,000 Km/sec.,
refers to a cluster in Hydra at an estimated distance of 800 million
light-years (revised scale).

cosmological models. However, according to a provisional discussion by Hubble in 1953, the linearity of the relation between apparent velocity and apparent photometric distance appears still to
hold up to the limit of the presently available data (Fig. 33).[1]

Nevertheless the complexity of the problem has become increasingly obvious as theoretical and practical difficulties have been

[1] In a general discussion of the extensive Lick–Mt. Wilson–Palomar
data, published in 1956, A. R. Sandage finds some evidence of slight departures from linearity for velocities in excess of 40,000 km./sec., but the
photometric data are not yet good enough for a final solution.

ore carefully discussed and the frailty of all pre-war work is now enerally acknowledged. One of the more far-reaching changes rought about by the application of the 200-in. telescope to extra-alactic studies has been the drastic revision of the scale of istances for the whole Universe beyond the boundaries of our own ialaxy. Extragalactic distances, it will be recalled, had been based nce the discovery of the period–luminosity relation among epheid variables on an early standardization of the zero-point of ie relation by Hertzsprung and Shapley (VIII, 42); it was lso assumed that nearby galactic cepheids followed the same –L relation as the cepheid variables in globular clusters and irther that the branches of the relation observed to operate mong cepheids in the Magellanic Clouds and other nearby alaxies could be directly compared with the relation observed in lobular clusters. In this way the apparent magnitude m of a epheid in an external galaxy gave by comparison with the absolute nagnitude M read off the calibration curve for the same period the pparent modulus $m-M$ of the system to which it belongs. Using istances of the Magellanic Clouds, the Andromeda spiral and ther galaxies determined in this way, the absolute magnitudes of ther objects such as novae, globular clusters, etc., observed in hese systems could be obtained. During the 1930's some dis-uieting discrepancies had already been noted between the absolute nagnitudes of these objects thus derived and the absolute magni-udes of the corresponding classes of objects obtained independently 1 our Galaxy, but the accuracy of the cepheid criterion had be-ome almost an article of faith among astronomers and most of hem preferred to follow the easy course of ignoring the discrepancy mounting to 1 or 2 magnitudes between extragalactic novae or lusters, and their galactic counterpart. K. Lundmark, of Lund, iweden, was almost the only astronomer to call attention to this liscrepancy in a series of papers published before and shortly after he war. In 1946, in particular, he showed that all criteria except he cepheids gave for the Andromeda nebula a distance about twice s large as that currently accepted.

An indication that something was wrong with the calibration of he P–L relation had indeed been obtained in 1945 by H. Mineur, in Paris, when he redetermined the zero-point of the relation from extensive new radial velocity data obtained by H. Joy at Mount Wilson, but he failed to see clearly the reason for and significance of his results. The final blow to the pre-war scale of extra-galactic distances was struck by W. Baade who announced in 1952 some results of a search for cluster-type variables in the Andromeda with the 200-in. telescope. The search was undertaken for the following reason: if the accepted distance of the Andromeda galaxy based on its long-period cepheids was correct then the fainter short-period cepheids, the so-called cluster-variables of periods less than one day observed in globular clusters, should have been within the reach of the 200-in. telescope. The thorough search conducted by Baade failed to detect these stars, hence the distance indicated by the long-period cepheids was wrong. If on the contrary the distance indicated by novae, globular clusters and other criteria was adopted the computed apparent magnitude of the cluster-variables in the Andromeda nebula was at or below the threshold of detection with the 200-in. so that the negative result was explained.

This conclusion was immediately confirmed by many other studies, in particular by observations of A. D. Thackeray and J. Wesselink who, with the 74-in. reflector at Pretoria, succeeded in detecting cluster-variables in some globular clusters associated with the Magellanic Clouds; these stars appeared at the 19th magnitude, while on the strength of the old distance modulus they had been previously sought in vain by the Harvard astronomers at the 17th magnitude. Globular clusters, novae, emission nebulae and other objects observed in the Magellanic Clouds fully confirmed the distance modulus of the Clouds to be about 1·5 mag greater than previously accepted and hence their distance double.

The reason for the error of the old calibration of the P–L relation was then quickly discovered: the long-period cepheids observed in our galactic neighbourhood belong to the stellar population of Type I typical of the spiral arms of the Galaxy and other similar systems (including the Clouds and the Andromeda nebula), and therefore do not follow the same P–L relation as the cluster variables typical of Type II systems such as the globular

lusters or the galactic nucleus. A thorough revision of the absolute
magnitudes of nearby galactic cepheids from their proper motions
published by A. Blaauw and H. R. Morgan in 1954 confirms that
the luminosity of these stars had previously been underestimated

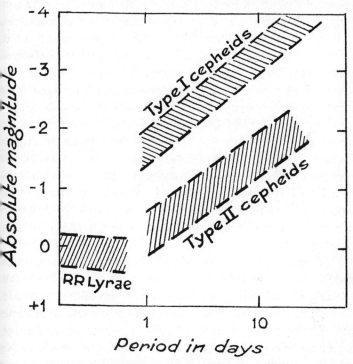

FIG. 34. THE REVISED PERIOD–LUMINOSITY RELA-
TIONS FOR CEPHEIDS (1953)

Classical (Type 1) cepheids observed in the Galaxy and external
systems follow a relation parallel to but 1·5 mag. brighter than the Type
II cepheids observed in globular clusters whose luminosities are determined by direct comparison with the short-period (RR Lyrae) cluster
variables. Compare with Fig. 22.

by a factor of nearly 4, i.e. that the distances derived from the old
P–L relation must be doubled.

It should be noted that since the distances of globular clusters
and of the galactic nucleus were based on cluster-variables no great

change of intra-galactic distances, and in particular of the dimen
sions of our Galaxy, is introduced by the revision, provided th
accepted median absolute magnitude of the cluster-variables
about 0·0, is correct (very recent estimates by American and
Russian astronomers place it at +0·2 or +0·5); but all extra
galactic distances based on the early erroneous calibration of th
classical cepheids must be nearly doubled. The question has, how
ever, not yet reached a final stage and further corrections may b
necessary when more distant objects are considered and the indica
tion is that a factor greater than 2 may be required to allow for
other errors in the old scale.

Nevertheless the drastic revision which the factor 2 involves has
been fully substantiated by a number of quite independent con
siderations. Thus not only certain theoretical difficulties in the
theory of cepheid pulsations have been removed by their increased
distances and consequent decreased densities, but the long-standing
mystery of the discrepancy between the age of the Earth as indi
cated by radioactivity and the age of the Universe as indicated by
the distance–velocity relation, often called Hubble's constant, is
now solved. In the old distance scale the velocity of expansion of
550 km./sec. per megaparsec led to an 'age' of no more than
1,800,000 years, about one-half only of the accepted age of the
Earth, 3,500,000 years (VIII, 45); this had given rise to ingenious
but unwarranted cosmological assumptions in order to stretch the
expansion time-scale sufficiently to include the radioactive time-
scale; with the new distance scale the velocity of expansion is
reduced to about 250 km./sec./Mpc. (perhaps less) and Hubble's
constant is now equal or greater than the age of the Earth, thus
dispensing with special assumptions in this respect. This agreement between the age of the Earth and of the Universe has in fact
been regarded as a strong argument in favour of such cosmologies
as the 'primeval atom' theory (VIII, 45) which envisage an
absolute and simultaneous beginning for all the visible universe in
some catastrophic event which took place only a few thousand
million years ago. The possibility that the agreement is only
fortuitous should, however, be kept in mind for it is obvious that
the last word has not yet been said on this question of the distance

cale, nor indeed on the more fundamental interpretation of the ed-shifts as evidence for an over-all expansion of the Universe.

Some astronomers, and foremost among them F. Zwicky, still ook for some flaw or some inconsistency in the observations and heir interpretation which will help avoid the unpalatable con-lusion that our universe started not very long ago in a big bang and is moving inexorably towards final dispersion into an inde-finitely expanding nothingness. But these efforts whether they eventually succeed or not belong rather to the future of astronomy han to an history of its past achievements.

52. Radio-astronomy

Despite the many striking advances achieved by optical astro-nomy since the war the single greatest development of the last decade has been the rise of radio-astronomy: the study of the heavens by means of cosmic radio-waves.

The possibility that the Sun might be a source of radio-waves had been discussed in the early years of radio, at the turn of the century, by some physicists in Britain and in France who con-ducted experiments in an effort to detect such waves. But the crude receivers of the time were much too insensitive for such experi-ments to succeed.

The first observation of radio-waves of extra-terrestrial origin came from a quite different and unexpected direction. In 1931–2 the American radio-engineer K. G. Jansky was investigating the 'atmospheric' sources of noise in short-wave radio receivers with a highly directive aerial pointed successively in different directions; he noticed that the noise was appreciably stronger when his aerials were pointing to certain particular regions of the celestial sphere closely corresponding to the path of the Milky Way. This 'cosmic noise' even passed through a sharp maximum of intensity when the aerial was directed towards the constellation of Sagittarius, the direction of the centre of the Galaxy.

These startling observations were soon repeated and extended by another American radio-engineer, G. Reber, who as early as 1936 set up the first 'radio-telescope' consisting of a large parabolic receiver, 30 ft. in aperture, and operating on a wavelength of about 2 metres. He was able to draw the first 'radio map' of the sky showing the contours of equal intensity of the cosmic noise; these radio-isophotes of the Milky Way were in general agreement with the optical isophotes. Even more surprising was the fact that despite the sensitivity of his apparatus Reber could not detect any radiation from the Sun.

There the matter rested until the end of the war, when the subject was taken up with great energy by several groups particularly in Great Britain and in Australia with the benefit of the considerable experience in radar techniques gained during the war.

It was actually during the war that the first radio signals from the Sun were detected by Army radar sets covering the coastline of Great Britain. On 26 February 1942 radar operators reported severe interference by abnormal signals the bearing of which for all stations placed the source in the direction of the Sun. The source of interference moved in step with the Sun during the day and disappeared at sunset. It reappeared the next day and the day after when the interference finally ceased. For security reasons this striking event was not made public at the time and was first announced only after the war, in 1946, by Sir Edward Appleton and J. S. Hey, of the Radar Research Establishment, Malvern. Since a large spot and associated flares had been crossing the central meridian of the Sun's disc at the time it was immediately realized that the source of such 'outbursts' of radiation as they came to be known was somehow associated with these outstanding optical disturbances.

Systematic observations were organized first in Britain and Australia, then in many other countries for the continuous watch and investigation of the radio-waves from the Sun. It was soon found that besides the great outbursts of energy, lasting for hours or days and associated with optical disturbances of the solar atmosphere, there are short-lived bursts lasting only a few seconds or minutes and a still weaker permanent emission, that of the 'disturbance-free' or 'quiet' Sun. The latter was first detected on 3 and 10 cm. with microwave radar receivers by Southworth in the

nited States in the later years of the war, although Reber also had
ally succeeded in detecting the solar radiation at a wavelength
1·9 metres. In both cases the intensity of the radiation detected
as far in excess of that expected for the thermal emission of the
otosphere at 6,000° K. The outbursts radiate mostly in the
etre wave-band, between 1 and 10 metres, while the ordinary
irsts show an emission spread out more evenly over the ultra-
ort radio-wave spectrum, increasing progressively with wave-
ngth from a few centimetres upwards; the radio spectrum of the
iet Sun, on the contrary, is most intense at the shorter wave-
ngths, below 1 cm., then decreases slowly as the wavelength of
ception is increased up to 1 metre and drops to a very low level at
eater wavelengths.

The amount of work on solar radio-waves since the war has been
ally enormous, because of the importance of solar phenomena for
vil and military radio-communications, but a rich harvest of
sults of astronomical interest has also been obtained. Only a few
itstanding developments can be noted here: one is the construc-
on in 1949 of a 'radio-spectroscope' by J. P. Wild and L. L.
cCready of the Radiophysics Laboratory, Sydney. With this
istrument which sweeps a broad band of frequencies every second
panoramic' receiver) they detected changes of frequency of the
nitted radiation during great outbursts and the occurrence of
armonics in this radiation. Such observations have been interpreted
giving evidence of the ejection by the Sun of fast particles with
elocities of the order of 1,000 km./sec.; these may be the same
hich, when striking the Earth, are responsible for magnetic
orms and aurorae. Radio observations have also indicated the
ection of ultra-fast particles moving at a velocity comparable with
at of light.

Another remarkable instrument is the 'radio interferometer'
eveloped in 1951 by W. Christiansen, also at Sydney. It consists
f an array of 32 parabolic mirrors constituting a sort of coarse
iffraction grating which gives a reception diagram formed by
arrow and widely spaced fringes. As the Sun crosses the field of
ie instrument each fringe scans the disc somewhat as the exit slit
f a spectroheliograph (VIII, 38) and localized sources of radio

emission can be pin-pointed with considerable accuracy. Th origin of enhanced radio emission in 'active' areas marked by spot bright hydrogen flocculi and other optical signs of disturbance i the solar atmosphere, has been established in detail with this instru ment.

Other important observations were made during eclipses whic afford a convenient means of studying the radio emission selected parts of the Sun's surface as the Moon moves in front it. All the mass of information gathered by these and other metho has been discussed by many theorists who have discovered sever mechanisms by which radio-waves originate in the solar atm sphere. The so-called 'plasma oscillations', for instance, in th ionized gas of the corona are an important source first suggested i 1946 by the Russian I. S. Shklovskii and in 1947 by D. F. Marty in Australia and discussed in recent years in great detail by man investigators. These are oscillations of large electrified gas clou which are likely to occur in the high-temperature, low-densit corona. Such mechanism may be responsible for the radio our bursts, but a great many details will have to be clarified before satisfactory theory of the complex phenomena disclosed by th study of solar radio-waves can be formulated.

While radar techniques have been instrumental in the quic progress of radio astronomy in general, the radio-telescopes use in the study of the Sun and cosmic noise play only a passive role collectors of electromagnetic energy much as an optical telescop acts as a 'light bucket'. There is, however, a branch of radi astronomy where the exact technique of radar is used, i.e. whe radio-waves are emitted through a directional aerial and th reflected signal, the 'echo', received back and detected: the obse vation of meteors. The first application of this method on a larg scale was carried out by a group led by A. C. B. Lovell, at th Jodrell Bank Experimental Station, near Manchester, during th great meteor display of 10 October 1946. This shower was th expected return of a fine display observed thirteen years earlie and known to be associated with a small comet of six and a ha years' period (Comet Giacobini-Zinner). Although observatio had been favoured by good weather in 1933, the Moon's presenc ıd the overcast sky over most of Europe greatly interfered in 946 with observation by orthodox methods. Radar methods, owever, could be used without difficulty, being unaffected by loon, clouds and even rain.

The advantage of the new method of observation became still iore obvious in 1947 when it enabled some very important meteor iowers to be observed in broad daylight; these showers until then ad been completely unknown to astronomers since their meteors re not visible at night. Some of the new meteor streams were eadily identified as associated with Halley's and Encke's comets.

Results of considerable interest for meteoric astronomy have ince been obtained by the Manchester group; they have suc-eeded, in particular, in solving a long-standing controversy egarding the origin of sporadic meteors. Visual observations had uggested that a fraction of the non-periodic meteors had velocities ı excess of the parabolic velocity, i.e. were visitors from outside he solar system. But visual observations of meteor velocities are xceedingly difficult and the results were uncertain. Thousands of neteor velocities measured at Jodrell Bank have definitely estab-ished that sporadic meteors, like shower meteors, follow elliptical rbits and are permanent members of the solar system. This is obviously of considerable importance for theories of the origin of neteors.[1]

Radar echoes from the Moon have been successfully received ince 1946 in several countries and theoretical studies have ndicated the possibility of obtaining echoes from the Sun and olanets. But the difficult experiment has not yet been attempted; t might conceivably be used to determine the Sun's distance and o probe the solar corona with radio beams. This, however, belongs o the future.

Notwithstanding the remarkable results achieved by radio nethods in the study of the Sun and meteors, it is in the vast field of galactic and extra-galactic studies that the most outstanding and ouzzling discoveries have been made by radio-astronomy.

[1] An excellent summary of techniques and results in 'Radio Astro-nomy' at Jodrell Bank was given by A. C. B. Lovell and his colleagues n the 'Occasional Notes' of the R. Ast. Soc., No. 16, 1954.

At first the early work of Reber was repeated and radio surve
of the general galactic radiation were made at several wavelength
ranging from 15 m. to 21 cm. in order to provide tests for th
various theories put forward to account for the cosmic radio nois
It appears that at the shorter wave lengths a good part at least
the noise is emitted in interstellar space by the so-called 'free
free' transitions between protons and electrons in the region
where the gas is ionized by the ultra-violet radiation of hot star
But it soon became apparent that this mechanism is incapable
accounting for the distribution of the radiation over the celesti
sphere, or for its spectral energy distribution. No general theory
yet available, but in the course of the observation some remarkab
and unexpected phenomena were discovered.

In 1946, during one of these surveys of galactic noise, J. S. Hey
S. J. Parsons and J. W. Phillips announced that the noise comin
from a small region in the constellation of Cygnus was not constar
but fluctuated as might happen in a localized variable source suc
as the Sun. In the following year J. G. Bolton and G. J. Stanley
using an interferometer technique based on interference betwee
the direct ray received by an aerial atop a high cliff and ray
reflected by the surface of the sea, near Sydney, proved that ther
was indeed in Cygnus a strong source of cosmic noise of ver
small apparent diameter. This was called a 'radio star' and th
year after another was discovered in Cassiopeia by M. Ryle an
F. G. Smith, of the Cavendish Laboratory, Cambridge. Since the
the number of 'radio stars' has increased rapidly, several hundre
having been detected in the systematic surveys conducted at Cam
bridge and Sydney since 1950.[1]

It was soon realized that the fluctuations of intensity which firs
attracted attention are not genuine, but are caused by irregularitie
in the ionosphere, much as the optical twinkling of the stars i
caused by inhomogeneities in the lower atmosphere. Careful inter
ferometer observations by B. Y. Mills, at the Radiophysics Labora
tory, Sydney, in 1953, also established that the sources of radiatio
are not points but have measurable, though generally small, appar

[1] More recent surveys (1955) have increased the total to well ove
1000.

t diameters and hence are not really 'stars'. The noncommittal
:signation of 'radio sources' is now preferred. Indeed, one of the
eat puzzles is that the majority of these radio sources, despite
.eir sometimes considerable intensity, cannot be identified with
ıy known star or optically visible celestial object. The two
rongest sources in Cassiopeia and Cygnus, for instance, are
most as intense as the quiet Sun.

After several years of feverish work by optical astronomers and
ıdio-astronomers cooperating closely to solve the problem, a few
f the stronger sources were finally identified with some rare and
eculiar galactic nebulosities or extra-galactic nebulae. The first
.ue came in 1949 when Bolton and Stanley found a fairly strong
ource in Taurus close to the position of the Crab Nebula, a strange
alactic nebulosity known to be the remnant of a supernova
bserved in A.D. 1054 by the Chinese (cf. VIII, 44). Then they
oticed that two strong sources in Virgo and Centaurus were located
ear the positions of peculiar galaxies, but as so many other sources
ad no obvious optical counterpart no conclusion could be drawn,
specially because of the low accuracy of the early radio positions.

One of the great difficulties confronting radio-astronomy is the
ıck of resolving power due to the great lengths of radio-waves and
he practical limitations on the sizes of radio-telescopes. The first
adio-telescopes had a resolving power measured in degrees,
housands of times poorer than that given by the smallest optical
elescope and indeed by the naked eye. This lack of positional
ccuracy was partly overcome by recourse to radio techniques
quivalent to the Michelson interferometer (cf. VIII, 42);
ccurate positions of the strongest sources obtained by F. G. Smith
.t Cambridge and B. Y. Mills at Sydney finally enabled W. Baade
nd R. Minkowski to establish firmly a few identifications with
»ptical objects observed with the 200-in. telescope. A puzzling
eature of these identifications published in 1954 is the variety of
ıstronomical objects found associated with radio sources: some
ike the Crab Nebula are gaseous remnants of supernovae, some
ike the source in Cassiopeia, peculiar galactic nebulosities of a
1ew type characterized by large random velocities indicating
riolent turbulence, others like the source in Cygnus, peculiar

external galaxies identified by Baade and Minkowski as a very fai
and distant pair in head-on collision. Other galaxies with di
concertingly different and unexplained peculiarities also coincid
with some of the strongest radio sources, but there is as yet n
general theory to explain why such peculiarities should give rise t
abnormal radio emission.

The much weaker radio emission of normal galaxies, such as ou
own, was first detected in 1950 by R. Hanbury Brown and C
Hazard at the Jodrell Bank Station with a large fixed radio-tele
scope 220 ft. in aperture consisting of metal wires stretched o
supports so as to form a rough paraboloid collecting the radio
waves from a small celestial area near the zenith of the station
Thanks to the great sensitivity and directivity of this instrumen
they succeeded in detecting the weak radio signals from the grea
spiral in Andromeda (Plate XV); the intensity was of the same orde
as that which would be received from our own Milky Way remove
to the same distance. Noise from several other great norther
spirals was received at Jodrell Bank in the following years, whil
in the southern hemisphere the radiation from the Magellani
Clouds and some other bright galaxies was detected in 1954 b
Mills with a new giant radio-telescope of original design recentl
put into operation near Sydney. This instrument, consisting o
two horizontal arrays of aerials arranged in the form of a cross wit
arms 1,500 ft. in length, constitutes at the moment by far th
greatest and most powerful radio-telescope in the world. Within :
few years, however, more versatile instruments will be put int
use which though of more modest aperture, some 200 to 250 ft.
will resemble more closely the conventional reflector of the optica
astronomer and give results more unequivocal than those obtaine
so far by radio-astronomers using ingenious but often complicate
and ambiguous methods to overcome the lack of resolving power o
existing instruments.

All the investigations discussed thus far have been based on th
continuous radio spectrum of the Sun, the Milky Way or the radio
sources. In 1944, H. C. Van de Hulst, of Leiden, predicted from
theoretical considerations of the hyperfine structure of the energy
levels of the hydrogen atom, that a discrete emission from neutra

terstellar hydrogen could be observed at a wavelength of 21 cm. This emission arises from a slight change of energy of the hydrogen tom as the spinning electron reverses spontaneously the direction f its spin from parallel to anti-parallel with respect to that of the roton. Even for an electron this is a difficult somersault and an ndividual atom spends an estimated 11 million years on the verage before emitting the 21-cm. line. Nevertheless, the line was uccessfully detected in 1951 independently by the American hysicists H. I. Ewen and E. M. Purcell, of Harvard College, then y C. A. Muller and J. H. Oort, in Holland, and shortly afterwards y W. Christiansen and J. V. Hindman, in Australia. By comparing he intensity at 21 cm. and in a small nearby region of the con-nuum, a slight excess could be detected as the Milky Way crossed he field of the receivers.

Since the first observation rapid progress has been made in the tudy of the radio emission of interstellar hydrogen with results of utstanding astronomical interest. The most significant was the letailed mapping of the outer spiral structure of the Galaxy by Muller, Oort and Van de Hulst in 1953–4, shortly after its first letection by optical methods (cf. section 50); this was possible because most of the interstellar hydrogen is concentrated in the piral arms of the Galaxy and its line emission provides a means of measuring accurately its radial velocity, by application of the Doppler principle to radio-waves; the measured velocity then gives he distance when a suitable model of galactic rotation is adopted.

While optical observations on account of interstellar absorption of light-waves permit the exploration of only a small section of the Galaxy in our neighbourhood, and then only in places where the ultra-violet radiations of high-temperature stars ionize the gas and excite its visible radiation (the so-called H II regions, cf. section 50), the radio observations can probe practically the whole extent of the galactic system, penetrating even beyond the galactic nucleus, to detect the radiation of the great bulk of interstellar hydrogen in its fundamental non-excited state (the H I regions).

A map of the spiral arms of the Galaxy obtained by Muller, Oort and Van de Hulst in 1954 is reproduced in Fig. 35.

The radio emission of neutral hydrogen at 21 cm. was also detected

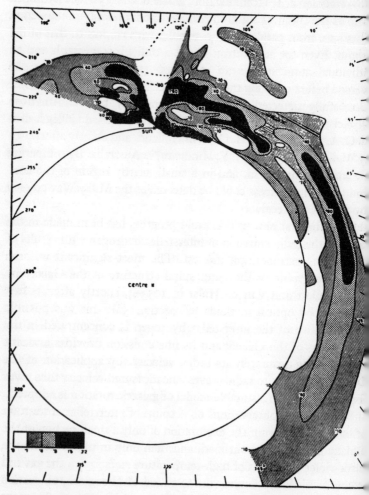

FIG. 35. SPIRAL STRUCTURE OF THE GALAXY FROM RADIO OBSERVATIONS, AFTER MULLER, OORT AND VAN DE HULST (1954)

The density of neutral hydrogen in interstellar space, deduced from measurements of the 21-cm. line radiation, is plotted in this map of the galactic plane.

the nearest external galaxies, the two Magellanic Clouds, in 1953
t Sydney by F. J. Kerr and J. V. Hindman, whose measurements
isclosed a very extensive hydrogen atmosphere to the Small
Cloud, extending towards the Large Cloud, as if due to some sort of
dal action; optical observations show an effect which is similar
lthough shorter and much narrower (section 51). The radial
elocities of the gas measured at a large number of points in both
Clouds, especially in the larger, were analysed for rotation in 1954
y Kerr and the author, who derived from them improved esti-
nates of the masses of the Clouds.

Studies in progress at the radio-astronomy station of the Harvard
College Observatory under the direction of B. J. Bok have indicated
hat the 21-cm. emission of neutral hydrogen can be detected over
nost of the sky and not only near the Milky Way; this may be an
ndication of a vast 'corona' of hydrogen surrounding our own
Galaxy, a late-type spiral according to current views.

Studies of the background radiation of the sky have also been
nade at several other wavelengths of the continuous radio spectrum,
n particular by R. Hanbury Brown and C. Hazard, at the Jodrell
Bank Station, and more recently by J. D. Kraus and H. C. Ko, at
he 'radio observatory' of the Ohio State University, Columbus.
Such investigations have disclosed that, besides the strong galactic
adiation and the discrete radio sources, a definite structure may be
liscovered in the weak background of radiation in regions away
rom the Milky Way, in the galactic polar caps. Earlier surveys,
such as those of Reber and others, had already shown that the
esidual radiation at the galactic poles is by no means negligible,
and in order to account for it it was found necessary to introduce,
besides the galactic radiation, a so-called 'isotropic component',
whose origin is still in doubt. Some radio-astronomers believe that
a spherical distribution of radio sources associated with our
Galaxy is responsible for it, others invoke the radiation of high-
speed ('relativistic') electrons moving in weak magnetic fields,
others attribute at least part of this background to the integrated
radiation of all distant galaxies.

In 1953 the Manchester and Columbus groups announced at a
few months' interval the discovery of a band of enhanced radiation

in the background, which band corresponds closely with the cloud and clusters of nearby galaxies marking the path of the 'Local Supergalaxy' (section 51); this is strong indication that at least part of the background radiation does indeed come from the large agglomerations of external galaxies. The observed intensity is however, much in excess of what could be predicted on the basis of known nebular counts and measured radio-optical emission ratios for individual nearby galaxies. Difficult questions of cosmology including the effect of red-shifts in optical and radio spectra will have to be clarified before definite conclusions can be formed; perhaps emission by a diffuse medium in the vast inter galactic spaces will have to be acknowledged and taken into account and this again could be of great cosmological significance.

At any rate it seems already certain that the new methods of radio-astronomy will prove of the utmost importance for the future progress of astronomy. A fascinating possibility is that some of the discrete sources and part of the background radiation may originate in regions of the Universe far beyond the limits of optical penetration of even the 200-in. telescope.

SELECTED ANALYTIC
BIBLIOGRAPHY

I. General Works

A. Berry: *A Short History of Astronomy*. J. Murray, London, 1898, 440 pp.

W. W. Bryant: *A History of Astronomy*. Methuen, London, 1907, 355 pp.

Two good general introductions which contain much valuable material on the ancient and classical periods.

G. Bigourdan: *L'Astronomie: Evolution des idées et des méthodes*. Flammarion, Paris, 1916, 396 pp.

This book, intended as a summary—although a very complete one—of the great fundamental classics,[1] is the most generally accessible source for the history of astronomical knowledge and observational methods in the ancient and classical periods. A reading of this book would be a useful supplement to our chapters I to III.

P. Doig: *A Concise History of Astronomy*. Chapman & Hall, London, 1950, 320 pp.

A good general introduction for the amateur, but the choice of the material is somewhat uncritical and unbalanced in favour of amateur activities in astronomy. In this respect it may prove more attractive to many readers than our own treatment of modern developments.

---

[1] J. Bailly: *Histoire de l'Astronomie ancienne*, Paris, 1781; *Histoire de l'Astronomie moderne*, Paris, 1785.

J. Delambre: *Histoire de l'Astronomie au Moyen-Age*, Paris, 1819; *Histoire de l'Astronomie moderne*, 2 vols., Paris, 1821; *Histoire de l'Astronomie au XVIIIème siècle*, Paris, 1827.

See also the two classical XIXth century treatises in English:

R. Grant: *History of Physical Astronomy*, Bohn, London, 1852, 638 pp.

G. Lewis: *Historical Survey of the Astronomy of the Ancients*, Parker, London, 1862, 527 pp.

H. Macpherson: *Makers of Astronomy*. Clarendon Press, Oxford 1933, 240 pp.

A history and commentary on the life and work of a large number of illustrious astronomers, from Copernicus to modern times. The selection is less strict than that of the following work and the choice is sometimes less justified, but it offers more variety and constitutes in any case an excellent introduction to it.

H. Shapley and H. E. Howarth: *A Source Book in Astronomy*. McGraw Hill, New York, 1929, 405 pp.

An important reference work containing, though without comment, the most characteristic passages in the main works which formed the landmarks of astronomical progress—from Copernicus to the end of the nineteenth century. It contains altogether some one hundred texts by some sixty authors and will be of tremendous interest to the reader who is acquainted with modern astronomy and has already some idea of its history.

G. Abetti: *The History of Astronomy* (translated from the Italian by Betti B. Abetti). Sidgwick & Jackson, London, 1954, 345 pp.

This book, with its emphasis on Italian astronomy, will be read with interest, as it reveals some little known contributions of Italian astronomers; it is marred by frequent misprints and mistranslation and illustrated by beautiful 200-inch photographs, which are however, mostly irrelevant.

E. Zinner: *Die Geschichte der Sternkunde von den ersten Anfangen bis zur Gegenwart*. Springer, Berlin, 1931, 673 pp.

A very complete, somewhat turgid account of the astronomical history of the various peoples, especially the Germanic races (300 pp.) the modern period is also included, but very briefly. There is a very complete bibliography.

II. Specialized Works

E. M. Antoniadi: *L'Astronomie égyptienne*. Gauthier-Villars, Paris 1934, 157 pp.

This book, based on original research by a learned Greek linguist and able planetary observer, gives a very detailed account of all that is known concerning the science and philosophy of the astronomer-priests of ancient Egypt and their contribution to Greek science. There are numerous references to, and original quotations from, Greek authors.

P. Duhem: *Le système du Monde, de Platon à Copernic*. 5 vols., Hermann, Paris, 1913–1917, about 3,000 pp.

This book is a monument of erudition and of analysis of ancient texts which should be consulted only by a reader truly interested in the details of the fantasies of Antiquity and of the Dark Ages. The intellectual gain which may be derived from such an account appears very limited to the modern astronomer. Additional volumes are to be published.

L. E. DREYER: *A History of the Planetary Systems from Thales to Kepler*. Cambridge Univ. Press, Cambridge, 1905, 432 pp. Reprinted as *A History of Astronomy from Thales to Kepler*. Dover Publ., New York, 1953, 438 pp.

This book, written by an astronomer, covers very much the same ground as the preceding work but with a more scientific outlook and within more manageable bounds. It is the standard reference volume for the period it covers.

). NEUGEBAUER: *The Exact Sciences in Antiquity*. Princeton University Press, 1952, 191 pp.

An excellent summary dealing mainly with the Astronomical knowledge of the Ancient Peoples.

E. ZINNER: *Entstehung und Ausbreitung der coppernicanischen Lehre*. Erlangen, 1943, 594 pp.

Published on the occasion of the fourth centenary of the death of Copernicus, this is an almost exhaustive history of the origins, the development and the expansion of the heliocentric doctrine and of the work of Copernicus, his predecessors and his successors. The index includes 785 references.

A. M. CLERKE: *A Popular History of Astronomy during the Nineteenth Century*. Black, London, 1885 (1st ed.); 1908 (4th ed.), 489 pp.

In a still conveniently limited space, this book presents a fascinating and fairly detailed account (documented with original references) of the history of the discoveries and advances in instrumental methods from 1774 to 1901 (4th ed.), chiefly in the field of physical astronomy. We have borrowed from it freely, and a reading of it will supplement with advantage our chapters IV, V and VI.

R. L. WATERFIELD: *A Hundred Years of Astronomy*. Duckworth, London, 1938, 526 pp.

A. ARMITAGE: *A Century of Astronomy*. Sampson Low, Marston & Co., London, 1950, 256 pp.

These two books cover very much the same ground and trace the development of modern astronomy—particularly of astrophysics—in the past century; the selection of material is not always very happy or well balanced and it is rather incomplete in places. However, either of them may be read as a supplement to our chapters V, VI, VII and VIII.

III. BIOGRAPHIES AND AUTOBIOGRAPHIES

A. ARMITAGE: *Copernicus. The Founder of Modern Astronomy.* G. Allen & Unwin, London, 1938, 183 pp.

A. ARMITAGE: *The World of Copernicus.* New American Library, New York, 1951, 165 pp.

H. KESTEN: *Copernicus and his World* (translated from the German). Secker & Warburg, New York, 1945, 408 pp.

J. L. E. DREYER: *Tycho Brahe.* Black, Edinburgh, 1890, 405 pp.

J. A. GADE: *The Life and Times of Tycho Brahe.* Princeton Univ. Press, Princeton, 1947, 209 pp.

M. CASPAR: *Johannes Kepler.* Kohlhammer, Stuttgart, 1948, 478 pp.

C. BAUMGARDT: *Johannes Kepler, Life and Letters.* Philosophical Library, New York, 1951, 209 pp.

TH. HENRI MARTIN: *Galilée, les droits de la Science et la méthode des sciences physiques.* Didier, Paris, 1868, 428 pp.

F. SHERWOOD TAYLOR: *Galileo and the Freedom of Thought.* Watts, London, 1938, 212 pp.

E. F. MACPIKE: *Hevelius, Flamsteed and Halley.* Taylor & Francis, London, 1937, 140 pp.

B. COHEN: *Roemer and the First Determination of the Velocity of Light.* Burndy, New York, 1944, 63 pp.

S. BRODETSKY: *Sir Isaac Newton. A Brief Account of his Life and Work.* Methuen, London, 1927, 161 pp.

E. N. DA C. ANDRADE: *Isaac Newton.* Max Parrish, London, 1950, 111 pp.

A. M. CLERKE: *The Herschels and Modern Astronomy.* Cassell, London, 1895, 224 pp.

J. B. SIDGWICK: *William Herschel, Explorer of the Heavens.* Faber & Faber, London, 1955, 228 pp.

C. A. LUBBOCK: *The Herschel Chronicle.* Cambridge Univ. Press, Cambridge, 1933, 388 pp.

G. B. AIRY: *Autobiography.* Cambridge Univ. Press, Cambridge, 1896, 414 pp.

S. NEWCOMB: *Reminiscences of an Astronomer.* Harper, New York, 1903, 424 pp.

G. FORBES: *David Gill, Man and Astronomer.* J. Murray, London, 1916, 418 pp.

E. B. FROST: *An Astronomer's Life*. Houghton Mifflin, Boston & New York, 1933, 300 pp.

E. A. MILNE: *Sir James Jeans, A Biography*. Cambridge University Press, Cambridge, 1952, 176 pp.

IV. INSTRUMENTS AND OBSERVATORIES

H. C. KING: *The History of the Telescope*. Charles Griffin, London, 1955, 456 pp.

This excellent and thorough treatise on the history of astronomical optics and instruments, with full references to the original publications, will be for a long time to come the standard reference volume. Its reading is warmly recommended as an indispensable complement to any astronomical history, such as the present one, which deals mainly with the results rather than the methods of Astronomy.

E. W. MAUNDER: *The Royal Observatory, Greenwich*. Religious Tract Society, London, 1900, 320 pp.

INDEX OF NAMES

SUBJECT INDEX